KNOWING YOUR TREES

By

G. H. COLLINGWOOD

With 529 photographs showing typical trees
and their leaves, bark, flowers, and fruits

THE AMERICAN FORESTRY ASSOCIATION

Washington, D. C.

FIRST PRINTING, NOVEMBER 1937
SECOND PRINTING, MARCH 1938
THIRD PRINTING, OCTOBER 1938
FOURTH PRINTING, APRIL 1940
FIFTH AND REVISED PRINTING, NOVEMBER 1941
SIXTH PRINTING, AUGUST 1943

PRINTED IN THE UNITED STATES OF AMERICA

CONTENTS

(See Alphabetical Index Page 211)

FOREWORD

A constant demand for information concerning the characteristic appearance of a tree typical of its species as recorded by the camera, together with its botanical features, its uses and economic importance, the meaning of its scientific name and the many details that distinguish it from its fellows of forest and roadside long have indicated the need for a book which brings together these pertinent facts as a guide to the ready identification of our important trees. This, ''Knowing Your Trees'' has undertaken to do in ways which it is hoped the reader will find attractive as well as informative.

The work of compiling ''Knowing Your Trees'' and collecting the hundreds of photographs which embellish its pages began ten years ago when in 1932, AMERICAN FORESTS magazine started the presentation of an illustrated feature devoted to trees. The magazine during the past decade has presented, within the limits of two pages, a tree species, illustrated and described in a manner designed to meet the recurring requests of grade school pupils, the more mature persons with an interest in trees, and the botanists and foresters with their high standards of scientific accuracy.

In 1937 after fifty trees had been presented in the magazine they were incorporated in a first edition of ''Knowing Your Trees.'' Between 1937 and 1940 three reprintings were necessary to meet demands for the book.

This revised and enlarged edition containing 101 tree descriptions is presented in response to increasing requests for a volume that includes the one hundred most important trees in the United States. In addition to the fifty-one added trees, it includes the fifty presented in previous editions and these have been corrected as respects statistical data to conform to the most recently available figures. Changes in the order of presenting the trees also have been made to conform with accepted practice among botanists and dendrologists.

In preparing these articles, the author owes much to constant encouragement and constructive criticism of the staff of AMERICAN FORESTS—especially Ovid Butler, Lilian Cromelin, Erle Kauffman and more recently Devereux Butcher. For aid in unraveling technical descriptions and in searching out the less well-known details of some trees, special appreciation is due William A. Dayton and the late Wilbur R. Mattoon of the Forest Service, Emanuel Fritz of the University of California and W. N. Harlow of the New York State College of Forestry. Similarly, the data reporting estimated stands and annual production were secured through the cooperation of Robert V. Reynolds and Albert H. Pierson of the Forest Service.

The illustrations are unique in that photographs of the leaves, fruit, and bark are frequently supplemented with one of the blossoms, and all deciduous broadleaved trees are shown under winter as well as summer conditions. To secure these pictures has required searches through all available collections of tree photographs, and an extensive correspondence with photographers throughout the country.

The photographic collection of the United States Forest Service was drawn upon so heavily that recognition for each picture is omitted. Accordingly, the unacknowledged illustrations may be credited to the Forest Service.

Changes in the common names of several trees have been made to accord with Sudworth's Check List as approved by the Acting Chief of the Forest Service on January 24, 1940.

—G. H. C.

EASTERN WHITE PINE

Pinus strobus, Linnaeus

Typical straight trunk of a forest-grown White
Pine whose whorls of horizontal branches form
a narrow irregular crown

T. F. Kouba

WHITE pine, long known as monarch of the eastern forests, flourishes from Newfoundland to Lake Winnipeg in Manitoba, southward through eastern Minnesota, to southeastern Iowa, and east through Wisconsin, Michigan, New York, New England and Pennsylvania, and along the Allegheny Mountains to northern Georgia. European foresters recognize it as Weymouth pine for Lord Weymouth, who planted it more than two hundred years ago on his English estate.

The sturdy, gradually tapering trunk and the horizontal limbs of the blue-green crown of white pine are a characteristic feature of many northern forests, where trees with trunks six feet in diameter and crowns reaching to a height of 250 feet were reported by the early lumbermen. Next to the sugar pine of California, northern white pine is the largest pine growing in the United States.

The blue-green needles, three to five inches long, are always borne in bunches of five, and remain on the tree from three to five years. A loose, papery, brown sheath surrounds their base during the spring and early summer. In May and June yellow staminate cone-like blossoms appear on the new shoots of the lower branches and produce quantities of pollen, which is borne great distances by the wind. At the same time, small bright pink cone-bearing ovulate flowers with purple scale margins occur on the end of the upper young shoots. The staminate blossoms wither and fall soon after they have lost their pollen, but by the end of the first season's growth the tiny upright, green cones are about an inch long. Early in the second season these elongate, turn down with increasing weight, and grow to a length of five to eleven inches before turning brown and maturing in August. In September the cone opens and winged seeds are discharged to be carried as far as a quarter of a mile by the wind. The scientific name *strobus* probably refers to the conspicuous cone, being derived from Greek and Latin words for pine cone.

On the branches and young trunks white pine bark is thin, smooth and greenish brown, but with increasing age it becomes fissured, ridged, darker and heavier, until it may vary from less than an inch to four inches in thickness according to the age and exposure.

During the first few years white pine develops a moderately long tap root with spreading lateral roots. This helps to make young trees easy to transplant. As the tree matures the lateral roots develop more vigorously than the tap root, resulting in a shallow root system similar to that of spruce.

White pine lumber ranks among the principal economic woods of North America. It is creamy white to reddish brown, soft, straight-grained, may be cut with ease, polishes well and when seasoned warps or swells but little. Almost everything from ships' masts to matches, including doors, floors, framing, finish, patterns, models, boxes, crating and novelties have been made of this versatile wood, but it is now largely restricted to the more exacting uses. A cubic foot when air-dry weighs twenty-four to twenty-seven pounds. It is probably the least resinous of all the pine woods, but has a mildly resinous odor. Although not noted for its strength, it compares favorably with ponderosa pine, cottonwood and basswood. In

1941 the total lumber production of white pine and Norway pine, with which it is commercially associated, was over 906,000,000 board feet. The largest amounts came from Maine, New Hampshire, Minnesota, Massachusetts and Wisconsin. The total commercial stand of white pine and Norway pine in the United States was estimated in 1936 to be slightly over 18,000,000,000 board feet, of which nearly two-thirds was in the northeastern states. The original stand was approximately 900,000,000,-000 board feet, about equally divided between the United States and Canada. Although literally king of American commercial woods before the present century, it is now fifth among the important sources of sawtimber.

White pine thrives on deep sandy loams, but will grow under a variety of soil conditions where adequate moisture is available. It grows in nearly pure stands and in mixture with hardwoods, as well as with hemlock and Norway pine. White pine of the original forests grew to be two hundred to two hundred and fifty years old, with occasional trees of three hundred to three hundred and fifty years. Under modern economic conditions, however, trees are usually cut at sixty to eighty years when they measure from twelve to seventeen inches in diameter and are from eighty to one hundred feet tall. Such stands may contain from 50,000 to 80,000 board feet to the acre. In the original forests, trees from thirty to forty inches in diameter required at least two hundred and forty years to grow. White pine reproduces readily from seed, and with fair soil, sunlight and moisture, will reach heights of ten feet in ten years, twenty-five feet in twenty years, sixty feet in forty years, thus averaging fifteen to eighteen inches each year. Similar trees forty years old may measure from seven to nine inches in diameter and yield fifty to eighty board feet of merchantable material. It is the most rapid growing northern forest tree, occasionally averaging a yearly growth of one thousand board feet an acre over periods of forty to eighty years. It responds to silvicultural treatment and has been more widely planted than any other American tree.

Fire, white pine blister rust and white pine weevil are the white pine's principal enemies, although other pests such as white pine scale, the pine sawyer and several root fungi and rots cause heavy damage. Forest fires are particularly damaging to the young growth. Fire is an enemy common to all trees, but white pine blister rust, which entered this country from Europe about thirty years ago, is peculiar to the five-needled pines and takes a heavy toll. This can be controlled by destroying all gooseberry and currant bushes, which are intermediate hosts of the disease, in the forest and for a distance of nine hundred feet from the trees to be protected. Without the leaves of these plants the disease can neither complete its life cycle nor infect other white pines.

Throughout portions of its range the leader shoots of white pine are killed by the white pine weevil. The tree is not killed, but frequently is so deformed as to make it valueless for lumber. No satisfactory control of the weevil has been developed.

White pine is seldom used for street or roadside purposes, but its vigorous growth and attractive color cause it to be favored as an ornamental tree for lawn and park purposes as well as for a background for other plantings. It is successfully grown considerably beyond its natural range, and has long been planted in northern Europe.

Long tapering cones, slender bluish green needles in bunches of five and clusters of yellow pollen-bearing blossoms

Broad, flat-topped, dark gray longitudinal ridges characterize White Pine bark

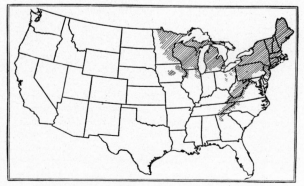

Natural range of White Pine in the United States

WESTERN WHITE PINE

Pinus monticola, **Douglas**

The tall shaft of Western White Pine reaches heights of one hundred feet or more and supports a narrow, symmetrical, pyramidal crown of short drooping branches. This open-grown tree has an unusually long crown. Frequently, more than half of the trunk is clear of branches

WESTERN white pine—the silver pine of the northwest, is native to the region from southern British Columbia across northern Idaho, Montana and Washington, southward through Oregon into California. True to its name, *monticola,* it is confined to the mountains, where in Idaho and Montana it is found at elevations of 2,000 to 5,000 feet above sea level, somewhat higher in Washington and Oregon and up to 10,000 feet in California.

Ranking among the important timber trees of America, western white pine frequently grows in dense stands and develops a tall, slender shaft with a peculiarly short-branched, narrow, symmetrical crown. The trunk is usually clear for a half to two-thirds of its length, has little taper and the slender drooping branches seldom extend more than twelve to fifteen feet. These trees may reach heights of 175 feet and be eight feet in diameter at breast height, but they are more often ninety to 110 feet high and two to three feet in diameter. Rapid growth is combined with long life, for trees of 200 to 500 years are not uncommon.

The silvery gray bark sometimes takes on a tone of purple and is broken into small oblong or rectangular blocks. Trees exposed to the wind become distinctly cinnamon in color. Even on mature trees the bark is seldom over one and one-quarter inches thick, while that of young trees and branches is thin, smooth and bright gray. Very young twigs and shoots are covered with a fine reddish down, which helps distinguish this tree from other white pines.

The pale bluish green leaves or needles are two to four inches long, commonly with a white, frosty appearance and are borne in bundles of five. They differ from the needles of the northern white pine in being thicker and more rigid. They persist on the twigs for three or four years or even longer.

The yellow pollen-bearing, staminate flowers or catkins are borne during early spring in clusters of six or seven on the lower branches, while near the ends of the high branches are pale purple ovulate flowers on long stalks. From these higher blossoms develop green or dark purple cones which first stand erect, becoming pendulous by the close of the first season. By the end of the second summer they turn a yellow-brown and mature to a length of six to ten inches—or occasionally eighteen inches. The slightly curved cones are longer than those of northern white pine and so slender as to give rise to the name "Finger-cone Pine." Trees seldom bear fertile cones before forty to sixty years of age, and then infrequently at intervals of two or more years. Under each cone scale may be found two pale red-brown seeds about a third of an inch long attached to a narrow membranous wing from three-quarters of an inch to an inch long. The seeds are shed in September and October soon after the cones ripen and may be carried by the wind several hundred feet from the parent tree. Buried in the duff and well shaded, the seeds retain their vitality several years. Over most of its range the tree reproduces sparingly and the seeds germinate best on exposed moist mineral soil, or on humus which keeps moist through the growing season. Many of the existing stands of white pine came into being as even-aged forests following the forest fires of 1889 and 1910, from seeds stored in the duff or released from cones that escaped destruction. Seedlings and young trees will endure shade, but as the tree becomes older more and more sunlight is demanded.

The pale brown to nearly white wood weighs only twenty-four to thirty pounds to the cubic foot, is straight-grained and easily worked. Although not strong, it is harder and stronger than northern white pine and for many purposes compares favorably with cypress, any of the spruces and Douglas fir. Its high commercial value is attested by the fact that among the species with which it is associated few command a higher price. With an estimated total stand of nearly twenty billion board feet of merchantable timber growing on some three million acres, the total cut in 1941 was 500,196,000 board feet. The peak of production for western white pine was reached in 1930 when 538,607,-000 board feet were cut. Idaho now has stands of over 13,500,000,000 board feet and Montana over 1,500,000,-000 board feet. These two States with Washington and Oregon are the chief sources of the species. Stands of 20,000 to 40,000 board feet to the acre are not uncommon, while a large area in Idaho yielded 40,000 board feet to the acre at 100 years of age, and another area about 150 years old cut 51,000 board feet to the acre. It is used widely for structural purposes, window and door frames, molding, matches and pattern stock.

Western white pine develops greatest size and highest economic importance in deep porous soils on gentle north slopes and flats in northern Idaho and Montana. It seldom grows in pure stands and is most frequently associated with western hemlock, Douglas fir, the several western firs and lodgepole pine. Deep snowfall, a mean annual precipitation of fifteen inches in California to sixty inches near Puget Sound, and a comparatively short growing-season characterize the regions where this pine grows.

While subject to disastrous losses from fire, protection against which is essential, its most dangerous enemy is the white pine blister rust. This fungus disease, first reported on the west coast in 1910, has made serious inroads upon scattered stands of young growth as far south as California. The fungus must find opportunity to live for a period upon the leaves of currant and gooseberry bushes before going over to the white pines, and cannot live where either the white pine or currant-gooseberry hosts are absent. Accordingly vigorous efforts are being made by the Federal Government, supported by the states and private land owners, to control the disease by destroying all the bushes in localities where the white pine is of commercial value.

The mountain pine bark beetle, *Dendroctonus monticolae*, is the principal insect enemy and causes losses amounting to thousands of dollars each year. Control can be secured by felling the infected trees, peeling the bark and burning it. It is subject also to other pests common to northern white pine, but no others are of special significance in its natural range.

David Douglas, the Scottish explorer and botanist, first reported western white pine on the slopes of Mount St. Helens in Washington in 1825. Soon after, seeds were sent to England where the tree grows successfully. Because of its extreme hardiness, attractive color, compact pyramidal form and rapid growth during the first years, it is highly desirable for ornamental purposes. Not only is it widely used on estates and home grounds in the northwestern states, but it has proved hardy in New York State, Massachusetts and as far north as Ottawa, Ontario.

Pale bluish green needles in bunches of five and slender, cylindrical cones six to ten inches long are characteristic features of this pine

The bark is sharply broken into rectangular blocks and may vary from silvery gray to a grayish purple, or a rich cinnamon color

Natural range of Western White Pine in the United States

11

SUGAR PINE

Pinus lambertiana, Douglas

SUGAR PINE is the tallest and most magnificent of all the pines. It is one of the *Quinae* — or five-leaves-in-a-bundle pines, and is confined to a narrow strip about 1,000 miles long extending from southwestern Oregon, along the western slopes of the Sierra and Coast Ranges of California at elevations of 1,000 to 9,000 feet above sea level, to lower California. Heights of 245 feet, and diameters, breast high, of twelve to eighteen feet, have been recorded, but trees 160 to 180 feet high and four to seven feet in diameter are more common. The straight cylindrical trunk of mature trees frequently rises fifty to eighty feet to the first few long horizontal limbs which form the base of a wide crown. These great branches sweep outward and downward in graceful curves. With maturity, the spire-like outline of young sugar pine assumes a flattened top similar to that of old eastern white pines. Trees attain ages of 300 to 500 years, and occasionally nearly 600 years, and stand on a broad, shallow root system.

First recorded in 1825, on the Multnomah River in southern Oregon, by David Douglas, it was named *Pinus lambertiana* in honor of his friend, Dr. Aylmer Bourke Lambert, a distinguished British botanist of that time, and author of a book on pines. The name sugar pine refers to the white crisp globules of resin which exude from the bark after injury. These are sweet, with a pleasant suggestion of pitch flavor, and possess certain cathartic qualities.

Like all true white pines, the deep blue-green needles which have a whitish tinge are borne in groups of five. They are two and a half to four inches long, stout, stiff, twisted, and remain on the twig through the third year. In early spring light yellow, pollen-bearing flowers, half an inch to an inch long, are borne in clusters on young twigs, simultaneously with light green or pale purple ovulate cones. Before maturing the cones become dark purple-brown, and stand erect, giving rise to the name "Purple-coned Sugar Pine." By August of the second year, the cones, which are the largest of all pine cones, become pendulous. They attain lengths of eleven to eighteen inches, or occasionally twenty-one inches, and two and a half to three and a half inches in diameter. In October the scales expand to release hundreds of dark, chestnut-brown, winged seeds. Each has a wing one and a half to five inches long, and an edible kernel about the size of a grain of corn, which is relished by many birds and mammals. The cones remain on the tree for two or three years. Heavy seed crops occur only at intervals of four to six years and trees under twenty inches in diameter seldom bear. The seeds are carried by the wind about the same distance as the height

Largest of all pines, the Sugar Pine, magnificent Pacific Coast tree, attains mature heights of 200 to 245 feet

of the tree. They germinate best on loose, moist soil with a little litter of decayed leaves.

The bark of mature trees is deeply and irregularly grooved into long plate-like ridges, covered with loose purple-brown to cinnamon-red scales, and is two to three inches thick. On young trees the bark is thin, smooth and dull dark gray in color.

The light colored, soft, straight-grained wood is fragrant, and satiny when planed. It is similar to that of eastern white pine, except that it is whiter, changes color less on exposure, has more conspicuous resin ducts, and has a slightly coarser texture. The wood weighs twenty-two to twenty-five pounds to the cubic foot when air dry. Although not as strong or stiff, it enters into all the uses of eastern white pine. Its remarkable freedom from any tendency to warp and twist with changing moisture, its durability in contact with the soil, and the large boards which are possible, cause it to be used for general construction, interior trim, patterns, and model making. It is also largely used for matches.

Sugar pine is produced commercially only in Oregon and California, where it ranks in volume with redwood and ponderosa pine, but exceeds either of them in value. The total production in 1941 was 369,843,000 board feet, compared with 106,139,000 board feet in 1931 and 205,159,000 board feet in 1930. Over a billion board feet have been cut since sugar pine was first commercially produced in 1901, yet the present stand is estimated by the Forest Service to be 25,000,000,000 board feet, of which about seven-eighths is in California.

It grows at elevations of 1,000 to 2,000 feet in the Coast Range, and from 6,500 to 9,000 feet in the Sierras, in loose, deep, moist but well drained sandy loams where air humidity as well as soil moisture are favorable. Best growth is found in the mountains where the annual precipitation is forty inches or more. Western yellow pine, white fir, Douglas fir, incense cedar, Jeffrey pine and Big Tree are its principal associates.

Seedlings and trees up to twelve inches in diameter are easily damaged by fire. Thereafter the thick bark and high crown protect the trees against ordinary fires. Lightning is a frequent source of damage because the larger trees stand out above their fellows. Young trees are occasionally attacked by mistletoe, which kills or stunts them. Snow frequently accumulates to a depth of ten or fifteen feet causing severe breakage to small trees, followed by insect damage, but until white pine blister rust entered the western forests, sugar pine was remarkably free from serious enemies. Because of its great value the federal government is cooperating with California and Oregon and with private owners to control the disease by destroying all currant and gooseberry bushes within its commercial range.

Sugar pine sustains a rapid rate of growth to a remarkably advanced age. During its first century of life, favorably located sugar pine will average one foot in height-growth each year. Many acres with 192,000 board feet of merchantable timber have been recorded, while 75,000 to 150,000 board feet to the acre are not uncommon. The ability of young sugar pine to endure shade enables it to start among other species, but as it grows older it demands more and more sunlight. It meets severe competition, however, from ponderosa pine.

Although not widely planted for reforestation or ornamental purposes in the West, individual specimens of sugar pine have been established in a number of eastern States. It has proved hardy in sheltered locations, as far north as Massachusetts, but under these conditions grows more slowly than the native eastern white pine, *Pinus strobus*. David Douglas introduced it in England in 1827, and occasionally specimens are now found among collections of trees in various parts of the British Isles.

Sugar pine cones are the largest of all pine cones, being ten to twenty inches long, madder-purple within, with the tips of the scales a rich lustrous chestnut-brown

The bark is two to three inches thick, gray-brown and broken into long, irregular ridges

Natural range of Sugar Pine in the United States

LIMBER PINE

Pinus flexilis, James

LIMBER PINE is one of the smaller white pines. It is usually bushy, with branching trunks, and when growing near timberline may be only a dwarf ground cover. It grows singly or in small groups throughout the higher eastern slopes of the Rocky Mountain region from Alberta and Montana to western Texas and northern Mexico, and westward into Nevada and southern California. It is fairly common at elevations between 4,000 and 12,000 feet on exposed, rocky slopes, the tops of ridges and foothills, and sometimes in moist canyons or along the banks of mountain streams.

Usually a low, many-branched tree, limber pine occasionally develops an undivided trunk thirty, fifty, or even eighty feet tall, whose diameter is two to five feet. Ordinarily, however, the trunk tapers rapidly, and is seldom clear of branches for more than ten to twenty feet. Distinctly regular whorls of slender, tough branches stand out at right angles to the main trunk of smaller trees, and may extend to the ground. Larger trees have extremely long branches which bend gracefully toward the ground. The outer ends of the branches of the upper crown tend to assume a vertical position, giving a peculiar up-reaching effect. The twigs and branches are capable of being bent to such an amazing extent that it is called limber pine, and scientists named it *flexilis.*

Growth is slow, but its life fairly long. Individual trees may take 200 years to attain diameters of nine or ten inches, while others may reach eighteen to twenty-two inches in 200 to 300 years. Some trees are believed to live 400 years or more. Trees of greatest size are found in the high mountains of Arizona and New Mexico.

Each stout, stiff, dark green needle is one and a half to three inches long in closely pressed clusters of five, which remain five or six years on the twig. They are forward pointing, densely crowded and compressed rather than flaring, and appear as short tufts on the ends of the branches. Under a magnifying glass the margins are smooth with only an occasional semblance of teeth.

Reddish, pollen-bearing, staminate flowers are borne on spikes throughout the crown, while the bright red-purple ovulate cone-bearing ones are generally

Limber Pine is a white pine of the high mountains with a relatively short trunk and long slender branches

14

in clusters near the top. The relatively thick, oval cones mature in late summer or early autumn of the second year, and shed their seed in September or early October. The cones are three to ten inches long, peculiar in that their broadly oval, light yellowish brown scales are greatly thickened, but without prickles, and are green or rarely purple at maturity. Instead of hanging down from the branch they remain erect, and at maturity stand out horizontally or decline only slightly. By early winter they fall from the trees without breaking up. The hard shelled, deep reddish brown seeds are mottled with black and from a third to a half inch long. Each narrow, rudimentary wing generally remains on the inner cone scale so as to leave a clean seed. Large seed crops occur at irregular intervals, but small quantities are released locally nearly every season. They are sought out by birds and rodents, who play an important part in disseminating them.

The large, hard shelled seeds, somewhat stubby and unarmed cones, which are horizontal rather than pendant on the branch, and the closely compressed bundles of smooth needles help separate this and its distinctly alpine associate, *Pinus albicaulis,* the white barked pine, from the other pines of America. With certain mountain pines of the old world they are classed as *cembrae* or stone pines, in distinction to the more common and usually larger white pines of the *strobi* group.

The bark of old trunks is dark brown or almost black, one and a half to two inches thick, with deep furrows between wide rectangular blocks. On trees eight to twelve inches in diameter the bark is broken into small, thin, gray-brown plates, while on younger trees it is a bright gray, often silvery, thin and smooth.

Its exceedingly slow growth and limby structure cause the light, soft wood to be dense and usually full of knots. The heartwood is pale lemon yellow, while the thin layer of sapwood is nearly white. The wood is very heavy when green, but a cubic foot when air dry weighs only about twenty-eight pounds, and is seldom found in commercial sizes. It is occasionally used for rough construction lumber, as well as for log cabins, fuel and mine props. There is no record of the amount cut or the volume of standing timber.

First observed on the upper slopes of Pikes Peak by Dr. Edwin James, an army surgeon attached to Stephen Harriman Long's Rocky Mountain Expedition of 1820, it was described and named in 1823.

Pure stands of limber pine are sometimes found, but it is more common as an individual, or in small groves in mixture with mountain hemlock, Lyall larch, white bark, lodgepole and bristle cone pines at high elevations, and with Douglas fir, white fir, Engelmann spruce, and ponderosa pine at lower elevations. It is less frequently found in the Pacific than in the Rocky Mountain region.

Young trees, especially, suffer heavily from surface fires, but the long tap root and the flexible limbs make all limber pines resistant to wind damage. Like all other five needled pines it is subject to white pine blister rust, but the small economic importance and generally scattered distribution seldom warrants special measures for protection from this disease.

While not suited for forest planting, its slow growth and unusual outline resulting from the horizontal and pendulous branches indicate possibilities for landscape use. It prospers under most western conditions, and thrives in the northeast when planted in well drained soil at the base of a moist slope.

One and two year old cones among the plump forward curved needles which are always in bundles of five

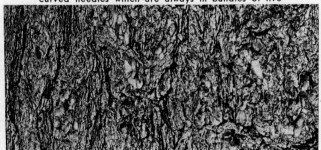

The silver gray bark of youth turns brown and rough, and becomes nearly two inches thick with maturity.
(Below) Natural range of limber pine

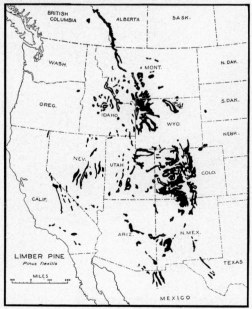

LIMBER PINE
Pinus flexilis

15

WHITEBARK PINE

Pinus albicaulis, Engelmann

THE wind distorted crown of whitebark pine is a feature of high mountain areas from North Central British Columbia, southward irregularly along the Rocky Mountain summits of Alberta, Montana, Idaho, Wyoming, and northern Utah, and again along the coast range summits of the Cascades and Sierras into southern California and Arizona. In its northern range this pine grows at elevations of 6,000 to 7,000 feet. Southward it thrives at increasing elevations up to 12,000 feet in the Sierra of California. On high summits temperatures of sixty degrees below zero are relieved by a scant three months of frosty summer, and prevailing winds often blow with such unabating force that most of the stout, flexible limbs develop on the leeward side of the thick, squatty trunk. At lower elevations and in protected coves, better soil and more encouraging surroundings combine to produce relatively tall and symmetrical trees. Even here, however, heights of more than sixty feet or diameters exceeding two feet at breast height are rare. Where undisturbed by wind the side branches, and especially those of the upper crown, stand almost erect.

Whitebark pine has five stout, stiff, slightly incurved needles in a bundle, therefore belonging to the whitepine group. They are one and a half to two and a half inches long and marked on the back with one to three rows of light colored pores or stomata. The bundles of five dark-green needles are usually clustered toward the end of the stout orange branchlets, and remain from four to eight years before being shed.

Scarlet male and female catkins appear on the past year's growth during early July. In late summer of the second year the ovulate ones develop into small round, almost stemless cones which are one and a half to three inches long. They ripen in August and are ordinarily a dark purplish brown. Inside and at the base of each cone scale are two sweet kerneled, winged seeds, plump on one side and flattened on the other. They are nearly half an inch long and about one-third of an inch in diameter. The narrow translucent wings stick to the sides of the cone scale so that the seeds must break loose. They are shed slowly through the late autumn and early winter. Squirrels, chipmunks, and other small animals and birds seek them greedily and are largely responsible for their sparse distribution. The busy rodents often store the seeds in narrow rock crevices on high, exposed elevations where germination may take place. Too often the tender young seedlings are whipped and worn in two against the sharp granite rocks by constant winds. At high elevations the surviving trees may sprawl over the rocks to form low springy mats of tough limbs, which provide shelter for mountain goats, bear, deer, and other animals, and not infrequently for an occasional traveler or sheep herder. Heavy snows keep the trees flattened for the better part of the year, leaving little time for the limbs to lift

Devereux Butcher

A dweller of high places, subject to unabating winds, Whitebark Pine develops a thick, squatty form which with age and depending on exposure may become distorted in shape

themselves. The bark of the larger trunks sometimes carries a whitish cast, while young trunks and twigs are clothed with fine, white pubescence. This is responsible for the common name "whitebark," as well as for the scientific name *Pinus albicaulis*, which may be translated as "the pine with the white stem."

The bark is scarcely more than half an inch thick and comparatively tender. For many years it remains characteristically smooth, but with maturity develops narrow vertical and horizontal cracks with the outer surface covered by thin light gray to brown scales. Beneath the scales, the inner bark is reddish brown. The winter buds are more or less egg shaped, and about one-third to one-half inch long.

Whitebark pines are seldom large enough or in sufficiently heavy stands to be of commercial importance. Occasionally, however, individual trees at lower elevations may be cut for fence posts or lumber. The wood is light in weight, nearly white, brittle, and marked by many close annular rings. Superficially, it resembles the wood of western white pine and, no doubt, small quantities are sawn and marketed with this more important relative. No figures are available covering either the estimate stand, the possible growth, or the annual cut of whitebark pine.

During its early development, whitebark pine is fairly tolerant to shade, but with maturity it demands full sunlight. Its growth is so slow that timberline trees scarcely five feet high have been found to be fully 500 years old. Other trees only three and a half inches in diameter have revealed as many as 225 annular rings. John Muir, with the aid of a magnifying glass, is reported to have counted seventy-five annular rings in a twig only one-eighth of an inch in diameter. A veteran tree with a trunk seventeen inches in diameter is recorded as being 800 years old.

Ordinarily whitebark pine associates with other hardy mountain trees such as alpine fir, limber pine, Engelmann spruce, foxtail pine, Lyall larch, western juniper, Rocky Mountain juniper, and knob-cone pine. Of all these trees whitebark pine is most frequently confused with limber pine, *Pinus flexilis*. In general the range of whitebark pine is more northerly, but the two trees may occupy the same area in several regions. Both are five needled pines with many common characteristics. They are best distinguished by their cones. Limber pine cones are three to ten inches long, with slightly reflexed scales, while those of whitebark pine are only one and a half to three inches long and more nearly cylindrical, with thickened scales armed with sharp points. The rows of light colored pores or stomata are on all sides of the limber pine needles instead of being limited to the back side as with whitebark pine.

Like all five needled pines, whitebark pine is susceptible to the white pine blister rust. Due to their scattered growth and relatively low commercial value, however, no special protective efforts are being made. Bark beetles also take a fairly heavy toll, but the greatest enemy is fire. Its natural habitat makes it particularly susceptible to lightning.

Whitebark pine is suitable for ornamental purposes and is so used to a limited extent. Trees selected from high elevations may maintain an inherited tendency to develop low spreading forms suitable for many landscape purposes.

Asahel Curtis

Of the whitepine group, the tree has stout, stiff, incurved needles, one to two and a half inches long, in bundles of five. The cones are small, almost stemless and a dark, purplish brown

Devereux Butcher

The whitish cast of the bark and stems gives Whitebark Pine its name

The natural range of Whitebark Pine

PIÑON PINE

Pinus edulis, Engelmann

Low, round-headed Piñon Pines, with far-reaching horizontal branches grow in open stands over the lower slopes of the southern Rocky Mountains

PIÑON, the two-leaved nut pine of the Southwest, grows in scattered groves and open stands on the dry foothills, mountain slopes, and canyon sides of the southern Rocky Mountains, at elevations between 5,000 and 8,000 feet above sea level. Small isolated specimens are found up to elevations of 9,000 feet.

A stand of piñon scattered over the arid slopes reminds one of an old apple orchard. It is one of the first trees to gain a foothold on the lava overflows so common throughout the Southwest, and often forms the advance growth as the forest encroaches upon more arid lands. Less resistant to frost and drought than the neighboring junipers, piñon will succeed on exposed slopes where the average annual precipitation is less than thirteen inches, and the annual range of temperatures extends from 110° F. to 25° below zero.

This is one of four nut pines of the Southwest.

Chief among the numerous details by which they may be distinguished is the manner in which the leaves or needles are borne. The Parry piñon, *Pinus parryana* has the needles in clusters of four; the Mexican piñon, *Pinus cembroides*, usually in clusters of three; the Singleleaf piñon, *Pinus monophylla*, usually as single leaves; and the stout, dark, yellowish green needles of *Pinus edulis* are borne in pairs or occasionally in clusters of three. Their ranges overlap, but all are confined to the Southwest. The needles of *Pinus edulis* are sharp pointed, often curved, with smooth margins, and seven-eighths of an inch to one and three-fourths inches long. Those of seedlings and of new growth are a bright bluish green. They remain on the branches as long as nine years but begin to fall with the fourth season.

This small, scraggy, nut pine grows associated with the western junipers, ponderosa pine, Gambel oak, the mountain mahoganies, and in pure stands over small areas. As the range extends south from northern Colorado over New Mexico to the Pecos River in Texas and throughout much of Arizona and southeastern Utah, it forms a woodland type of considerable local importance. Best growth is attained on mesas and slopes where the sandy or gravelly soil is moderately deep and rich, but the tree is more frequently found on poor rocky soils.

In the early spring elongated clusters of dark red, pollen-bearing, staminate flowers cover the tree, while on the ends of the twigs are short-stalked, purplish, ovulate blossoms. The staminate flowers soon drop, but the ovulate ones develop in August and September of the second year into egg-shaped, shiny, yellowish brown cones about an inch to two inches long. The cone scales are relatively few in number and without prickles. In pairs, on the scales near the middle of each cone are two to thirty red-brown, mottled, nut-like seeds.

Piñon (pin-yone) is the name given by the early Spanish explorers and was described by Cabeza de Vaca in 1536. Although several other pines produce edible seeds, the scientific name *Pinus edulis* refers specifically to the large seeds of this tree.

Piñon nuts were formerly a staple item in the fall and winter diet of southwestern Indians and Mexicans, but are now largely sold for use as a delicacy. To prevent the seeds from spoiling and to retain their flavor, they are usually baked immediately after being gathered. Individual trees produce one to eight bushels of cones, and stands of trees may yield 300 pounds of seed to the acre.

The reddish brown bark is irregularly furrowed with shallow diagonal ridges and varies from a half an inch to an inch thick.

The piñon tree is usually only fifteen to twenty feet high, but reaches heights of thirty-five to fifty feet. The trunk is rarely free from branches for more than six or eight feet. Trees may attain breast high diameters of twelve to thirty inches in 150 to 375 years, but the growth is always slow. The root system is shallow.

The wood is soft, without special strength, and weighs about thirty-seven pounds to the cubic foot when air dry. Considerable quantities are used locally for fuel, fence posts, corral posts, telephone poles, mine logging, charcoal, and general construction. It is not durable in contact with the soil. There are no authentic estimates of the total stand of piñon pine.

Although piñon bears abundant crops of seeds at intervals of two to five years, only a small percentage are fertile, and the power to germinate is soon lost. So large a part of the crop is eaten by birds, small animals, and gathered by Indians or local settlers that natural reproduction is poor. Weevils may also enter the seed before the cones open. Accordingly, the maintenance and reproduction of natural stands is difficult.

Piñon is seldom injured by fire, but excessive grazing may destroy the seedlings. The worst enemy is probably a two-host fungus disease similar to white pine blister rust. As in the case of the white pine pest, the alternate host of the "piñon blister rust" is a wild currant, and the damage is chiefly sustained by seedlings and younger trees.

Although peculiar to the Southwest, this tree has been successfully planted in the eastern states where it has proved a hardy, slow growing, compact, bushy evergreen as far north as Massachusetts.

Mature trunks are clothed with reddish brown bark whose shallow irregular ridges may be broken into small detachable scales

Dark, yellowish green needles are borne in pairs, and the large edible nuts grow in egg-shaped cones, at the ends of the branches

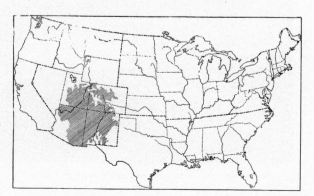

Natural range of Pinon Pine within the United States

Pinus resinosa, Aiton

THE straight clean trunk and reddish brown bark of the red pine is a familiar feature of the forest stands of the northeast from south-

Red Pine attains heights of eighty feet or more

ern Canada throughout the northern states from Maine to Minnesota, and south as far as Pennsylvania. Scattered specimens are found in West Virginia. It reaches its optimum development on sandy plains in the Great Lakes region, as well as on dry, gravelly ridges of the more eastern states.

Known widely as Norway pine, this tree is usually from sixty to eighty feet high with trunk diameters two to three feet at breast height. Occasional trees attain a height of 140 feet with a diameter of four and a half feet. It seldom attains an age of more than 300 years and declines in vigor after 200 to 230 years. During the first sixty or seventy years, the red pine is capable of an average height growth of one foot a year. Thereafter, the height growth gradually declines until it practically ceases at around one hundred years. The crown is symmetrically conical, and the whorled branches extend at right angles from the main trunk. Under forest conditions the trunk may be free of branches for one-half to two-thirds the total height.

Stands in Massachusetts have attained an average height of ninety-one feet with breast high diameters of sixteen inches in eighty-eight years, while average trees in a Minnesota stand were over 200 years old and measured nearly nineteen inches in diameter.

The dark green, glossy leaves are borne in pairs held together by long, persistent membraneous sheaths. Each leaf is four to six inches long, flexible, and sharply pointed. They occur in tufts near the ends of the branches and remain on the tree four or five seasons.

In May or June dense clusters of dark purple staminate blossoms about half an inch long occur at the base of the current season's growth, while near the ends of the upper branches on the same tree are less evident pairs of short-stalked, broadly egg-shaped, scarlet, ovulate flowers. The short compact character of the ovulate flower is retained as the cone develops to maturity through the succeeding two seasons.

The light, chestnut-brown, broadly conical cone is about two inches long, and grows without a stalk at right angles to the parent stem. Each cone scale is slightly thickened at the end, and unarmed. No other pine tree native to the northeastern states has cone scales without a spine or bristle. While the cone may remain on the tree through the winter, most of the winged seeds are shed early in the autumn. Ordinarily, a bushel of cones will yield a half to three quarters of a pound of mottled brown, oval seeds about an eighth of an inch long and requiring some 50,000 to make a pound. Never a prolific seed bearer, the cones occur, high in the crown, at intervals of two to four years. Except during logging operations seeds are difficult to gather and bring relatively high prices.

An outstanding feature of the tree is the reddish brown bark, divided by shallow fissures into broad, flat ridges, with thin, irregular, flaky scales. The bark is three-fourths to one and one-half inches thick, and rich in tannin. The color is partly responsible for the common name—red pine.

The name *resinosa* is not particularly appropriate in that it indicates a pine "full of resin." Living red pines have never been a source of turpentine, but gum spirits are sometimes produced in a small way by burning the stumps in specially constructed stills. An accepted name—Norway pine—is credited to an early explorer who confused the tree with Scotch pine, *Pinus sylvestris*, which grows in Norway.

The pale red, close-grained heartwood, surrounded by a moderately thick layer of light yellow sapwood, weighs thirty to thirty-four pounds to the cubic foot when air dry. The annual rings are fairly conspicuous. Heavier than white pine, it is also stronger and stiffer. It is, however, neither so heavy nor so strong as longleaf pine. The wood is of considerable commercial importance, being used for general construction, piles, door and window frames, sash, flooring, boxes, crates, ship masts, and ship flooring. It is not durable when used without treatment in contact with the soil. In commerce it is frequently sold in mixture with white pine, and there are no separate figures of its annual production.

In 1914 the existing stand of red pine was estimated to be 17,000,000,000 board feet. At that time red pine was believed to have furnished fifteen percent of all of the pine lumber which had been cut from the Lake States. Were these figures applied to the 906,556,000 board feet credited to northern white pine in 1941, the production of red pine for that year would have been about 135,000,000 board feet. The peak of production was probably about 1889, when according to the same ratio more than 1,411,000,000 board feet were produced.

While pure stands of red pine are found in the Lake States, it grows more frequently in mixture with white pine and jack pine. It also grows in mixture with hardwoods.

While the thick bark is fairly resistant to fire, red pine has the ability to reproduce heavily after fire, and to grow rapidly during the seedling and sapling stages. It is more resistant to insects and diseases than white pine, but even less tolerant of shade, and is frequently used for forest planting in the northeastern states. Its rich color, attractive form, vigorous growth, and the ease with which it may be transplanted make it popular for ornamental planting. The quality of the lumber gives it a place of increasing importance in forest management. It is seldom planted for street or shade.

William M. Harlow

Each pair of needles is four to six inches long, while the cone is without spines or prickles

The reddish brown bark flakes off in irregular scales

Natural range of Red Pine in the United States

PONDEROSA PINE

Pinus ponderosa, Douglas

KNOWN until recently as western yellow pine, and by a variety of other names, this tree of the western mountains is now recognized as ponderosa pine. It grows in fairly open stands from British Columbia and the Black Hills of the Dakotas southward in the Pacific and Rocky Mountain regions to western Texas, New Mexico, Arizona and on into northern Mexico and lower California. Northern and Pacific Coast forms have been differentiated from the southwestern ones but this description includes all forms under the single heading. In different parts of its range there is noticeable variation in length and thickness of the needles, size of the cones, color of the bark and texture of the wood.

It grows on well drained uplands and mountain slopes up to elevations of 12,000 feet in the southern part of its range and in dry valleys at lower elevations in the north. In the Colorado plateau of northern Arizona and New Mexico it constitutes over four-fifths of the stand in vast valuable forests at elevations of 6,500 feet to 10,500 feet above sea level.

Members of the Lewis and Clark expedition first reported it in 1804, while going up the Missouri River. Twenty-two years later, David Douglas found trees growing near the Spokane River in eastern Washington. He suggested the name *ponderosa,* because of the ponderous bulk, and sent seeds to European gardeners.

Ponderosa pine trees attain heights of 150 to 230 feet and five to eight feet in diameter at breast height. They may be 350 to 500 years old and the regular spire-like head surmounts a massive trunk whose irregularly divided scaly bark is cinnamon-brown to orange-yellow. Until the trees are eighty to one hundred years old the bark is less broken and dark brown to nearly black. This accounts for the name black jack pine and the occasional idea that the dark barked trees are unrelated to the older trees with the brighter colored bark.

Grouped botanically among the pitch pines, ponderosa pine has needles five to ten inches long which are borne in clusters of two and three. Normally these remain on the twigs from three to seven years.

The brown cones are three to six inches long and are frequently in a cluster. Before the seeds ripen the cones are bright green or purple and stand erect on their short stalks. As they ripen they become a reddish brown, turn down and the scales spread open for the winged seeds to escape. Ordinarily there are two full rounded somewhat triangular seeds about a quarter of an inch long under each scale. The wings are broadest below the middle and an inch to an inch and a quarter long, are so balanced with the seed as to carry it on a wind from 200 to 1,000 feet from the parent tree. Frequently when the mature cones break off, a few of the scales are left hanging to the stems.

Although the seeds have a strong resinous flavor, making them inedible, the Western Indians strip the bark in spring and scrape it for the

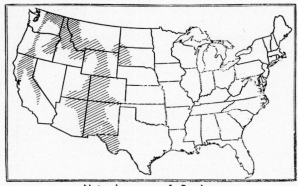

Natural range of Ponderosa
Pine in the United States

Forest grown trees may lift their crowns
more than 200 feet above the ground,
and attain an age of 500 years

sweet nutritious layer of living cambium. A spicy odor as of orange peel which sometimes seems to pervade the entire forest is given off by the twigs when crushed.

The hard, strong, comparatively fine-grained wood is light red with a narrow band of nearly white sapwood and weighs twenty-five to twenty-eight pounds to the cubic foot when air dry. The light weight has led to its confusion with white pine. A fungus known as "blue stain" frequently disfigures the sapwood of trees cut in warm, damp weather, but does not materially reduce its strength. The wood is widely used for general construction, interior finish, boxing and crating. It is not strong enough for heavy construction and is too easily attacked by fungi to be used in contact with the soil.

The estimated merchantable stand of 225,000,000,-000 board feet of timber is second only to the stand of Douglas fir in this country, while the amount of lumber cut ranks third. In 1941 the cut of ponderosa pine in the United States was 4,249,928,000 board feet with the largest amounts coming from Oregon, California, Washington, Idaho, Arizona, New Mexico and Montana.

Ponderosa pine grows vigorously from seed and adapts itself to forest plantings. It has been successfully planted over its natural range, and to a considerable extent in the eastern states, but is not generally a rapid grower. There are so many other trees better adapted to eastern conditions that it is not recommended for planting outside of the area where it is native.

Subject to a number of insect and fungus enemies, the resistance of the tree is evidenced by its wide distribution, the large areas of forest in which ponderosa pine predominates, and the great age and size which it frequently attains. Next to fire, the two most serious enemies of ponderosa pine are the *dendroctonus* bark beetle and mistletoe. Attacks by bark beetles may follow fire damage and frequently accompany mistletoe. This is a less showy form of mistletoe than that associated with Christmas decorations, but is a parasite to be reckoned with in any form of forest management. The mistletoe centers its attack largely upon the limbs and branches, while the bark beetles channel beneath the bark of the trunk and kill the tree more quickly.

Two forms of needle disease are common which either distort the needles or cause them to die. In neither case do these diseases kill the trees, but they materially reduce the rate of growth.

In Oregon and other parts of the West caterpillars of the pandora moth have eaten the needles from large areas of merchantable pine. They reach proportions of an epidemic at fairly regular intervals of twenty or thirty years, and continue abundant for six to eight years.

The size of the trees, the great area over which they grow and the relative inaccessibility of many of the timber stands make absolute control impracticable. Although mature trees are fire-resistant, foresters in charge of forests of ponderosa pine face a real problem in keeping its enemies, including fire, within bounds.

Woodbridge Metcalf

The green cones maintain an upright position into their second year, when they become brown, turn down and release the seeds from between the back-spread scales. Usually three, but occasionally two needles are held in a cluster

Close pressed papery layers or scales make up the bark, which is cinnamon-brown to orange-yellow in the older trees, but nearly black in trees younger than eighty or 100 years

LODGEPOLE PINE

Pinus contorta, Loudon

LODGEPOLE PINE has been referred to as the most common conifer of the Northern Rockies. It grows from sea level to elevations of 11,500 feet, extending from the Yukon River down the coast of Alaska and British Columbia, through Washington, Oregon and California, and most of the Rocky Mountain region. Along the seacoast and in the bogs of the far North, the tree is frequently gnarled and stunted so as to deserve the name "scrub pine." Doubtless, the technical name, *Pinus contorta,* refers to the twisted branches of the botanical type characteristic of the coast, which is also reflected in the local name, "screw pine." In parts of the Rocky Mountains where it grows with Douglas fir, Englemann spruce, alpine fir, and other trees, lodgepole pine is of commercial importance.

While commonly sixty to eighty feet high, it occasionally reaches 150 feet, and thirty to forty inches in diameter. Trees mature in about 140 years and may live to be 300 years old. It develops stands of more than 10,000 board feet to the acre. Ranking seventh among Western conifers, lodgepole pine stands are estimated to contain over 38,000,000,000 board feet, of which more than half is in the southern and central Rocky Mountains. About two billion board feet are growing in the Pacific Coast region. The lumber cut for 1941 was reported as 71,618,000 board feet and was largely from Colorado and Wyoming, with additional small amounts from Utah, Montana and Idaho.

Some botanists recognize the more upstanding tree of the high mountains as a distinct species, while others call it a variety of the shore pine. Accordingly, it may be referred to as *Pinus murrayana,* or *Pinus contorta* variety *murrayana.*

The needles or leaves are bright yellow-green, occur in pairs, range from one inch to three inches but average about two inches in length, and remain on the trees six to eight years.

Fertile cones are borne nearly every year after the trees are fifteen years old. Heavy seed crops occur at intervals of three or four years. The cones are glossy, light yellow-brown, three quarters of an inch to two inches long, and often occur in clusters of a half dozen or more. Each thin scale is armed with a slender more or less recurved prickle. The cones ripen in August or September of the second season but may hang on the branches for years before opening and liberating their seed. Lodgepole pine seed have been known to show life after forty years.

In dense stands tall, clean, gradually tapering shafts with short rounded small-branched crowns are developed. Such shafts, five or six inches in

Lodgepole Pine of the Rocky Mountains frequently grows in dense, even-aged stands, attaining a height of one hundred and fifty feet, with breast high diameter of three feet or more

diameter, and flexible, were used by Indians to make their lodges or tepees, whence the name "lodgepole pine." Open stands result in dense rounded or pyramidal crowns of large, much-forked branches which may extend down to the ground.

The thin scaly bark of the trunk is pale brown with a grayish tinge, from half an inch to an inch thick, and irregularly divided by vertical and cross fissures into small oblong plates. The inner bark is prepared as food by the Indians of the Northwest and of Alaska. They also work it into baskets.

The wood is hard, stiff, somewhat brittle and straight grained. The heartwood is usually light brown, tinged with red, while the thick sapwood is nearly white. A pebbled appearance on some boards has led to the name "bird's eye pine." The wood from Coast trees is heavier, stronger and more dense than that from trees grown in the mountains, a cubic foot weighing about thirty-six pounds as compared with about twenty-five pounds for the mountain form. Lodgepole pine is used for railroad ties, construction lumber, fence and corral poles, house logs and fuel.

Although native only to the West, lodgepole pine has been successfully planted in various parts of the East. Specimens growing in the Arnold Arboretum, in Massachusetts, were planted about 1877 and others have been grown successfully at Letchworth Park in western New York since 1912 and 1914. Under natural conditions it avoids limestone soils and demands full sunlight for best growth.

Fire destroys large areas of valuable lodgepole timber, but at the same time it prepares ideal conditions for the seedlings by exposing the mineral soil, removing competing vegetation and killing or driving away the birds and rodents who would otherwise feed on the seed. In dense lodgepole stands fires quickly develop into disastrous crown blazes, which destroy everything in their path. Even surface fires quickly burn through the thin bark and severely damage the stands. The cone scales, however, insulate many of the seed against damage, yet open most readily in the presence of heat, so that a heavy distribution of seeds frequently follows after a fire. The resulting lodgepole seedlings grow quickly in the fire-cleaned area, producing a dense stand without competition from other kinds of trees. This accounts for the phoenix-like power of lodgepole pine to take possession of areas following fires.

Mistletoe distorts many lodgepole trees, causing them to have thin crowns, sickly, pale, short needles and slow growth. Trees badly covered with mistletoe should be cut and removed when practicable. Heart rot is caused by canker infections from several kinds of wood-destroying fungi.

Serious damage is done great areas of lodgepole pine by western pine bark beetles, which bore under the bark and eventually girdle and kill the trees. Bark beetles can be controlled by peeling the bark from the trunk and stump of the tree and then burning it. Porcupines prove a lesser menace by gnawing off the bark from many trees.

The bright yellow-green needles are about two inches long and borne in pairs. The cones range up to two inches long and may remain on the tree for years before releasing their seeds

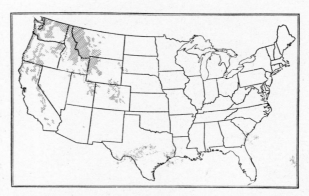

Natural range of Lodgepole Pine in the United States

The pale brown bark of the main trunk is made up of many thin, irregular scales and is seldom more than an inch thick

LOBLOLLY PINE

Pinus taeda, Linnaeus

LOBLOLLY pine is one of the four important Southern yellow pines. Frequently known as "old field pine," it extends over the coastal plain and lower Piedmont sections from southern Delaware, south and west into the river valleys of eastern Texas and southern Arkansas. It often grows in moist depressions locally called "loblollies,"—

Loblolly pine usually grows on flat moist land and develops a clean, straight trunk and broad open crown

hence the name, loblolly pine. The tall, straight, cinnamon colored trunk supports a relatively short, open, spreading crown. Trees have attained a height of 170 feet with a breast-high diameter of six feet while trees ninety to 120 feet high and three to four feet in diameter are not uncommon. The trunk may be sixty to eighty feet to the first limb. Trees occasionally reach an age of 150 years, although few trees live over one hundred years. The lower limbs of the crown spread horizontally and droop at the outer ends while those in the upper portions of the tree are more erect.

The red-brown to cinnamon colored bark is deeply furrowed into broad, flat oblong plates made up of many thin, closely pressed scales, and is usually from three-quarters of an inch to one and one-half inches thick. The slender brown twigs have a tinge of yellow and may be distinguished from other three-needled pines by a fine bloom or fuzz during their first season. The pale green needles are five to nine inches long, are borne in threes, held together at the base by a fibrous sheath, and stay on the twig for three or four years. They are slender, stiff, slightly twisted and tipped with a rigid sharp point. The buds are without resin.

From the middle of March to the first of April yellow pollen-bearing staminate flowers appear crowded at the base of the lower twigs, while higher up in the trees are single or occasionally clustered yellow ovulate flowers. At the end of the second season these mature into light reddish brown, broad, more or less egg-shaped cones three to six inches long. Each woody cone scale is tipped with a stout triangular spine.

Blackish, winged seeds are discharged from October to late November of the second season, but the cones hang on the trees for months before they break off leaving a short stock. The seeds are carried considerable distances by the wind and usually germinate the following spring. They grow best on exposed mineral soil such as abandoned agricultural land. Accordingly, the tree is called "old field pine." Open grown trees may seed abundantly when twenty to thirty years old and the seeds are highly fertile. Loblolly pine is essentially moisture-loving and reaches its best growth where the water table is close to the surface of the ground, or where the soil is able to hold moisture during the growing season.

The light brown, coarse-grained wood is resinous and, while lighter and softer than the wood of longleaf pine, is nearly as strong. It weighs about thirty-four to thirty-eight pounds to the cubic foot when air-dry and is used for construction, interior finish, bridges, freight cars, barrel shooks, boxes, crating and tobacco hogsheads. When treated with creosote to prevent decay, it is used for railroad ties and piling. More recently it has been successfully used in the manufacture of paper. While no separate figures are available, loblolly is one of the most important of the four Southern pines and makes a considerable part of the annual cut of "yellow pine," which totaled 10,311,696,000 board feet in 1941 and over 7,000,000,000 feet in 1930. The estimated stand of all Southern yellow pines in 1936 was 197,000,000,000 board feet. Wounds exude pitch or "gum," but this tree does not produce the gum in sufficient quantities to be a source of "naval stores."

Because loblolly pine has a thick bark and grows largely on low sites or in damp soils it is relatively resistant to fire. Heavy losses frequently occur, however, on higher land and in no case is it benefited by fire. It is also subject to attacks from the ravages of the pine sawyer and the Southern pine bark beetle, and a bud moth which destroys the terminal shoots of young pines. The first two insects are small beetles which bore in the bark and cambium. Insect attacks may be controlled by cutting all infested trees as soon as the foliage begins to brown. While the logs may be used, the bark and branches should be burned as quickly as possible. Similarly, when trees are cut from May to October the logs should be peeled and the bark burned along with any limbs or fresh woody trash.

Loblolly pine grows faster over long periods than any other Southern pine. In fairly open stands, with ample space for the branches and roots of each tree to spread, they may attain diameters of nine to fourteen inches and heights of forty-seven to seventy-five feet in thirty years, depending upon the character of the soil. Where natural seeding fails, loblolly pine seedlings may be planted about six feet apart. Thinnings may be necessary as the trees grow.

A well stocked acre may produce from 300 to nearly 1,000 board feet of saw timber yearly. The production depends, as with other crops, upon the character of the soil, and the protection from fire and pests. Individual stands have been measured that had averaged 1,800 board feet a year on each acre for thirty-two years. After seventy years on fair to good growing sites 40,-000 to 50,000 board feet of timber is a reasonable yield and stands may produce an income from thinning within thirty years.

Sharp triangular spines are on each scale of the three to six-inch reddish brown cones

Deep furrows break the cinnamon-red bark into flat, oblong, scaly plates

A crowded cluster of yellow pollen-bearing blossoms and the early spring growth of a young Loblolly Pine

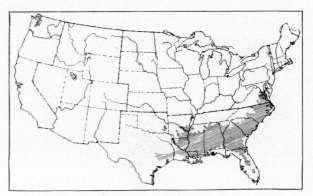

Natural range of Loblolly Pine

27

Pinus rigida, Miller

PITCH pine belongs to the group of hard pines, and is the only three-needled pine of the northeastern states. Its wide, scraggy top is common to the rougher, sterile slopes, and is occasionally found in swamps from northeastern Maine to northern Georgia, west along the slopes of the Alleghenies through eastern Tennessee, Kentucky, Ohio, Pennsylvania, and New York to the eastern Great Lakes and the St. Lawrence River.

Trees from forty to fifty feet high and one to two feet in diameter are common, while broad-crowned individuals of about 200 years may attain heights of eighty to 100 feet with a trunk up to thirty inches in diameter. In youth pitch pine is fairly symmetrical, but with age the wide crown may become irregular or even scraggy and grotesque. It is generally considered a slow-growing tree, for where other pines mark each season's growth with a single whorl of branches and one growth ring, pitch pine may put on two or sometimes three whorls of branches, and as many growth rings in a single year. Few trees of the eastern states have been studied less than pitch pine, but reports from Pennsylvania indicate that trees will attain a height of fifty feet in as many years. With increasing age the growth slows down so that at one hundred years the tree may be seventy-five feet high, and about eighteen inches in diameter.

The Latin name *rigida* refers to the stiffness of the wide spreading, sharply pointed, yellowish green needles which are often twisted and two and a half to five inches long. They are usually in clusters of three, with exceptional clusters of two. Each leaf stands out almost at right angles to the twig where it remains two years, and the trio are bound at the base by a fibrous sheath.

In April or May clusters of yellow, cylindrical, staminate flowers are produced at the base of the new season's growth, and send forth clouds of yellow pollen. More or less simultaneously with these, ovulate flowers appear as individuals or in clusters along the sides of the new twigs. Two years after fertilization, these mature as two to three inch, dark

The hardy Pitch Pine assumes an unconventional form with age, and ordinarily attains heights of fifty to eighty feet with trunk diameters at breast height of about two feet

green, pointed cones closely attached to the parent stem, and may remain on the tree for years. Each cone scale is broadly thickened at the end and armed with a stout recurved prickle. In the fall or winter, the cones may open to release many brown, winged seeds, so small that 65,000 to 75,000 are required to make a pound. Because the cones frequently hang on several years before opening, the crown may be filled with cones of varying ages. Pitch pine seeds that are shed in midwinter are sometimes an important source of food for squirrels, quail, and small birds. While primarily dependent upon seeds for reproduction, vigorous stump sprouts will grow to merchantable size. This ability to produce sprouts has been observed in trees up to four to eight inches in diameter.

On young trees and branches the rough bark is broken into reddish brown scales, while on mature trees it is deeply furrowed and broken into large irregular plates. It is so resistant to fire that the bark may be severely blackened and scarred for several feet above the ground. Clusters of leaves and short branches, known as "water sprouts," may be produced along the trunk and main branches, which. like the ability to reproduce from stump sprouts, is unique among northern pines. Such considerable quantities of pitch flow when the bark is broken, and are contained in the wood, that at one time logs and branches were destructively distilled for naval stores as far north as Pennsylvania. This is no longer done to any extent, but the name "pitch pine" continues.

The soft, coarse-grained, yellowish wood is only moderately strong and full of resin. It weighs about thirty-two pounds to the cubic foot, and is used for rough construction, mine props, fencing, fuel, pulp, crating, and railroad ties. When grown under favorable conditions the wood is of good quality and as valuable as that of the other eastern hard pines, but no estimates of the present stand or total annual production are available.

Pitch pine has few enemies, has remarkable resistance to fire, and no pine east of the Mississippi River maintains itself under such unfavorable conditions. It is not demanding as to soil or moisture, and will grow under a variety of soil and climatic conditions. Accordingly, it is frequently found on dry, burned-over, gravelly slopes, on rocky cliffs at high elevations and also in swamps. Best growth is frequently found when the trees grow in mixture with hardwoods. It can be established either directly from seed or by means of nursery-grown seedlings and transplants. While of no value for street planting, the contorted forms occasionally lend themselves to landscape purposes.

The stiff, yellow-green needles are usually in clusters of three, while the scales of the broad based cones have thick ends, each armed with a short recurved prickle

Deeply furrowed reddish brown bark sometimes an inch and a half thick and highly fire resistant is found on mature Pitch Pine trees

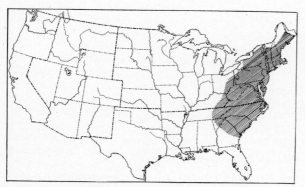

Natural range of Pitch Pine in the United States

POND PINE

Pinus rigida serotina, (Michaux) Loudon

Pond Pine is a relatively small, usually shaggy looking southern hard pine

ONE of the least important of some twenty-two so-called hard pines, pond pine prefers to have its roots in moist, sandy soil. This usually shaggy looking, comparatively short trunked tree inhabits stream banks, the border of ponds, or small swampy areas, as well as undrained peaty soils, and low, wet, sandy flats and islands. Full details of its range are not reported, but it grows from Cape May, New Jersey, southward along the coastal plain to the banks of the St. John's River in Florida and west into southeastern Alabama. Occasionally it occurs as far inland as the eastern edge of the Piedmont Plateau in North Carolina.

Pond pine bears such local names as marsh pine, bay pine, and pocoson pine. The latter is a local name for a dry swamp. It is closely related to pitch pine, *Pinus rigida,* while the added name *serotina* means "late." This probably refers to the habit of retaining the cones for several years and the somewhat delayed dispersal of seeds. As a result, the first impression made by pond pine on most people is of an irregular crown, overloaded with cones. Many of these, however, are old and empty, so that the tree is not as prolific a seeder as might be supposed.

With trunk diameters of one to three feet, it ranges from forty to eighty feet high. Only under most favorable locations does it approach a hundred feet in height. When grown in crowded stands, the trunk is clean and fairly straight. The stout, sometimes contorted, branches tend to be pendulous at the ends, forming an irregular and open crown or top. The numerous slender twigs are dark green, turning orange in their first winter and brown to almost black by the fourth or fifth year.

The dark, reddish brown bark is irregularly broken by narrow grooves into broad, squarish flat plates of thin closely pressed scales. It is a half to three quarters of an inch thick and resembles that of loblolly pine.

The slender, dull yellow-green needles are in clusters of three, or occasionally in fours. They resemble those of pitch pine but are longer, measuring six to eight inches or occasionally ten inches. Moreover, they are slightly twisted, marked with several rows of stomata or tiny breathing pores on the three faces, and hang on until the third or fourth year. The tendency for the trunk and limbs to sprout bunches of leaves and short twigs is noticeable in Pond pine.

Spring finds the trees adorned with crowded spikes of dark orange staminate catkins while the greenish pistillate ones are borne in pairs or clusters on stout stems near the ends of the twigs. Like pitch pine, many mature cones remain closed for several years while others open during the first fall or early spring. They are reddish brown, turning gray when weathered, two to two and a half inches long, and like those of pitch pine are

The broadly egg-shaped, red-brown cones are about two inches
long, while the long slender needles are usually in clusters of three

short and broadly pyramidal, or like a long pointed
egg. The thin, almost flat scales of the newly mature
cones are tipped with a slender prickle which soon
drops off.

The seeds are about an eighth of an inch long, nearly
triangular, sometimes ridged beneath, and fully rounded at the side. The thin, dark rough shell forms a
wide border, and the wings, narrowed toward the ends,
are broadest in the middle. They measure a scant quarter inch in width and three quarters inch in length.

Trees growing in close stands seldom bear seed before
thirty or thirty-five years of age, but thereafter with
fair abundance. The cones often hang on the trees for
six or more years, but usually they are empty and seed-
less. The seeds are, however, credited with retaining
their vitality for several years. They germinate readily
when they fall on ground which has sufficient moisture.
There the young trees quickly take possession of poorly
drained and otherwise valueless land, or of open and
abandoned pastures and fields. In common with pitch
pine, but few others, young pond pine reproduces from
stump shoots which appear after the tree is cut or
killed by fire.

Pond pine trees do not grow rapidly but develop into
merchantable timber of fair quality. The wood ranks
as medium heavy for pine, weighing thirty-eight pounds
to the cubic foot when dry. It is soft, coarse-grained,
resinous and brittle, without any qualities of special
importance. The dark orange heartwood is surrounded
by a wide area of pale sapwood. Its qualities of
strength and flexibility are comparable to those of slash
pine, pitch pine, and longleaf pine with which the lumber is frequently marketed. It is sparingly used for
general construction lumber, small masts for local demands, and for other general uses. When pond pines
occur with slash or longleaf pines, they are occasionally tapped for turpentine, often by mistake of the
operator.

Like other pines, it is unsatisfactory for shade, but
its pleasing foliage and form encourage its use as an
ornamental in southern parks where the soil is wet and
sandy. Because of its natural moist habitat, it seldom
develops a tap root. The wet sites, however, usually
offer partial protection from fire. Moreover, it has no
severe insect or fungus enemies.

Many thin, angular plates serve
to build up the thin brown bark

Natural range of Pond Pine

31

Pinus virginiana, Miller

Virginia Pine is seldom over fifty feet high with a short trunk and an open straggly crown. (Right) Natural range of Virginia Pine

and frequently in dense stands, but with maturity the crown becomes flat topped, open and straggly—supported on a relatively short trunk, with long horizontal or tortuously pendulous branches in remote whorls. Over most of its range the usual heights are thirty or forty feet with breast high diameters up to eighteen inches, but occasional heights of 110 feet with diameters of three feet are attained. It matures in 100 to 150 years and seldom lives longer than 200 years. Ordinarily it grows on poor, light sandy soils, and always demands full sunlight. While it prospers on moist, fertile soils it usually suffers from competition with other species and is crowded out.

The stiff, divergently twisted, sharp pointed, grayish green leaves are one and a half to three inches long, and usually in pairs. They are closely distributed along the smooth, tough branchlets and are shed irregularly during the third and fourth years. The purplish, waxy bloom on the slender young shoots distinguishes *Pinus virginiana* from all other two-needled pines.

With early spring, clusters of yellowish brown staminate flowers appear at the base of the new growth and scatter clouds of fine yellow pollen. The purplish, long-stalked ovulate blooms appear like small prickly cones on the same branches. They may be single, in pairs, or in whorls, and unlike most pines are produced in all portions of the crown.

After two growing seasons they mature in the autumn as bright red-brown cones two to three inches long, which grow tight to the parent stem. Each thin cone scale is armed with a

FROM Long Island and the sand barrens of New Jersey to central Georgia and westward on shale hills and mountain bases across the Alleghenies to southern Indiana and western Kentucky, the Virginia pine is a common and occasionally important forest tree. It grows from sea level to about 3,000 feet, and attains its largest size in the low hills of Indiana.

Appearing under a variety of names, it is frequently called scrub pine, over much of the northern coastal area it is Jersey pine, and throughout a considerable portion of the south it is spruce pine — or simply spruce. Young trees are roughly pyramidal in form

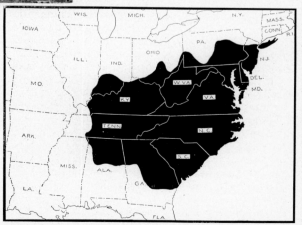

slender, persistent spine or prickle. The cones may open any time during the next three or four years to shed the small pale brown winged seeds.

The dark brown bark is broken by shallow fissures with flat scaly ridges. It is smoother than the bark of any of its associated pines and seldom more than a quarter to a half inch thick.

Until recently the light orange to yellow wood which is soft, coarse grained, brittle, and knotty had little value. Because of its small size its use was largely limited to mine props, railroad ties, rough lumber, and fuel. Early settlers burned the wood in kilns for tar and charcoal. More recently, however, the pulpwood market has opened up a steady demand, and from Pennsylvania to the south it is being recognized as an important feature of the forest. A cubic foot when air dry weighs about thirty-three pounds. Although extensively cut, no separate estimates of stand or commercial use are available.

L. W. Brownell

Yellowish brown staminate and purplish cone-like ovulate flowers develop during early spring at the base of the new growth

Trees bear seed by their twentieth year and produce heavy crops every two or three years thereafter. While the wings are too small to carry the seed far, seedlings usually appear in all surrounding places where the soil is exposed. This means that with the aid of a comparatively few seed trees direct planting is unnecessary to secure satisfactory restocking of the land.

Pure stands of young Virginia pine frequently follow on old fields when agriculture is abandoned, but they persist only on the more sterile, sand and clay areas of its range. Elsewhere pure stands of this tree are temporary in character and eventually give way to other competing conifers and hardwoods, leaving only individual Virginia pines or small groups of them. Because of its extensive range, this pine grows in combination with a variety of hardwoods and conifers, such as red maple, black cherry, dogwood, white oak, together with pitch, loblolly, and shortleaf pines, depending upon the locality. It is an early and prolific producer of seeds which germinate readily on open land. For this reason its greatest value is probably to reclothe worn out or neglected lands, and as a nurse crop for more useful trees.

Over much of its range Virginia pine shows a growth rate sufficiently rapid to warrant its encouragement. This can be accomplished by selective cutting or by cutting to a diameter limit. By combining this with a reasonable amount of weeding the encroaching hardwood trees can be kept under control.

It has few enemies, other than fire, to which it quickly succumbs, because of its thin bark and relatively shallow root system. Although not considered a vigorous species, its habit of retreating to poor soils where there is little competition gives assurance that its ranks may never be seriously reduced.

Although almost never planted for shade or ornamental purposes, home owners in new residential developments frequently enhance the beauty of their grounds by protecting and encouraging a few individuals. It was introduced in England in 1739 but has never been extensively planted.

The thin, shallowly furrowed, rather scaly bark becomes dark brown with maturity

Each scale of the narrowly conical red-brown cone bears a persistent prickle or spine

SHORTLEAF PINE

Pinus echinata, Miller

SHORTLEAF pine—one of four important Southern yellow pines—attains commercial importance in Arkansas, Virginia, Missouri, Louisiana, Mississippi, Texas, South Carolina and North Carolina, but is found in varying abundance from Long Island and southwestern Pennsylvania south and westerly to eastern Texas and Oklahoma. It prefers well-drained light sandy or gravelly clay soil. On moist soils along the coastal plain it is crowded out by loblolly pine and longleaf pine with which it is often sold as lumber. It is able to withstand lower winter temperatures than any of the other Southern pines.

The long clean trunk has little taper and is surmounted by a relatively short, pyramidal or rounded crown consisting of limbs arranged in more or less regular whorls. The oldest and stoutest of the limbs are rarely over twenty-five feet long and somewhat drooping. Trees eighty to one hundred feet high and two to three feet in diameter are not uncommon, but trees one hundred and twenty feet tall and four feet in diameter have been recorded. It reaches maturity at about one hundred and twenty years and occasionally lives over three hundred years. The bark of old trees is yellow tinged with cinnamon-red, broken into irregular plates which peel off into thin scales. Bark on young trees and branches is smooth and green, becoming brown and scaly with age.

The slender dark bluish green leaves are three to five inches long, occur in clusters of two or three and remain on the tree for two to five years.

In April or May the pale purple pollen-bearing staminate blossoms cluster at the base of the new leaf growth, while the cone-bearing ovulate flowers are borne two or four in a whorl on stout erect stems below the new growth. The short-stalked, dull brown, egg-shaped cones reach a length of one and a half to two and a half inches and mature in two seasons. They are the smallest cones of the four important Southern pines. Each cone scale is terminated with a temporary prickle or broad-based spine. This characteristic is responsible for the scientific name *echinata* derived from the Latin word *echinus*, meaning hedgehog. Under each central cone scale are two pale brown triangular seeds about three-sixteenths of an inch long, each provided with a wing about one-half an inch long and one-eighth of an inch wide. When the cone opens the seeds drop out and may be carried several hundred feet by the wind. They germinate evenly and quickly, and frequently find places for growth in abandoned open fields, which gives rise to the common name "old field pine." It is more often called yellow or "short straw" pine, and rosemary pine.

It is unusual among all pines because of its ability to sprout

Maryland State Department of Forestry

Shortleaf Pine frequently grows in open fields and is commonly called "old field pine." Its broad, rounded, dark bluish green crown with long somewhat drooping branches surmounts a straight cinnamon-red trunk

from the stump, or when injured by fire. This is characteristic of young trees and is lost after they are six or eight inches in diameter.

The yellowish wood is noticeably grained, moderately hard, strong and stiff. It resembles that of longleaf pine with which it is frequently sold, but is lighter and less strong. A cubic foot of air-dry shortleaf wood weighs thirty-six to thirty-nine pounds, as compared with forty to forty-four pounds for longleaf pine. It is used extensively for house-building materials, including framing, ceiling, weather-boarding, panels, window and door frames, casing and carved work. The grain shows well in natural finish or when stained. Frames of overstuffed furniture, chairs, desks, agricultural machinery, excelsior, wood pulp, mine props, barrels and crates are also made of shortleaf pine.

Commercial estimates of standing timber are combined under the general heading "yellow pine," which amounted to 197,000,000,000 board feet in 1936. About twenty-eight per cent or nearly 55,000,000,000 board feet is probably shortleaf pine. The same ratio might be applied to the eight billion board feet of yellow pine cut and sold in 1939.

It grows associated with loblolly pine, oaks, hickories and sweet gum, but extensively in stands comprised only of shortleaf pine. Whole stands frequently attain an average height of fifty or sixty feet and nearly nine inches in diameter in thirty years. Such a stand may contain nearly fifty cords of wood capable of being cut into about 6,000 board feet of lumber. Assuming that the trees are sound and straight, the volume rapidly increases as the trees mature. At fifty years they may be ten to twelve inches in diameter and the volume of saw material will be from 20,000 to 40,000 board feet to the acre. Stands of more than 50,000 board feet to the acre are relatively uncommon as the timber is usually cut before it reaches that size.

Shortleaf pine, along with all other southern forest trees, suffers from the yearly burning of the woods. Not only are the immature trees killed, but the mature ones are seared and weakened, leaving them prey to injurious insects and fungi. The ability to sprout only partially offsets the damage and in no case makes up for the removal of the natural mulch of leaf litter from the soil. Next to the loss from fire is that from attacks of the Southern pine beetle. This insect attacks the living trees and is particularly active after long dry periods, but will not live through winter temperatures of zero or colder. Other enemies include such insects as the pine sawyer, the Nantucket tip moth, and fungus diseases such as "red heart," whose spores frequently enter the tree through wounds caused by fire.

Aside from its value for timber, the broad pyramidal head, straight symmetrical trunk, and general vigor result in shortleaf pine being recognized as a handsome park or lawn tree. It may be planted for ornamental purposes from New York to Georgia and west to Missouri and Texas.

The three to five-inch long needles are borne in clusters of two or three. Prickles on each cone scale help distinguish this tree

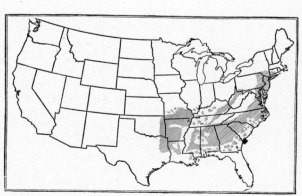

Natural range of Shortleaf Pine

The scaly bark of mature trees is almost cinnamon-red and broken into more or less rectangular plates

JACK PINE

Pinus banksiana, Lambert

Jack pine frequently attains heights of sixty feet or more, and young trees usually carry branches well down to the ground

TYPICAL of light sandy soils and the heavy snow country of the north, Jack pine grows throughout northern New England, northeastern New York, the greater part of the Lake States, and south as far as the Illinois shores of Lake Michigan. In British Columbia the range lacks scarcely three hundred miles of being transcontinental, extending from the southern shores of Hudson Bay to the upper waters of the Mackenzie River. Approaching within one and a half degrees of the Arctic Circle, it is the most northern of all American pines. The range reaches some 1,600 miles to the south, and the spread from east to west is 2,500 miles.

Generally considered an inferior tree, as implied by the name "Jack," it is scrubby and dwarfed on its outer limits of distribution, but under favorable conditions of soil and climate attains heights of twenty-five to sixty feet and breast-high diameters of eight to twenty inches. Occasional trees reach heights of seventy-five to ninety feet and are two feet in diameter.

Barren, sandy or rocky land at elevations from 100 feet to 1,200 feet above sea level are its usual habitat, but the largest trees develop on moist soils of good quality. Jack pine is given little consideration in New England, but it is assuming increasing importance in the Lake States, and reaches its largest size on the sandy barrens northwest of Lake Winnipeg in the provinces of Manitoba and Saskatchewan.

Jack pine is essentially a pioneering tree in that it follows closely after lumbering operations and fires to provide shelter for more desirable species that may follow. During the first twenty to twenty-five years, it grows faster than either red pine or white pine, but a few years later these species will overtake it and dominate the stand. Open grown trees six to fifteen inches in diameter may be twenty-five to eighty-five years old, while trees growing in dense stands may take seventy-five years to attain a diameter of six inches. Naturally shortlived, the oldest Jack pine trees do not exceed 125 to 150 years, and few stands which have been lumbered exceed 110 years in age.

Botanists classify Jack pine with the twenty-four hard, pitch or "yellow" pines, which grow throughout the country, and until 1905 was known as *Pinus divaricata*. The stubby, flat, grayish green needles, held two in a cluster, are among the shortest of the entire pine group. They vary from less than an inch to an inch and a half in length, are scanty and somewhat clustered at the ends of the twigs and remain two or three seasons before dropping.

After the trees are four to eight years old, crowded clusters of yellow, pollen-bearing cone-like blossoms appear in the early spring on the ends of the past season's growth, while the upper branches of the same tree carry clusters of dark, purple ovulate flowers. After fertilization the ovulate ones develop into lopsided cones incurved like a ram's horn and about one to two inches long, by a half inch to an inch in diameter. These ripen during September of the second season. Pressed closely against the stem or sometimes growing more or less at right angles to it, these light, clay-brown cones may remain attached and closed for twenty-five years or longer. They open irregularly to release some of the small, brown-winged, blackish seeds which drift before the wind for long distances. The unusual capacity of this tree to retain its seeds and liberate them during warm weather or after a fire, and the fact that many of the seed which land on open soil grow to seedling or sapling stage, frequently causes Jack pine to be the first to reclothe burned land. In fact, Jack pine's greatest usefulness is to clothe poor, sandy, or gravelly land with tree growth and hold the ground for other more desirable species that will follow.

Short, flat needles borne in pairs cluster toward the end of tough branches, and the lopsided cones may retain their seed for years

The relatively thin, dull red-brown bark of mature trees is narrowly ridged and furrowed. The irregular main vertical ridges are connected by smaller lateral ones.

Taken as a whole the tree is easily identified by its short leaves which are always in pairs, its persistent curved cones, and by its many crooked branches.

Jack pine is of increasing commercial importance. There are about 3,000,000 acres of jack pine in the three Lake States with approximately 2,500,000,000 board feet and 6,000,000 cords of standing timber. The brownish-yellow heartwood, surrounded by a layer of creamy sapwood, varies in texture and weighs twenty-nine to thirty pounds to the cubic foot when air dry. It lacks strength, is brittle, and decays rapidly when left in contact with the soil. Clear lumber resembles that of red pine, and is so marketed, but it is usually low grade and knotty.

The dull red-brown bark consists of narrow, intermeshed ridges of closely pressed scales

Used locally for fuel and rough lumber, there are increasing demands for its use as pulpwood, packing cases, slack cooperage, mine timbers, posts, and light traffic railroad ties.

Jack pine has few enemies other than fire and from this it reseeds itself with remarkable ability. While not satisfactory as a street or shade tree, the peculiar green of its foliage makes it desired for some ornamental purposes. Recently it has been used for forest plantings as a means of restoring growth on poor sandy lands, and has succeeded on the sandy soils of northwestern Nebraska.

First reported by French explorers and early settlers in eastern Canada, it was planted in England as early as 1735. It has, however, proved better adapted to the soil and climate conditions of Germany and Russia than to England.

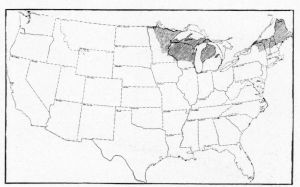

Natural range of Jack Pine within the United States

LONGLEAF PINE

Pinus palustris, Miller

IN the original southern pine forest, longleaf pine outranked shortleaf, loblolly and slash pines, and was comparable to the present rank of Douglas fir in national importance. The temperate almost sub-tropical climate, combined with ample rainfall of the coastal plain from southeastern Virginia through North and South Carolinas, Georgia, Florida, Alabama, Mississippi, Louisiana and eastern Texas, furnishes desirable growing conditions. Trees of best development are found on moist but well drained, deep, sandy loam, but they grow well on all sandy and gravelly soils within this range.

Literally translated, its botanical name *Pinus palustris* means the pine that lives in marshy places, but it grows on many different kinds of soil. Frequently growing with shortleaf, loblolly, and slash pines, it shares with them the common name of Southern yellow pine, and in certain respects is the most desirable of them all. It is commonly known as "longstraw" pine.

The leaves, or needles, are eight to eighteen inches long, held three in a bundle, and drop off before the end of the second season. Like all other pines, separate male and female flowers are borne on the same tree during early spring. The male flowers appear as dark rose-purple catkins around the base of young shoots and bear yellow pollen. These shrivel and fall shortly after the wind has carried the pollen to fertilize the ovulate or female blossoms, which appear in pairs or small clusters at the ends of the upper branches. During the second season after fertilization these grow into cones five to ten inches long, and having matured, release the winged seeds which develop in pairs under each of the cone scales.

Longleaf pine frequently grows to heights of 100 to 120 feet, with a tall slight tapering trunk from two to three feet in diameter. The orange-brown bark of mature trees is made up of many closely pressed papery scales and may be a half-inch thick.

The light red to orange-yellow heartwood is exceedingly hard, strong and durable, and within the tree is surrounded by a thin nearly white layer of sapwood. A cubic foot of heartwood weighs forty to forty-three pounds when air dry. Its great strength and the large sizes in which it is available cause it to be favored above most others for construction. It is used for heavy girders in buildings and bridges, mast and spars, railway-ties, flooring, interior finish and general construction, as well as for fuel and charcoal.

The annual cut of longleaf pine is not known, but it probably amounts to about one third of all the Southern yellow pine lumber cut. During 1939 the total was almost eight billion board feet, of which more than half was produced in Alabama, Mississippi, Louisiana, and Texas.

Longleaf Pine—The aristocrat of the Southern pines, frequently attains heights of 100 to 120 feet on the light sandy soils of the coastal plain from southeastern Virginia to western Texas

Recent estimates indicate that the region occupied by Southern pines now contains about 200,000,000,000 board feet of saw timber. The total volume of these Southern yellow pines ranks fourth in our national storehouse of forest wealth, being exceeded only by Douglas fir, ponderosa pine and the Western firs.

No description of longleaf pine is complete without reference to the naval stores industry. This general term applies chiefly to turpentine and rosin, the principal products derived from the distillation of the pitch or crude gum which exudes from pine trees when "chipped" or wounded. It also is applied to similar products obtained by distilling the pine wood. Longleaf and slash pines are the chief gum-running trees from which naval stores are secured. Most of this is produced in the region from South Carolina to Mississippi. The value of these according to the 1939 United States census exceeded $30,000,000. Paint and varnish, soap, shoe polish, paper, and printing ink use up most of the naval stores. Chipping of the trees and distilling the gum employs several thousand people and is one of the major forest industries of some portions of the southeast.

Longleaf pine produces vigorous seedlings which grow slowly above ground during the first few years because of the energy spent developing a long tap root and large root system. After four or five years the longleaf saplings begin to grow rapidly and continue for thirty-five to fifty years, producing in that period trees fifty-five to eighty feet tall and seven to eleven inches in diameter. Timber growth of 300 to 500 board feet an acre a year in full stands is not uncommon throughout the longleaf area.

Fire and hogs are the worst enemies of longleaf pine. During the early seedling stage light grass fires do comparatively little harm, but this apparent immunity becomes less effective as the trees get taller. While the small trees have what is sometimes called an "asbestus bud," their sweet succulent roots appeal to hogs that range much of the Southern pine country. A single "razorback" hog with a taste for pine roots may destroy hundreds of little trees in a day.

Again, after the trees have attained a fair size and have been wounded or "faced" for gum, they are easily damaged by fire. These faces start a few inches from the ground, and being covered with dry gum or pitch burn easily. In spite of constant efforts fires continue to rob the South of millions of dollars in present and future timber values.

Various insects and fungus diseases attack longleaf pine, but the one most generally recognized is the Southern pine beetle. Attacks by these tiny insects upon the living trees may be partially prevented by not cutting timber in the hot season, or if it must be cut, by piling and burning the brush as quickly as possible. Infested trees should be used at once, and all brush and bark should be burned.

Longleaf pine bears large crops of seeds at intervals of three to five years, with a few seed from open stands nearly every year. Where seed trees are left, and fire and hogs kept out, it re-establishes itself after a lumbering operation. Since 1920 Louisiana has required timber operators to leave at least one seed tree, eight inches in diameter, to the acre.

Where seed trees are not available seedlings may be grown in a nursery and transplanted after the first year. Set out at intervals of six to eight feet there will be from 700 to 1,200 trees to the acre. Successful plantations have been established in many parts of the South, and with fire protection are producing from 100 to 500 board feet to the acre yearly.

The orange-brown bark, furrowed and crossed into closely pressed scales may be confused with that of some other pines, but the long, flexible, shiny, dark-green needles, held in groups of threes, are characteristic of Longleaf Pine. The reddish brown mature cones are five to ten inches long, with thick scales that turn back to release the winged seeds. At the base of the leaves is a cluster of pollen-bearing staminate blossoms

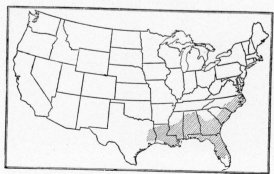

Natural range of Longleaf Pine in the United States

SLASH PINE

Pinus caribaea, Morelet

SLASH PINE ranks high among the rapid growing, early maturing pines of the southern coastal plain. Because of its ability to produce heavy stands of timber and its yield of high quality resin, it is probably the most profitable of all southern timber trees.

It grows on low ground and on hummocks in swamps or moist "slashes" from southern South Carolina to the keys of Florida and westward across Georgia, Alabama, and Mississippi to eastern Louisiana. It also occurs in Central America, Cuba, the Isle of Pines, the Bahamas, and other islands of the Carribean Sea, which explains its scientific name *Pinus caribaea*. The southern extremity of its range, including lower Florida, produces pure forests of slash pine, while elsewhere it may be associated with loblolly and longleaf pine.

Best growth and purest stands are attained in Florida and southern Georgia, where trees rise to heights of eighty to 150 feet and attain trunk diameters of two to three feet. The average height is about 100 feet, with clear lengths of sixty or seventy feet surmounted by a dense, rounded crown of heavy horizontal limbs. During its first twenty to fifty years, slash pine exceeds all of the southern pines in growth, reaching heights of forty-five feet and diameters of six inches in twenty years, and attains over eighty feet in height and fifteen inches in diameter by fifty years. Trees mature at about one hundred years but may reach ages of 150 to 200 years.

The dark lustrous green needles grow in bundles of two, three, or more—but are most frequently in pairs. They are eight to twelve inches long, forming dense clusters near the ends of the branches, and drop off in their second season. While shorter than those of longleaf pine, they are longer than loblolly, and darker green than either.

In spring the reddish brown terminal bud elongates into a light gray "candle" about the thickness of a large pencil in contrast to similar "candles" from the larger terminal bud of longleaf pine, which are an inch or more in diameter.

The rapid growing, early-maturing Slash Pine is one of the profitable timber trees of the South Atlantic and Gulf States

During January and February, before leaf growth starts, dark purple staminate flowers appear in crowded clusters at the base of twigs of the previous year's growth, while at the ends of the same or similar twigs are pink ovulate flowers on long stems which develop into small erect cones. They hang down during the second season, and by October have matured into glossy, leathery brown, egg-shaped cones three to six inches long. The thin, flexible cone scales are each armed with a slender, slightly recurved prickle. These prickles, borne on the varnished end of each cone scale, are peculiar to slash pine.

Under each cone scale is a pair of mottled dark gray winged seeds. Large crops are borne every two or three years, which are carried by the wind to assist in this tree's aggressive reclamation of old fields and cutover areas. There are 16,000 to 18,000 clear seed in a pound, with sixty to ninety out of every 100 seed fertile.

The bark is clear orange to red-brown, one-half to three-quarters of an inch thick, consisting of many overlapping, irregular plates or scales which form broad flat ridges on the trunk. Turpentine workers invariably associate the orange bark with free flowing resin qualities, for slash pine excels all other southern pines in production of rosin or gum containing a large content of spirits of turpentine.

The light brown to rich orange wood is coarse-grained, resinous, brittle, without durability in contact with the soil, and a cubic foot weighs — when air dry — about forty-eight pounds. Accordingly, it is the heaviest of all pines and comparable to the hickories and white oaks. The wide sapwood is nearly white. It so closely resembles the wood of longleaf pine that a distinction is seldom made when the lumber is marketed. Large quantities of second growth timber are cut for railroad ties, increasing amounts for wood pulp, and mature trees are used for general construction and interior trim.

The moist location of most slash pine stands provides natural protection against fire, but trees are often subject to red heart rot.

Slash pine is one of the most rapid growing and early-maturing of all eastern forest trees. Because of its capacity to produce wood pulp, fuel, lumber, and naval stores, as well as its adaptability to moist, sandy soils within its range, it is being extensively planted in several of the southern coastal states. Moreover, it is recognized for its unusual beauty and is being used to an increasing extent for landscape and roadside planting in the South.

William M. Harlow

The short-stalked three to six inch cones are armed with distinct prickles on each cone scale. Leaves are in bundles of two or three

Irregular orange colored plates lie one over the other to make a half-inch layer of bark

Natural range of Slash Pine in the United States

SCOTCH PINE

Pinus sylvestris, Linnaeus

Photographs by Devereux Butcher

SCOTCH pine has been more extensively planted for forestry purposes in eastern North America than any other European tree. Its irregular crown, and the orange-red bark of the upper trunk and limbs are seen in many parks and cemeteries. Plantations, windbreaks, and ornamental plantings from western North Carolina to Quebec, and across the Lake States to Saskatchewan and northwestern Nebraska testify to this tree's indifference to soil and climate conditions. In its native Europe it is found over most of the continent and much of northern Asia, comprising the bulk of the forested area of northern Germany and enormous forests in Russia. It thrives on well drained sites where the soil is deep and moist, but grows on dry, sterile sands and thin soils of rocky outcrops to elevations of 8,000 feet in the Caucasian Mountains.

Although commercially important in Europe, Scotch pine has an unhappy record as a timber producer in this country. Early plantings were largely from seed of low, stunted, high mountain trees, producing crooked trunks and poor quality wood. Since 1920, increasing numbers of trees from seed of selected origin have been planted including a variety from the vicinity of Riga, in northeastern Europe. The American grown trees of this variety are expected to inherit their parents' tall, straight form.

Scotch pine attains heights of sixty to ninety feet in America with diameters of one to three feet, but under favorable western European conditions it reaches 150 feet and diameters of five feet. When young, it has an irregularly pyramidal crown, but with age a broad, irregularly round-topped head, often described as picturesque, develops. Forest grown trees are tall with a straight unbranched trunk of relatively little taper and a short crown. Trees grown in the open retain their branches well down toward the ground, several of which may develop long, and horizontal in form. At a distance this tree resembles pitch pine.

The needles are one and a half to three and a half inches long, borne in sheathed clusters of two or rarely three. They are dull blue-green, appreciably flattened, rigid, sharp-

Field grown Scotch Pine has a short trunk, an open, irregular crown, and heights of sixty feet or more

pointed and usually twisted. The needles are shorter than those of red pine, stouter than shortleaf pine, and more blunt pointed than Table Mountain pine. They extend along the length of medium thick, grayish yellow twigs which are rougher than those of Virginia pine. Each twig is terminated by blunt orange-red buds whose small scales turn backward.

Dense clusters of egg-shaped, yellow, pollen-bearing cone-like staminate blossoms about two-fifths of an inch long are borne near the base of the new growth in May or June. The seed-producing ovulate blooms appear simultaneously, singly or in pairs near the ends of the new growth in the upper crown. These mature in the second season as backward pointing, somewhat curved, dull, tawny yellow, short stalked cones, one to two and a half inches long. The cone scales are swollen at the base and are usually armed with a tiny prickle. The small dark gray winged seeds may be carried several hundred feet on the wind.

The bark of the upper trunk and larger limbs is orange-red, thin, and peels off in papery flakes. That of the older trunks is grayish brown, about a half inch thick near the base, with longitudinal scaly plates and irregular furrows which reveal streaks of orange-red inner bark.

The pale reddish brown resinous heartwood is hard, tough, and moderately light—a cubic foot weighing thirty-three to thirty-four pounds when air seasoned. The heartwood becomes increasingly distinguishable from the lighter colored sapwood on prolonged exposure to the air. The annual rings are clearly apparent. It is moderately durable in contact with the ground, drys well in the air, but is susceptible to blue stain, and is suitable for outside work. Throughout Europe, it is widely used for general construction. Its many uses include buildings, bridges, scaffolding, ships' masts, mine props, fencing, paving, and the better grades are selected for joinery. The wood gives good results with paint or varnish, can be effectively stained, and is easily glued.

Within its European range, and especially on poor soils, Scotch pine forms pure stands of considerable extent. On better sites, it associates with Norway spruce, silver fir and European larch. In the Scottish highlands it is found with European white birch, and on the peat moors with aspen and alder.

In America Scotch pine is reasonably free of fungus diseases and insect pests, but in Europe no other tree is more susceptible to injurious insects. Bark beetles, weevils, wood borers and various needle feeding insects are especially active where trees grow on poor soil. Fungus diseases also do considerable damage. The thin bark makes young trees susceptible to ground fire damage, but the thicker bark on older trees resists fire to a considerable extent.

Scotch pine has proved a hardy pioneer, especially when planted on long-abandoned, trampled pastures, and on blow sand. Even on such sites, however, native species will grow with equal or greater vigor, and the resulting forest products are usually superior. Like other trees from Europe and Asia it shows strong tendencies to establish itself by natural seeding. Extensive stands of volunteer second generation Scotch pine may be expected over the northern and eastern states, and the better strains will undoubtedly provide this country with sources of good timber.

Clusters of yellow pollen bearing blossoms appear at the base of the new spring growth

The gray-brown bark near the base of old trees is broken by shallow, longitudinal fissures

Two flat, twisted, blue-green needles are in each sheath and the short-stalked cone which bends backward is seldom more than two inches long

TAMARACK

Larix Laricina, (DuRoi) Koch

FROM the Atlantic to the valley of the Yukon, north to the limit of tree growth near the Arctic circle and along the shores of Hudson Bay, tamarack, or eastern larch extends south throughout much of Canada, New England and New York, into Pennsylvania, West Vir-

companions drop out from south to north, until the last to remain are black spruce, red spruce, aspen, paper birch and finally, the willows. Toward the Arctic circle growth is scattered and dwarfed. This tree sustains itself from sea level to elevations of 4,000 feet; from the relatively mild climate and humidity of the Atlantic Coast to the interior of Alaska.

The broad, shallow root system is adapted to swampy ground, but best growth is made in fresh, well-drained soils.

The straight, slender tamarack is seldom more than fifty to sixty feet tall with a trunk eighteen to twenty inches in diameter, but on the low benches north of Lake Winnipeg trees reach one hundred feet or more with diameters of two feet.

In youth the crown is narrowly pyramidal, with a

Devereux Butcher

Slender and sparsely foliaged, tamaracks
are often fifty or sixty feet tall

ginia, Ohio, Michigan, Indiana, Illinois, Wisconsin and Minnesota. Its slender, sparse and feathery, clear green summer crown contrasts with the dark green heavier foliage of other conifers. In winter its bare orange-brown branches form a delicate tracery.

On well-drained uplands and occasional cool sphagnum swamps of its southern range tamarack grows in mixture with black, red, and white spruces, hemlock, balsam, aspen, paper birch, alder, northern white cedar, willow and red maple. The occasional pure even-aged stands are crowded. One by one its tree

From late September until April the crown
and horizontal branches are bare of foliage

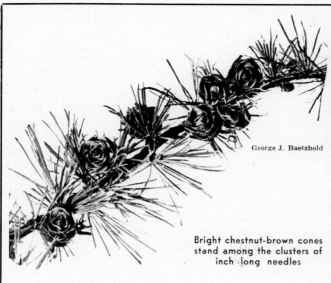

George J. Baetzhold

Bright chestnut-brown cones
stand among the clusters of
inch long needles

Frank Wallace

Pale green new leaves of early spring
appear with rose red ovulate blooms

flexible terminal shoot. With age trees become irregular, and those grown in the open maintain a low
broad head. The slender upper branches are horizontal or slightly ascending, the lower ones droop in
long sweeps, and the straight trunk tapers rapidly.
Trees grown within forest competition may be clear of
branches for half or more their length.

Clusters of twelve to twenty bright green, soft,
bristle-like leaves grow on wood of the previous year,
or singly on the new shoots. They are three-quarters
of an inch to an inch and a quarter long and triangular in cross section. The upper side is rounded,
and the lower sharply keeled. In early spring the new
leaves are marked with breathing pores or stomata.
By September or October the leaves turn yellow and
fall. This feature was noted by the Iroquois Indians
whose name "Ka-neh-tens" means "the leaves fall."

The delicate green tracery of the spring foliage is
punctuated with clusters of inconspicuous, stemless
yellow staminate or pollen-bearing blooms on the one
or two year old orange-brown branchlets. The more
showy ovulate cones grow on short lateral stalks of
one to three year old twigs. They are like small
flattened spheres, with green-tipped, rose-colored
bracts growing out between the red scales. At first
they stand erect, with scales spread ready for pollination. Later they droop and close their scales while
the seeds develop. By autumn they stand erect again,
are chestnut-brown and one-half to three-quarters of
an inch long. During the fall and winter the scales
spread to liberate the chestnut-brown winged seed.

The reddish brown bark of mature trunks is a half
to three quarters of an inch thick. Its surface is
broken into thin, brown, closely pressed, roundish
scales. Young bark is smooth and light orange.

A cubic foot of the tough, resinous, coarse-grained
wood when dry weighs about thirty-nine pounds. It
is light brown, with thin, nearly white sapwood. Because it is durable in contact with the soil it is used
for railroad ties, posts, sills and for boats. Its other
uses include excelsior, refrigerators, cabinet work, interior finish and telephone poles. In 1941 eight northeastern states from Minnesota to New England produced 2,846,000 board feet of lumber.

Next to fire, its worst enemy is the larch saw-fly
which often kills large areas of tamarack forest.

George J. Baetzhold

The reddish brown bark has shallow
furrows and is about half an inch thick

Natural range of Tamarack

45

WESTERN LARCH

Larix occidentalis, Nuttall

Western Larch attains heights of over two hundred feet and develops a slender symmetrical crown covered with satiny, pale green foliage

THE most important, as well as the largest and most massive of all the larches or tamaracks is western larch, whose natural range is restricted to the high mountain valleys and slopes of southeastern British Columbia and the upper Columbia River basin bounded by the Rocky Mountains on the east and the Cascade Mountains on the west. This tree is seldom found below 2,000 feet or higher than 7,000 feet above sea level, and attains its greatest size and abundance in Montana.

Short, horizontal branches on a tall straight trunk form a crown whose narrow, pyramidal form runs to a slender point. The crown usually occupies from one-half to one-third of the total height, so that trees 160 to 200 feet tall may have sixty to over one hundred feet of clear trunk. Such individuals which occasionally attain diameters of six or seven feet, may be 600 or 700 years old, while trees sixteen to twenty inches in diameter may be 250 to 400 years old.

The larches and the southern cypress are unique among coniferous trees in that they shed their leaves in the autumn. The light green, flatly triangular pointed needles are one to one and five-eighths inches long. First appearing singly in spirals on the twig, they later develop on a scaly spur in bundles of thirty to forty. They turn yellow in the fall and drop, but new ones develop on the same spur for several years thereafter. The foliage is sparse, and gives the crown a pale green, satiny appearance.

Separate male and female flowers are borne close together on the same tree during the early spring on growth of the previous year. The yellow green, pollen-bearing male flowers are about the size of a pea, while developing on the same twigs are small scaly, bright purple or red ovulate flowers, each of which is surrounded by a bundle of leaves. These flowers, when fertilized, develop into broadly egg-shaped cones, one to one and a half inches long, with slender bracts which extend beyond the cone scales. In the early fall the small, chestnut-brown, winged seeds are shed, and by the end of October or November the cones have dropped from the trees. Cones are seldom produced on trees younger than twenty-five years old, and heavy crops are not produced until the trees are forty years or older.

The conspicuous bract extending beyond the cone scale as in the case of Douglas fir cones, the white woolly coating of hairs near the base of the cone, their larger size, and the fine hairy growth on the young twigs help distinguish western larch from the other larches. The leaves or needles are triangular in cross-section and longer, and the tree attains the greatest size of all the larches.

Mature trees have deeply furrowed dull, reddish cinnamon - brown bark composed of innumerable overlapping rounded plates broken to form a zig-zag pattern of many imperfect diamonds. It is three to six inches thick near the base. Higher up on the trunk and on the branches, the bark is relatively thin, scaly and more brown than red. The thick bark on the lower trunk often proves an effective protection against fire. This, together with the natural tolerance of the tree, helps explain the pure stands of western larch which frequently follow the destruction of lodgepole pine and other associates by fire. The hard, fine-grained, reddish brown wood is not only the heaviest of all the larches, but one of the heaviest of all the conifers. It weighs thirty-six to thirty-nine pounds to the cubic foot when air dry, and is remarkably durable in contact with the soil. It works well with tools and is used to an increasing extent for interior finish, boxes, boats, and furniture, as well as for telephone poles, railroad ties, mine timbers, and posts. Its largest use is probably as rough lumber in local construction. The butt logs, however, are so heavy, and frequently so full of defects that they are often left in the woods. Pulping experiments indicate that western larch is suitable for the production of high-grade wrapping paper.

With an estimated stand of 25,000,000,000 board feet of sawtimber, most of which is in national forests, the lumber production for all western species of larch in 1941 was reported as 145,842,000 board feet. Over one-half of this was cut from the forests of Montana, and the remainder from Idaho, Washington, and Oregon. The high point in the production of western larch was in 1920 when the cut was 338,000,000 board feet. During the twenty years from 1910 to 1930 the average annual lumber cut was 275,000,000 board feet.

Western larch sometimes occurs in pure open forests, but is usually associated with other species. In mixture with ponderosa pine, in eastern Oregon, stands of about 2,000 board feet an acre are common, while in western Montana in mixture with western white pine, Douglas fir, lodgepole pine, lowland white fir, alpine fir, and Engelmann spruce the stand may reach 10,000 to 12,000 board feet to the acre.

Throughout its range the natural reproduction is increased by fires, because the seedlings require a large amount of light, and because of the relative resistance which large trees have to fire. In this respect western larch finds lodgepole pine its chief competitor. Favorite areas for pure larch reproduction are those so thoroughly burned over as practically to prevent any immediate heavy reproduction of lodgepole pine.

The precipitation throughout much of its range is from twenty to thirty inches, with long seasons of moderately heavy snowfall, frequent rains in the spring and fall, but hot dry summers.

While relatively resistant to fire, western larch is subject to the attack of a number of wood-destroying fungi, the most common of which is a chalky quinine fungus which causes a brown heart rot. It is also subject to what the lumbermen call "shake"—a breaking or disintegration along the growth rings of the lower trunk.

There is evidence that the larches have existed for millions of years in the north temperate and subarctic zones of North America and Europe. Of the nine species inhabiting the world four are native to this continent. In addition to western larch, there is the eastern tamarack common to the northeastern states and extending westward to southern Alaska, alpine larch found in the high mountains of the Northwest, and Alaska larch limited to a portion of that territory.

Larix occidentalis may be translated directly to mean the larch of the western world. David Douglas first observed and described it in April, 1826, in northwestern Washington near Kettle Falls on the Columbia River

Elongated cones one to one and five-eighths inches long grow on the branches along with the clusters of thirty to forty fine, flexible needles

The dull cinnamon-brown bark, composed of many small irregularly rounded plates, may be three to six inches thick near the base of the trunk

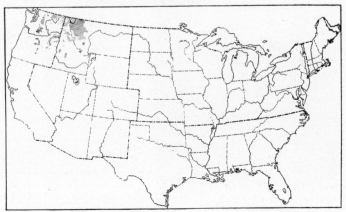

Natural range of Western Larch in the United States

47

BLACK SPRUCE

Picea mariana, (Miller) Britton, Sterns and Poggenberg

WHILE the form of black spruce varies according to site, its most noticeable characteristics are its slender straight trunk, irregular open conical crown, comparatively short branches, and small cones. In favored situations at the southern extremity of the range, it sometimes attains a height of one hundred feet with a trunk diameter of two or three feet, and on good sites in the north it occasionally grows to seventy feet or more with a trunk that measures ten or twelve inches in diameter. As a rule, however, it is only thirty to fifty feet tall. Toward the northern limits of its range it is reduced to a shrub with heights up to twelve feet. A moisture-loving species, it inhabits cold sphagnum bogs, springy swamps and lake shores. It may be found on sandy or rocky hillsides and uplands, but as in the case of bog-grown trees where ice remains around roots and base of trunk well into spring or early summer, and those growing on upland sites where there is insufficient moisture, the trees are stunted. It is found at elevations from one hundred to thirty-five hundred feet above sea level.

Black spruce is a slow growing tree, especially when in swampy locations. Trees in these sites will add only an inch or two to their trunk diameters in seventy-five or a hundred years. In such areas there is little competition so that it is most abundant and develops thick pure stands. It grows also on glacial drift and clay soils, but best growth occurs in well-drained alluvial soils that are constantly moist. Black spruce does not demand deep soils because the root system is shallow. It is a fairly long-lived tree, and specimens of average size are from one hundred and twenty-five to two hundred years old.

The range of black spruce is transcontinental, extending from Labrador, Newfoundland and Nova Scotia southward through New England, northern New Jersey, Pennsylvania, and along the Appalachian Mountains to northern West Virginia. In the lake states it occurs in Michigan, Wisconsin and northeastern Minnesota, and thence from Hudson Bay and southern Manitoba northwestward in a broad belt to the west coast of Alaska.

Bark on the mature trunk is a quarter to a half inch thick, dark reddish brown turning gray with age, and is broken on the surface into flaky, thin, rather closely pressed scales. Trunks of trees growing in the open are clothed to the ground with branches, the upper ones being horizontal, while the lower ones droop and turn upward at the tip. Occasionally the basal branches of isolated trees sweep the ground taking root and sending up shoots. Middle-aged trees in dense stands have their trunks clear of branches for half their height, and trees forming thick, pure stands in bogs often have only a few short branches clustered at the top of the tree.

The sharp-pointed buds of black spruce are covered with light reddish brown overlapping scales and measure an eighth to a third of an inch long. Twigs of the year are yellowish brown, covered with short reddish brown hairs later turning dark brown and becoming scaly. The four-angled, blunt-tipped needles measure a quarter to three-quarters of an inch in length and are slightly incurved above the middle. They are dark bluish green with a whitish bloom, and have rows of tiny white stomata on each of the four sides. They grow in spirals along the twig, standing out on all sides from it, and remain on the tree for from seven to ten years.

Flowers of black spruce appear in May or June, and are situated near or at the tips of the branches and measure about one-eighth of an inch in length. The staminate or pollen-bearing ones are dark red and nearly stemless, while the ovulate or seed-producing flowers are purple and are composed of rounded scales.

The clustered, drooping, grayish brown cones measuring one-half to one and a half inches in length mature in August. When the scales open the cones are nearly round. They fall entire, but remain on the trees for

The most noticeable features of black spruce are its slender straight form, comparatively short branches and small size

twenty or thirty years, the oldest being at the base of branches nearest the trunk. Scales are brittle, rounded, slightly hairy, and have notched, uneven edges. The dark brown winged oblong, pointed seeds measure a half-inch in length and an eighth inch in width. Black spruce bears large seed crops only at infrequent intervals. Seeds retain their vitality for a long time. Their rate of germination is fairly high, and is best on mineral soil or humus that is constantly moist, and on wet decayed wood, needle littler, or moss. During their first year or two, seedlings require little or no direct sunlight. Older trees also are very tolerant of shade, especially on wet sites, and up to an advanced age are able to recover from suppression. Though often forming pure forests, this tree is found in mixture with larch, aspen, willow, alder, cottonwood, balsam fir, white cedar, and black ash. Black spruce, eastern larch and willow, all three of dwarf size, make the most northerly outpost of trees where their ranges draw close to the edge of the Arctic Sea in the Mackenzie Bay region.

Heavier than the wood of any other North American spruce, that of black spruce weighs about thirty-three pounds to the cubic foot when dry. It is pale buff yellow or with a reddish tinge, and has a few inconspicuous resin ducts. Because of slow growth, the annual rings are narrow and the sapwood thin. It is soft, straight-grained, not strong, and is commercially less important than the other two eastern spruces, — red spruce and white spruce, — because the tree is small and slow growing. The wood, however, has much the same properties as the others. The chief use to which black spruce is put is in the manufacture of paper pulp for which it is ideally suited owing to the long white fibres which make up the wood and which need little or no bleaching. It is used also for canoe paddles, oars, ladder rails, construction, ship building, and for many other purposes requiring a light, stiff wood. Chewing gum is made from the resin, and formerly spruce beer was made by boiling the branch tips. Today young trees are increasingly in demand for the Christmas tree market.

Other common names for black spruce are blue spruce, spruce pine, eastern spruce, bog spruce, and swamp spruce. The scientific name *Picea mariana* means Maryland spruce.

Its thin bark and resinous exudations on the trunk make black spruce susceptible to injury by fire, but this is lessened by the wet locations in which it grows. The tree is attacked by several kinds of fungi and by insects, especially the spruce budworm.

Black spruce is rarely planted as an ornamental tree because it is short-lived in cultivation. Moreover, it has an uneven, unkempt appearance owing to an accumulation of dead branches.

From 1928-1937 the combined average annual cut of the three eastern spruces in the United States was 132,600,000 board feet. There are no available figures to show the amount of standing black spruce sawtimber, but in 1930 the combined stand of red, white, and black spruces, and balsam fir in the United States was estimated at 21,533,000,000 board feet.

The grayish brown cones are clustered and drooping, and the bluish green, four-angled needles grow in spirals along the twigs

At first reddish brown, the bark turns gray with age, and is cracked into thin, closely pressed scales

Natural range of Black Spruce

RED SPRUCE

Picea rubra, **Link**

THE narrow, dark yellow-green crowns of red spruce pierce the forest skyline from southeastern Canada through New England, eastern New York and the Appalachian Mountains to Georgia. Frequently in mixture with white pine, hemlock, balsam fir, sugar maple, yellow birch, or beech, pure stands are usually limited to swamps and mountain tops. In its northern range, red spruce grows on well drained soils near sea level, but ascends in the Adirondacks to altitudes of 4,500 feet and in the Southern Appalachians is seldom found below 5,000 feet.

Red spruce of the north reaches heights of sixty to eighty feet, with trunk diameters of nearly two feet. Larger sizes are attained in the Southern Appalachians with occasional trees over one hundred feet high and up to four feet in diameter. Some botanists classify these southern mountain spruce as *Picea australis*. The crown of red spruce is less regularly symmetrical than that of most other spruces, and with maturity becomes open and widespreading. Numerous large, irregular branches droop as they extend outward, before turning up at the tips.

The plump four-sided, dark, shiny, yellow-green needles are about half an inch long and grow singly from all sides of the twigs and branches. They are slightly incurved, usually blunt-pointed, and have a prominent midrib on the lower surface. They remain on the twigs about six years. A reddish coat of down persists on the slender new twigs through the first year. This, together with the short incurved needles helps distinguish red spruce from all but black spruce whose needles are more nearly blue-green, and without the midrib on the lower surface.

Bright red, oval, pollen-bearing staminate flowers about half an inch long grow close to the twig near the ends of the previous year's growth in April and May. The ovulate flowers appear simultaneously but on the ends of different branches of the same

The open, wide-spreading crown of Red Spruce reaches heights of sixty to one hundred feet

Devereux Butcher

tree. They are reddish green, oblong, cylindrical cones about three-quarters of an inch long. Standing erect at first, they hang down after being fertilized, and in the autumn of the same year mature as elongated egg-shaped cones one to two and a half inches long. Purplish or light green during the spring and early summer, they become a light, glossy, reddish brown when ripe. The rounded, entire margins of the scales help distinguish these cones from those of black spruce. Also, the cone scales are thicker and less flexible than those of white spruce. The dark mottled brown seeds are shed through fall and early winter, and the cones drop by the end of the following year. The seed are about an eighth of an inch long, and with the full rounded wing are nearly half an inch long.

The red cones apparently attracted the German botanist, Johann Heinrich Friedrich Link who is responsible for the name *Picea rubra,* as early as 1841.

Old trunks have dark, reddish brown bark often appearing as if washed with gray. It is hard, firm, and about half an inch thick.

The light, soft, narrow-ringed wood is faintly tinged with red, but a layer of sapwood often two inches thick is almost white. Averaging about twenty-eight pounds to the cubic foot when air dry, the wood is easy to work, free from pitch or distinctive flavor, and holds paint fairly well. The combination of strength and stiffness in relation to weight gives spruce a special place in the construction of ladder rails, canoe paddles, and light oars, but the long straight fibres and light color favor it for the manufacture of paper. Spruce furnishes nearly one-third of the pulpwood for American paper manufacture. Domestic spruce production in 1937 was 2,010,720 cords, of which 1,400,000 cords may have been red spruce. That year some 120,000,000 board feet were cut for lumber.

The saw timber stand of red, white, and black spruce within the northeastern United States has been estimated at sixteen billion board feet. Probably two-thirds of this is red spruce. The Canadian supply of the several spruces is not only greater but of better quality. Growth on the whole is slow. On better sites an acre of trees up to ten inches in diameter will produce about a cord each year, but the average is more nearly half of this.

Fire is the worst enemy of spruce. Fortunately, however, its preference for damp situations usually retards a real conflagration. Occasionally, the heavy accumulation of debris becomes dry and fires sweep into the dense crowns with disastrous results. Less spectacular ground fires are especially damaging to the young growth.

Of the many insects which prey upon the foliage, bark, wood, and twigs of spruce, the European spruce sawfly is the worst. Its ravages now extend through much of Canada, New England and eastern New York.

Glossy red-brown cones emerge from last year's dark yellow-green needles

The dark reddish-brown bark of mature trunks is hard and firm, often appearing as if washed with gray

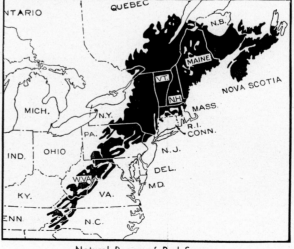

Natural Range of Red Spruce

51

WHITE SPRUCE

Picea glauca, (Moench) Voss

STRETCHING from Labrador to Alaska, southward to Montana, the Lake States, northern New York and northern New England is the white spruce. Its most westerly, and perhaps most northerly stand is near the Arctic Ocean, in Alaska, at Latitude 68°. One of the two most widely distributed of the seven American spruces, it is of less commercial importance than red spruce, but of greater importance than black spruce which accompanies it across the continent. It grows best on moist, well drained, porous soils, from sea level to elevations of 5,000 feet.

Ordinarily a tree forty to seventy feet tall with trunk diameters of one or two feet, it sometimes reaches heights of eighty to 140 feet with diameters up to four feet. Such trees may be 250 to 350 years old. In British Columbia and Alberta white spruce attains large dimensions and constitutes the bulk of the forest. Toward the northern extremity of its range in Alaska it is dwarf but attains fair size on higher ground along streams. Almost invariably with a straight central trunk, when grown alone or in the open it forms a narrow, regular cone clothed with whorls of long, thick branches, which bend toward the ground, then turn up, and carry the crown nearly to the ground. As the tree matures, numerous small side branchlets droop down from the main branches, and the crown becomes wider and less pointed. In dense forest conditions the straight, smooth trunk may be clear of branches for a third to two-thirds of its length. It often grows in dense pure forests, or in mixture with black spruce, Engelmann spruce, larch, birch, and aspen.

Open grown white spruce develops a pyramidal "crown," and under forest conditions it rises to heights from forty feet to more than a hundred and forty feet

There is some confusion regarding its scientific name. *Picea glauca,* as adopted in this description, has been approved by three leading American dendrologists—Sargent, Sudworth, and Rehder. Some botanists use *canadensis,* published in 1768 by Philip Miller, the English botanist and contemporary of Linnaeus, but Miller seems to have described white and black spruces and hemlock under this name. The word *glauca* applies to the pale blue, hoary, or even whitish tinge of the new needles, and provides one reason for the common name, white spruce.

The four-angled, pointed needles are one-third to two-thirds of an inch long and grow singly from all sides of the twig. When crushed or bruised they give off a peculiarly offensive polecat odor, which explains the local names of cat or skunk spruce. They remain on the stout twigs seven to ten years before beginning to fall off. The young shoots are slender and without the fine hairs characteristic of other associated spruces.

In May or early June, conspicuous pale red catkins half an inch or more in length, with stalks of nearly equal length appear near the twig ends throughout the crown. These are the staminate flowers whose wealth of pollen soon makes the catkins more yellow than pink. On the ends of neighboring branches in the upper portion of the same tree are also reddish or yellowish green, cone-like ovulate flowers of about the same size.

With fertilization the fruit blossoms bend down, and mature by the end of summer as pendulous, oblong-cylindrical, flexible cones varying from an inch to nearly two and a half inches long. The thin rounded cone scales are first a light grass-green tinged with rose-red, but become a glossy, light clay-brown. One of the means of distinguishing white spruce from Engelmann spruce, is by the cone scales. Those of white spruce are relatively broad and generally with a smooth margin, while those of Engelmann spruce are narrower with an irregularly toothed margin. The cones begin dropping from the trees immediately after the seed are released, but many hang on until the following spring. In New England heavy seed crops are borne at intervals of about eight years. The seed are only moderately fertile and germinate best on moist moss over organic soil. The seedlings thrive under heavy shade for many years.

The new bark of the twigs is orange-brown, but ashen gray on the older trunk. On young trunks or branches the bark is relatively smooth or only slightly roughened, but with maturity a scaly, pale gray to reddish brown formation develops.

The pale, yellowish-white wood is soft, straight grained with narrow growth rings. A cubic foot weighs about twenty-eight pounds when air dry. In this respect it ranks midway among the seven native spruces. It is an important source of paper pulp, general construction lumber and interior finish. Like other spruces, the clear wood is prized for sounding boards of musical instruments.

The stand within the United States is one billion to one and a half billion board feet. Much larger volumes are available in Canada. No attempt is made to distinguish the several spruces in the trade. In 1936 spruce of all kinds, from the United States, furnished 1,757,000 cords of pulpwood and 349,383,000 board feet of lumber. Of this amount approximately ten per cent, or 175,700 cords and possibly 34,938,300 board feet were white spruce. In that same year, white spruce constituted an even larger portion of the 735,300 cords of pulpwood imported from Canada.

White spruce is an easy victim of fire, because of its thin bark, resinous exudations, and readily inflammable foliage. It is also subject to attack by trunk and root fungi of several kinds, and by various insects such as the spruce bud worm and the European sawfly.

First introduced into England about 1700, its ability to endure extremes of temperature as well as drought and its attractive light bluish green foliage have caused it to be widely used for ornamental purposes. Fully a dozen subspecies distinguished by the color of the foliage, size of tree, and other features are known to the nursery trade.

The shiny brown, flexible cones which may be two and a half inches long, grow at the ends of twigs clothed with light blue-green, sharp pointed needles

The ashen brown bark is scaly and scarcely half an inch thick

Natural range of White Spruce

ENGELMANN SPRUCE

Picea engelmannii, **Engelmann**

THE narrow pyramidal deep blue-green crown of Engelmann spruce is a feature of the high Rocky Mountains from the Yukon territory to Arizona. In the western Cascade Mountains of Oregon and Washington it grows at elevations of around 6,000 feet, and at steadily increasing elevations as the range extends into Arizona and New Mexico, where it is found from 8,500 to 12,000 feet above sea level. As a rule it finds sufficient soil moisture only at higher elevations, so its lower range is limited to moist canyons and north slopes. In dense stands Engelmann spruce has a straight, slightly tapering trunk and a fairly short, narrow pyramidal crown of small branches. The lower branches droop and when grown in the open extend to the ground. Numerous tassel-like side branchlets hanging from the main horizontal branches give a compact appearance to the crown. Trees attain heights of eighty to 110 feet, with diameters at breast height from eighteen inches to thirty-six inches, and clear trunk lengths of twenty-five feet. Such trees may be 500 to 600 years old. At high altitudes exposed to wind and low temperatures, trees two to four feet high with slender, spike-like stems may live for a hundred years or more.

The deep blue-green leaves or needles are an inch or more in length, four-angled, more or less directed forward, rather soft and flexible to the touch with a relatively short, flat point. On young trees and on those which do not bear cones, the needles are spreading and evenly scattered, while on the cone-bearing twigs they are commonly crowded and usually shorter. Ordinarily deep blue green, some trees are decidedly silvery. This is particularly true of the younger trees. The young shoots, which are covered with fine hairs for the first three years, and the leaves, give off a disagreeable odor when crushed. These features, together with the smaller cones, help distinguish it from the Colorado spruce, *Picea pungens*.

The dark, purplish brown or russet red bark is one-quarter to one-half an inch thick, and broken into thin, loosely attached, small scales. Even young trees have the characteristic scaly bark.

In the spring each tree carries dark purple male flowers, and bright scarlet female flowers, like little catkins, near the top of the tree. The latter develop by the following August into cylindrical light brown cones, an inch to three inches long. The small, dark brown, winged seeds are soon shed and by early winter the empty cones drop from the trees. Large crops of seed are borne at intervals of three or four years from the time the tree is about twenty-five years to an advanced age. While the crops are heavy and seeds which lie protected in the forest duff continue to be fertile for four or five years after they have been shed, natural reproduction is usually sparse.

The deep blue-green spires of the Engelmann Spruce dominate the landscape of the higher western Rockies from the Yukon territory to Arizona

The light yellowish or faintly reddish brown wood is fine-grained and lighter in weight than white pine. A single cubic foot when air dry weighs about twenty-three pounds. It is strong for its weight, and carefully selected spruce lumber was used in the early airplanes. It is used locally for telephone and telegraph lines, and also for doors, window sash and interior trim.

Picea is the Latin name for spruce and is derived from *pix*, meaning pitch, while *engelmannii* refers to George Engelmann, a distinguished botanist of St. Louis, Missouri, whose identifying description of this spruce first appeared in 1863.

It is the most important of the Rocky Mountain spruces. The 1941 production was reported as 62,-581,000 board feet, with the largest amounts from California, Montana and Idaho. No figures of the estimated stand of Engelmann spruce are available, but of the 63,000,000,000 board feet of western spruce, now estimated to exist, a large part consists of this species.

While Engelmann spruce grows at the upper limits of tree growth, varying from 6,000 feet above sea level in the north to 12,000 feet in the south, with variations according to local climatic conditions, the merchantable sizes are found at the middle and lower levels. Even these are relatively high elevations, however, and the resulting inaccessibility is the chief reason for its minor commercial importance.

Within its range it is frequently the dominating species and is commonly associated with alpine fir, white fir, lodgepole pine, limber pine and Douglas fir. In the north it may also be found with western white pine and in the south with corkbark fir. Because it surpasses most of its associates in its tolerance of shade, the forest invariably contains Engelmann spruce of all ages and sizes, varying from seedlings and saplings to trees of saw-log size. These are more tolerant in youth than in old age, but the small suppressed growth shows remarkable ability to respond after it has been released by the removal of larger trees. Even after years of shading, trees will make good growth after the source of suppression is removed.

Fortunately the season of great fire hazard at high elevations is relatively short, but once started, fire is almost impossible to control when it gets into the heavy crowns of this spruce. Fire, as well as extensive timber cutting, may be followed by considerable windfall because of the shallow root system.

Engelmann spruce has few insect or fungus enemies, but is susceptible to the spruce budworm. Control under the mountainous forest conditions would be difficult, but thus far the attacks have never been extensive.

Although native to the high western mountains, it can adapt itself to eastern conditions and has been successful as an ornamental tree on northern exposures in relatively moist clay loam soils, but cannot stand the hot dry winds of open prairies. The singular beauty of color and form makes it increasingly favored for landscape purposes. Probably first cultivated in the Arnold Arboretum, it has been introduced successfully into England and parts of Germany. The lower branches are maintained for forty or fifty years, and while the tree loses symmetry with age, it is always beautiful.

The soft, flexible, four-angled needles are an inch or more long and usually curved forward, while the light brown cones are one to three inches long

Many small, thin, loosely attached scales are laid one over the other to form the thin, russet-red bark

Natural range of Engelmann Spruce in the United States

BLUE SPRUCE

Picea pungens, Engelmann

Jackson W. Space

The symmetrical, pyramidal crown of Blue Spruce with its crisp, cool, blue-green foliage is frequently seventy to ninety feet high or higher

BLUE SPRUCE, one of the most admired and widely known of all American evergreens, grows naturally in a relatively limited area within the Central Rocky Mountain region, where the pyramidal crown and cool, crisp, silvery blue foliage of the young trees is frequently a striking feature of the landscape. After the tree is thirty-five to fifty years old the crown becomes thin and irregular, the lower limbs disappear revealing a clean, tapering trunk one-fourth to one-half the total height of the tree, and the silvery blue hue of the foliage gives way to a less distinctive green. Trees commonly attain heights of seventy to ninety feet with breast-high diameters of sixteen to twenty-four inches in 275 to 350 years. Occasional trees in favorable locations may be 110 to 130 feet high and four feet in diameter. Growth is often extremely slow, but trees may live to be 400 and possibly 600 years old.

Pure forest stands of blue spruce are seldom found, but individuals or scattered groves are fairly common along stream banks. There it grows in moderately rich, dry to moist gravelly or rocky soils and is commonly associated with Douglas fir, Engelmann spruce, alpine fir, and occasionally with narrow-leaf cottonwood. Although usually found at elevations of 6,000 to 8,500 feet above sea level, trees may ascend to nearly 10,000 feet.

While found as far north as Glacier National Park in northern Montana, the chief distribution is in Colorado, eastern Utah, north central Arizona, and eastern New Mexico.

The stiff, sharp-pointed, four-angled, single needles are a half inch to an inch and a quarter long. They range from dull gray-green to blue-green or silvery white depending upon the age of the tree and the location of the leaves. The frosted, silvery appearance is due to a fine powdery substance on the surface of the needles. Most of this may be removed by rubbing them between the fingers. New growth carries more of the silvery blue hue than does the old foliage. Accordingly, the trees assume their most striking appearance in mid-summer, shortly after the new foliage is fully grown. The leaves remain on the twigs eight or nine years and become darker with age. Each needle is borne on a brown, stalk-like base which remains on the twig several years after the green leaf has fallen. These leaf-bases give the branchlets, from which the needles have fallen, a rough appearance.

Blue spruce differs from Engelmann spruce in having more definitely blue, very stiff, keenly-pointed leaves. This gives rise to the local name "prickly spruce," and to the scientific name *pungens*, which comes from a Latin word meaning "to prick." The crushed leaves of blue spruce do not smell as rank as do those of

Engelmann spruce, and are largely free of the "catty" odor. At one time blue spruce was named *Picea parryana*, after Dr. C. C. Parry, who described it in 1862.

The light ashy brown bark is composed of many thin scales divided into vertical ridges, while the bark of Engelmann spruce is seldom ridged or furrowed. The bark of mature blue spruce trees is a half inch to over an inch thick, but that of young trees is thinner, less broken, and often tinged with cinnamon-red. The twigs are stout and smooth, differing from those of Engelmann spruce, which are pubescent.

In the early spring each tree may bear male and female flowers near the ends of twigs of the previous year's growth. The drooping, pollen-bearing, staminate blooms are yellow, tinged with red, and may develop over much of the tree. Usually higher on the tree and on the ends of the branches are green to purple, ovulate, female cone-like flowers. While in blossom these stand erect with broad, oblong scales expanded to catch the wind-blown pollen. Soon after being fertilized they turn down and become pendulous. By the following autumn they mature as shiny, light brown cylindrical cones two to four inches long. This is nearly twice the length of the Engelmann spruce cone. Under each of the thin cone scales may be two small chestnut brown seeds, each fitted to a pale yellow-brown wing. The seeds are discharged in the late autumn or early winter.

The wood is light, moderately soft, nearly white in color, brittle and weak. It is frequently knotty, is the least valuable for commercial purposes of all American spruces, but is used locally for corral posts and poles, fuel, house logs, and occasionally for railroad ties and temporary mine props.

Blue spruce is best known as an ornamental tree, and is widely used in northern Europe as well as throughout the United States. Seedlings may show a wide variety in the intensity of the blue color of the foliage, so the bluest specimens are selected by nurserymen for ornamental planting. Koster's blue spruce, with its brilliant silvery blue foliage is a particularly fine form of this spruce, which is propagated by being grafted upon spruce seedlings or transplants. For economical reasons most of the selected blue specimens are grafted on stock of Norway spruce, *Picea excelsa*, but any other spruce can be used.

Forest grown trees are subject to fire injury and to several insect and fungous pests, many of which extend their activities to the trees planted for ornamentation. Spruce gall aphis and red spider are common enemies, and like other spruces it is subject to defoliation by the European spruce sawfly. While difficult to control under forest conditions, these pests can all be successfully combated when the trees are growing on lawns or in parks.

Shiny, pale chestnut-brown cones about three inches long are borne on the ends of second-year twigs near the top of the trees, and mature in a single season

The ash-brown bark of old tree trunks which may be an inch or more thick is vertically divided into broad rounded ridges

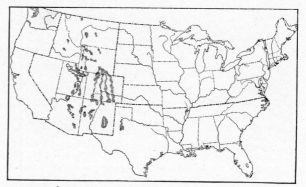

Natural range of Blue Spruce in the United States

SITKA SPRUCE

Picea sitchensis, (Bongard) Carrière

LARGEST of the eighteen species of *Picea* inhabiting the northern hemisphere and towering over the six other spruces occurring in North America is the Sitka spruce of the north Pacific region. From sea level to elevations of 3,000 feet, it occupies a narrow coastal ribbon forty to fifty miles wide and some 2,000 miles long from Mendocino County in northern California to the east end of Kodiak Island in Alaska.

Ranking with redwood and Douglas fir, Sitka spruce is one of America's fastest growing conifers. Heights of over 200 feet have been attained in one hundred years, yet it may live 800 to 850 years. Trees are ordinarily eighty to 125 feet high and three and a half to six feet in diameter, but heights over 280 feet have been recorded, and in low, wet valleys and flatlands, they reach 160 to 200 feet with diameters of eight to ten feet above the buttressed base. The swollen buttresses of the long clean trunks and the protruding roots help distinguish Sitka spruce from associated redwoods, western red cedars, lowland firs, and yellow cedars, as well as the smaller Pacific yew and black hemlock with which it is frequently associated. It also grows in company with Douglas fir, broadleaf maple, vine maple, alder, black cottonwood, and willows. To the north and in Alaska it forms pure stands or includes western hemlock, but in the extreme northwest where it extends beyond all other conifers, it is reduced to a low shrub.

In dense stands it is clear of branches for forty to eighty feet with a thin, open conical crown of small branches. Open grown individuals seldom attain the height of those in the forest and the rapidly tapering trunk is clothed to the ground with huge sweeping branches.

Sitka spruce is unique among American spruces in having thick, flattened leaves whose four angles are indistinct. They grow on smooth stems and are bright bluish green, half an inch to a little over an inch long, keenly pointed and with broad silvery bands of stomata usually confined to the lower surface. In the tops of tall trees the leaves are thicker, more crowded, and with stomata marking the upper surface. The prickly needles stand straight out around the branch, and lack the musky odor characteristic of Englemann spruce.

Dark red, pollen-bearing flowers adorn the ends of the drooping side branches in early spring, while high up on stiff terminal shoots are the

Courtesy "Forest Trees of the Pacific Slope" by W. A. Eliot

Sitka towers above all other spruces, and even open grown trees reach heights of 160 feet

short stalked oval female cones. A single growing season matures these as pale yellow or reddish brown, flexible cones two to four inches long, which hang conspicuously on the pendulous branches. They ripen in the early fall, and from their thin, papery, oval scales, whose margins are unevenly toothed, are shed tiny, clay-brown winged seeds. Heavy crops of fertile seed may occur every two to three years. They will grow on any wet or constantly moist soil, but for the first few years the seedlings are sensitive to frost.

Deep reddish brown or dark purple bark, with the surface broken into large, thin, easily detached scales, clothes old trunks to a thickness of about half an inch. On branches and trunks of young trees the bark is scaly and dark grayish brown, while the dark yellow-brown twigs are smooth.

Without odor or taste, the pale, pinkish brown wood is soft, straight grained and light—a cubic foot weighing about twenty-five pounds when air dry. It works easily and the planed surfaces have a silky sheen. Remarkably strong for its weight, it is easily kiln dried and shrinks and swells only moderately. Large quantities were used during the first World War for wing beams, struts and members in airplane construction, but the bulk of the 303,684,000 board feet cut in 1941 was used for boxes and crates, planing mill products, doors, blinds, sash, and general mill work. The annual consumption of more than 70,000 cords for pulp indicates its excellence for the manufacture of paper. Small quantities of slowly grown highly resonant timbers are specially selected for piano sounding-boards. Special orders for pieces thirty to forty inches wide, three to four inches thick, and sixteen to twenty feet long are occasionally filled.

Of some 11,050,000,000 board feet of Sitka spruce growing in this country 8,400,000,000 board feet is in Washington, while Oregon has about 2,600,000,000 board feet. Alaska's stand is estimated at 18,500,000,-000 board feet and British Columbia has some 16,000,000,000 board feet. Single trees contain 8,000 to 10,000 and occasionally 40,000 board feet, while the selected Sitka spruce, which grows in mixture with associated species, frequently amounts to 40,000 to 60,000 board feet to the acre.

While the thin bark leaves individual Sitka spruce easy victims of fire, the humidity of its coastal range partly protects old stands from severe damage. Organized fire protection during the two or three dry summer months is, however, essential to the natural reproduction that follows logging. It is frequently harmed by one of the bark beetles, and is defoliated by the Douglas fir chermes. Although attacked by two rust diseases, and by several wood rotting fungi, this spruce is more free from decay than either Douglas fir or western hemlock.

Archibald Menzies, a distinguished English traveller, serving as physician and surgeon with Vancouver, is credited with its discovery on Puget Sound in 1792. For a time it was known as Menzies spruce, *Picea menziesii*, but botanists now accept the geographical name, *Picea sitchensis*, in which the French botanist Bongard recognized the heavy stands of this tree in the vicinity of Sitka, Alaska.

Sitka spruce demands a cool, humid climate and is successfully grown for forest as well as ornamental purposes in England and western Europe, where it was introduced by Douglas in 1831. It is less adapted to our middle Atlantic States, while the hot, dry summers of New England and the eastern states have proved too severe, unless the trees are watered or heavily mulched. Wherever it grows well it is especially attractive because of the contrasting colors of its leaves.

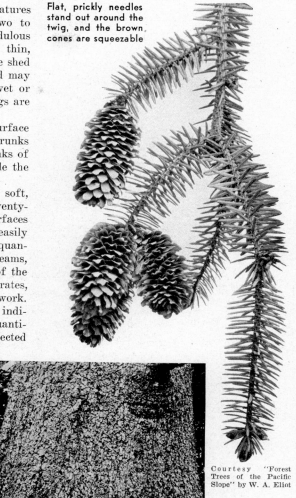

Flat, prickly needles stand out around the twig, and the brown cones are squeezable

Courtesy "Forest Trees of the Pacific Slope" by W. A. Eliot

The reddish brown scaly bark is about half an inch thick

Natural range of Sitka Spruce

NORWAY SPRUCE

Picea excelsa, Link

NORWAY spruce, the common spruce of Europe, is widely planted in the United States. Its native range extends beyond Norway to nearly all of middle and northern Europe, where it is at home from sea level to the higher mountain slopes where moisture is abundant but not stagnant. Early introduced in this country, it is hardy in all of our northern states as far west as North Dakota, and again in many western states. Like other spruces, it grows naturally in cool humid climates but may be planted with comparative success as far south as the southern highlands of Georgia, Tennessee, and Arkansas. Although preferring well drained, sandy loam, it has been successfully planted on almost all soils except those which are sour or permanently water-soaked. It has been widely planted for windbreaks and shelterbelts in the western prairies, but is happier in the more humid regions of the northern, eastern, and Pacific Coast states, where it may live to a hundred years or more. Frequently, however, some of our native trees would have been better adapted to many of the regions where it has been planted.

Occasionally attaining a height of 150 feet, with diameters of three feet or more, American-grown Norway spruce usually begins to deteriorate before reaching sixty feet and it seldom lives over 100 years. Young open-grown trees up to a height of twenty-five or thirty feet are symmetrically cone-shaped, with a single straight tapering trunk, and branches arranged more or less in annual whorls. These grow heavier and more spreading with age, and may be retained to the ground through the life of individual trees. With increasing age, the tree assumes a ragged, unkempt appearance, for the foliage becomes thin, and numerous long slender branches grow as if suspended from the main branches.

The bark is reddish brown, scaly and seldom more than half an inch thick. Reddish or light brown cone-shaped winter buds, without resin, form before late summer, and each needle or leaf is attached to the twig separately. Although the shiny dark green needles point upward and forward, their bases entirely surround the twig. They are a half to three-quarters of an inch long, have four sides, each with tiny white lines, and remain on the twig for six or seven years.

As Norway Spruce attains maturity the spread of the side branches increases and the pendulous branchlets become more apparent

Unlike the pines, all spruce trees mature their cones and seed in a single season. In the spring, male and female blossoms may be found on the same trees. The male or staminate flowers are like little yellow catkins on the ends of the twigs, while the ovulate ones are usually higher on the tree and range from green to purple. They stand upright on the twig until fertilized, and gradually turn down until they mature in the fall as pendulous, cylindrical cones four to seven inches long and light brown in color. During the late winter and early spring the scales spread back to release the winged seed.

The scientific name, *Picea excelsa*, was given this tree by a Swedish botanist named Link in 1841. *Picea* is an ancient Latin word for spruce, derived from *pix*, meaning pitch, while *excelsa* comes from the Latin word *excelsus*, meaning elevated or tall.

The wood of Norway spruce is soft, weighs about twenty-five pounds to the cubic foot, is straight grained and easily worked. Although not durable in contact with the soil it is widely used for construction purposes. The heartwood is yellowish white, and the thin sapwood is white. It is an important source of pulp for the manufacture of paper, and has been planted in many of the northern and eastern States for that purpose.

Although extensively planted for forest purposes in many parts of the north and east, Norway spruce has proved especially successful as an ornamental tree and for farm windbreaks and shelter-belts in the middle west. It may be pruned and can be used for hedges. Christmas tree plantations have proved financially successful, but the early shedding of the needles, after the tree is set up in a warm house, makes all spruces less desirable than the firs.

There are relatively few enemies of importance. Chief among these are the red spider and several parasitic fungi, but ornamental trees probably suffer most for lack of moisture and because the soil around the roots becomes too severely packed. Grass fires may do severe damage, and in many localities late frosts may destroy the leader and some of the terminal buds. The tree recovers, however, with only a slight deformity.

Norway spruce has shown ability to adapt itself to a wide variety of American conditions, and is generally accepted as readily as a native tree.

Light-brown cones four to seven inches long grow near the tree top, and ripen in a single season

Upper: Catkin-like staminate blossom. Lower: The cone-like pistillate blossom stands erect with the scales separated

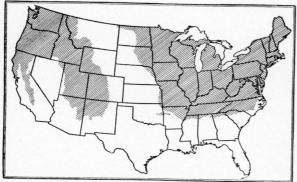

Approximate areas within the United States where Norway Spruce may be grown

The circular growth in the reddish brown bark is where the stub of a former branch has been overgrown

EASTERN HEMLOCK

Tsuga canadensis, (Linnaeus) Carriere

EASTERN hemlock with its irregular crown of dark green foliage, its slender gracefully drooping leader, and its massive trunk is a feature of the forest and open country on cool, moist slopes and in well drained, fertile valleys throughout the northeastern states from northern Maine to northeastern Minnesota, south through Wisconsin, southern Michigan and Indiana, and southward along the mountains from Pennsylvania and West Virginia into northern Alabama and Georgia.

Of relatively slow growth, it reaches maturity in 250 to 300 years and often lives for 600 years or more. While many trees are sixty to eighty feet high and two to three feet in diameter, heights of over 100 feet and diameters exceeding four feet are not uncommon. Occasional individuals 160 feet high and six feet in diameter have been measured.

The flat narrow leaves are one-third to two-thirds of an inch long, rounded or minutely notched at the end, shiny dark green above, light green below, and marked with two parallel white lines of white dots or stomata beneath. Each leaf or needle grows on a thread-like stem or petiole, and while borne spirally on the branchlets they appear to be two-ranked, like a flat spray. The early spring foliage is a delicate light yellow-green contrasting with the darker green of previous years. The needles remain on the twigs for three or more years, and upon falling, the base of the petiole remains, giving the twig a roughened appearance.

Early in May each tree bears separate male and female flowers on twigs of the previous year. The small, yellow, globular male blossoms appear singly in the axils of the previous season's leaves and occasionally near the ends of the twigs, while the small seed-bearing female flowers are erect and greenish, with circular scales from the upper surface of which may appear thin bracts. Blossoms appear on all parts of a tree, from the top to the lowest branches. By October at the end of one season the fertilized ovulate flowers develop into broadly oval, green to purple cones, one-half to one inch long which become reddish brown and hang down singly from short stalks as they reach maturity. These are among the smallest of all tree cones. Under each fertile scale are two light brown seeds whose transparent wings help carry them on the wind. The partially empty cones remain on the twigs through the fall and much of the winter. A single seed is about one-sixteenth of an inch long, and 400,000 are in a pound. In spite of the many seeds produced each year, hemlock reproduces poorly. Seedlings cannot endure strong light and reproduction is best in moist,

Hemlock reveals its rugged beauty and massive proportions when growing in the open or near the edge of a forest. Trees may attain heights of seventy-five to 160 feet and diameters of two to four feet or more

shady places. Later when the roots have developed they respond to increased light with more vigorous growth.

The tiny, glossy, resin-coated. reddish brown buds are alternate and the slender, yellowish brown twigs are coated with fine hairs in the first winter, but later become smooth and dark gray or purplish brown. The branching is irregular rather than in whorls as with the pines and firs.

Deeply divided cinnamon-red to brown bark, two to three inches thick, the surface of whose broad, longitudinal ridges are finely scaly covers the rapidly tapering trunk of mature hemlocks. The bark may comprise fifteen to nineteen per cent of the cubic volume of a tree. The value of the tannin was for years so great in comparison with the lumber that great trees were frequently left to decay in the forest after the bark had been removed. The bark is peeled off in rectangular sheets about four feet square and is still so greatly in demand by the leather industry that lumbering operations are usually confined to the spring and summer when it "slips" easily. From 70,000 to 130,000 tons of bark are produced each year.

With scarcity of other lumber, the light buff, soft, coarse-grained wood of hemlock has become of increasing importance. It weighs only twenty-four to thirty-one pounds to the cubic foot when air dry, is practically without taste or odor, is not durable when exposed to the elements, and is frequently splintery and subject to wind-shakes. The lumber is used for boxing, crating, general construction, and railroad ties, and recently as a source of mechanical pulp for the manufacture of paper. Hemlock possesses unusual power to hold nails and spikes. It is low in fuel value.

With an estimated stand of 17,500,000,000 board feet the bulk of the cut for 1941 amounting to 565,270,000 board feet came from Wisconsin, Michigan, Maine, Pennsylvania, West Virginia, New Hampshire, and New York. Until about 1928 the normal annual production was shown to exceed 750,000,000 board feet. In the north the common associates of hemlock are white pine, beech, yellow birch, and the maples, while in the southern mountains it grows with tulip trees, red maple. the hickories, oaks, and chestnut. Hemlock stands have yielded 25,000 board feet to the acre, but 15,000 to 20,000 board feet is more common. Individual trees frequently yield 1,500 board feet of lumber.

Hemlock is a member of the pine family and is of ancient origin. Remains of leaves, cones and wood have been found in early geological strata of America and Asia. Of the nine known species four are found on this continent, two being native to the eastern states and two to the northwestern mountains. The others are in Japan, China, and the Himalayan Mountains between India and Tibet. There are no native hemlocks. in Europe. The name *Tsuga* was first applied to the genus in 1847 by the dendrologist, Stephen L. Endlicher, and is a Japanese word meaning yew-leaved, while *canadensis* means Canadian, although the tree is so common south of the international boundary as to be ranked among the important sources of timber in the United States. Since June 22, 1931, it has been Pennsylvania's state tree.

Few insect and fungus pests are of importance in the life of the eastern hemlock and they seldom occur in serious epidemic. Next to ground-fires which may burn through the deep humus and kill the trees, and severe winds which may tip them over, the most destructive enemy is the flat-headed eastern hemlock borer.

Hemlock ranks high among all coniferous evergreens for ornamental planting, and in its juvenile stages it lends itself to border and background plantings.

George J. Baetzhold
The two-ranked sprays of narrow, flat, round-tipped needles are dark green on the upper surface and light green beneath. The cones are a quarter to a half inch long and begin shedding their seeds in the early fall

The cinnamon-red bark, broken into broad ridges by long, longitudinal fissures, may be two to three inches thick and is an important source of tannin

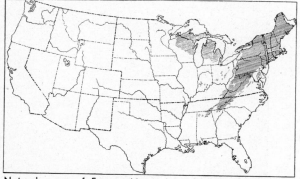

Natural range of Eastern Hemlock in the United States

63

Western Hemlock, largest of eight hemlock species, attains heights of 150 to 250 feet, and diameters up to eight or ten feet

Tsuga heterophylla, (Rafinesque) Sargent

WESTERN hemlock, a tree of increasing economic importance, is found in the deep forests of the humid coast regions from Prince William Sound in Alaska for a thousand miles to Marin County, California, just north of San Francisco, and inland as far as northern Idaho and northwestern Montana. It grows best in cool, moist locations on the seaward side of the Cascade Mountains, at elevations from 1,500 to 3,500 feet above sea level, but ascends from sea level to altitudes of 6,000 feet.

Growing to greater dimensions than its eastern relatives, this tree under favorable conditions may become 130 to 150 feet high and from seventeen to twenty-one inches in diameter in one hundred years. Occasionally, western hemlock reaches an age of 500 years or more, when it develops to heights of 175 to 250 feet with diameters ranging to eight or ten feet.

Everywhere it is a dignified tree, with grave and massive outline, but in the dense forest the crown of irregular, slender, pendulous branches is narrow and pyramidal. The long, clean, cylindrical trunk has little taper, and the base is often suddenly buttressed. Open-grown trees have a broad crown which may extend to the base of the trunk. Being tolerant of shade, it clears its trunk of branches somewhat slowly.

The flat, narrow, distinctly grooved leaves are a dark, highly lustrous green from one-third to three-fourths of an inch long. They remain on the branchlets three to six years. Closely resembling the leaves of eastern hemlock, the ends are distinctly rounded and the two bands of white stomata on the under side of each leaf are less well defined. *Tsuga* is the Japanese name for hemlock, while *heterophylla* is derived from two Greek words meaning other or different leaves. Apparently it was applied by Rafinesque in an effort to indicate the slight distinguishing differences of the leaf from that of *Tsuga canadensis,* the eastern hemlock.

Male and female blossoms are borne separately on sprays of the preceding season, on different parts of the same tree. Yellow, pollen-bearing, male flowers grow singly at the base of leaves near the ends of the branchlets, while the small, purple, scaly female flowers are at the ends of the sprays.

By the middle or end of August, the reddish clay-brown cones which develop from the pistillate blossoms are mature and ready to discharge their winged seeds. These cones hang from the ends of the branchlets, are nearly twice the size of those of eastern hemlock, being three-fourths to one and one-fourth inches long, and are more acutely pointed. Each cone is attached by a short thread-like stem, and drops during the succeeding winter. The thin, overlapping scales are faintly downy on the outer surface. Under each scale may be two light brown seeds, about one-eighth of an inch long, whose ample wing carries them considerable distances on the wind.

Open grown trees begin to bear seed when twenty-five to thirty years old, but those growing in dense forests at a much older age. Some seed are produced nearly every year, but heavy crops occur at intervals of two or three years. The seed, which are borne in large amounts, are fairly high in germinative ability, retain their vitality for several years, and develop best on wet moss, decaying wood or moist humus. This tree reproduces freely under a variety of conditions, and while the seedlings can endure dense shade, they grow more rapidly in the sunlight.

On old trunks the dark russet-brown, deeply furrowed bark may be one and one-half inches thick. It is even richer in tannin than that of eastern hemlock, having twelve to fifteen percent, as compared with ten to thirteen percent for the eastern variety.

The pale, yellowish brown heartwood contrasts with the narrow area of white sapwood, and weighs about twenty-nine pounds to the cubic foot when air dry. It is heavier, harder, and stronger than the wood of eastern hemlock, is less splintery, and because of its soft, fine, non-resinous texture and straight grain is finding an increasing demand in commerce. The wood is relatively resistant to attacks by termites, but is not durable when used untreated under conditions that favor decay. When commercially dry it is suitable for all but the heaviest construction work, and is extensively used for framing material, house sheathing, planing mill products, boxes, barrels, railroad ties, concrete forms, and is rapidly becoming one of the most important pulp woods grown on this continent.

The total stand of western hemlock in the United States is estimated to be some 115 billion board feet, of which over half is in Washington. In addition some sixty-three billion board feet are in Alaska. In 1941 the cut amounted to 434,908,000 board feet, of which nearly 235,000,000 board feet came from the forests of Washington. The peak of western hemlock production was reached in 1927, when 1,418,000,000 board feet were cut.

The comparatively thin bark and shallow root system make it highly susceptible to fire injury and to windfall. While less frequently damaged by "wind shake" than the eastern hemlock, it suffers heavily from insects and fungi, against which little can be done.

Its ability to withstand shade makes it desirable for ornamental purposes, but it does not thrive in the central and eastern states.

Round-tipped, flat, glossy green leaves, and narrowly pointed, pendent cones are three-fourths of an inch to an inch and a quarter long

The deeply furrowed russet-brown bark is over an inch thick and rich in tannin

The natural range of Western Hemlock extends along the Pacific Coast into Alaska

MOUNTAIN HEMLOCK

Tsuga mertensiana, (Bongard) Sargent

MOUNTAIN hemlocks clothed in dense blue-green foliage frequently stand silhouetted against high mountain skylines, and are called black hemlock. In southern Alaska it grows at elevations from tidewater to 4,000 feet above sea level. On the slopes of the Cascade and Olympic Mountains of Washington, it grows at elevations from 5,000 to 7,000 feet, while in California it is found at 6,000 to 11,000 feet. It grows in the high mountains from the south fork of the Kings River Canyon in California, north through Oregon and Washington, northern Idaho and Montana, into British Columbia and Alaska. Northern exposures are usually preferred because of the cool, moist soil conditions. At high elevations it occurs in mixture with white bark pine, alpine fir, alpine larch and Engelmann spruce. At lower elevations its associates are lowland white fir, lodgepole pine, and western white pine.

The sharp pointed, narrowly pyramidal crowns bear little resemblance to the western hemlock of lower elevations, but it has the same dropping branches and deeply furrowed, dark reddish brown trunk. On steep slopes the trunk may be bent in a wide curve like a sled runner or a great saber. This started when the tree was a slender sapling bent down by heavy snows.

Like other timberline trees mountain hemlock is usually short and distorted, reaching only twenty-five to sixty feet in height and ten to twenty inches in diameter, while those exposed to buffeting winds may be low sprawling trees only a few feet high. On gentle slopes and at the heads of moist valleys, trees seventy-five to eighty feet high are not uncommon, with occasional heights of 100 to 150 feet and diameters of two and a half to three and a half feet. Such trees are undoubtedly of great age, for trees eighteen to twenty inches in diameter are 180 to 260 years old. In contrast to the rapid growth of low country trees,

Mountain Hemlock occurs in the high mountains of the Pacific Slope

those which grow on wind-swept ridges may take sixty to eighty years to grow five to seven inches in diameter.

The blue-green, bluntly pointed leaves are plump but flat, arranged spirally so as to stand out from all sides of the twig, and range from a twelfth of an inch to an inch in length. Because of the needle arrangement the tree is frequently mistaken for a spruce. Like the leaves of all other hemlocks, each stands on a separate petiole or stem, and unlike the three other American hemlocks, both leaf surfaces are marked with parallel lines of white stomata. The leaves drop off during the third and fourth years.

Purple cones up to three inches long are produced near the branch ends

Richly colored male and female flowers are borne on the same tree. Violet-purple staminate ones hang on slender, drooping, hairy stems of the previous year, while erect lustrous purple or yellow-green ovulate ones appear near the ends of the branches at about the same time. These develop into broad scaled, blunt pointed cones three-fourths of an inch to three inches long. They stand erect until half grown and then become pendulous, ranging in color from yellowish green to a bluish purple. Under each cone scale may be two small, light brown seeds with large wings capable of being carried considerable distances on the wind when they ripen in September or October. Large quantities of seed are produced annually, but relatively few germinate. These will endure shade and suppression for years, and resume normal growth when given full light.

The dark cinnamon to lavender-brown bark is an inch or more thick, with deep, narrowly furrowed, rounded ridges.

The pale brown to red, close grained, soft wood while light in weight is the heaviest of all the American hemlocks, weighing thirty-three pounds to the cubic foot when air dry. It is without special strength and is only used locally for cabins and rough log shelters.

Mountain hemlock is a tree of unusual beauty suited for ornamental planting in cool moist soils in the northern Pacific States and in the east as far north as Massachusetts. Outside its natural habitat, however, it seldom achieves the grace and vigor of the wild mountain trees.

The name *mertensiana* honors a German physician and naturalist Karl Heinrich Mertens, who lived from 1795 to 1830. *Tsuga* (tsü-ga) is the Japanese name for the hemlock genus.

The rich brown, narrowly furrowed bark is an inch or more thick

Natural range of Mountain Hemlock in the United States

In the mountains of the northwest Douglas fir attains
magnificent proportions, sometimes reaching a height
of over two hundred feet

DOUGLAS FIR

Pseudotsuga taxifolia, Britton

DOUGLAS fir is a widely distributed Western tree. It grows naturally throughout the Rocky Mountains, from their eastern base to the Pacific Coast, and northern Mexico and the mountains of western Texas, southern New Mexico and Arizona to British Columbia. It attains its largest size near sea-level in the coast region of southern British Columbia, Washington, Oregon and on the western foothills of the Cascade Mountains. No attempt is made in this description to distinguish between the Oregon variety and the slower growing, more hardy Douglas fir native to Colorado and the interior mountains. It is frequently called red fir, Oregon pine, Douglas spruce, or Douglas yew, but Douglas fir is generally accepted.

Three hundred and twenty-five foot heights have been recorded with trunk diameters of ten to seventeen feet, and are often characterized by a clear shaft for a third of their height. The larger trees may be from four hundred to one thousand years old. The reddish brown bark of large mature trees is broken into oblong longitudinal plates and may be ten to twelve inches thick. The smooth thinner bark of young trees is more of the color of ashes, has resin blisters like the true firs, but thickens as the tree grows larger and becomes reddish brown in color.

The tree is in the nature of a botanical puzzle, for it bears strong resemblance to spruce and fir as well as to the hemlock and yew. Accordingly, the botanists went to the Greek to describe it as a "false hemlock with a yewlike leaf." It was first discovered by Dr. Archibald Menzies in 1791, on the west coast of Vancouver Island; later it was rediscovered by the Scottish traveler David Douglas, who introduced it into England in 1827. Since then it has been widely planted on the British Isles.

The soft, flattened, slightly pointed needles are one-half to one and one-half inches long and grow around the branch so as to give it a full rounded appearance. They are grooved on the upper surface, and have a white band on each side of a prominent midrib beneath. When pulled off they leave an oval scar on top of a little projection. They remain on the trees five to eight years before they fall. Frequently the dark orange-red pointed terminal bud is one-fourth of an inch long, while the side buds are about half as large.

The oval cones are pendulous like those of the spruce and pine. They are an inch and a half to four and one-half inches long and mature in the first autumn from reddish ovulate flowers that grow well out on the ends of the branches. The three-lobed "Neptune's trident" is especially noticeable in the blossom stage. On the same tree are the bright red staminate or male flowers, which appear in the early spring on the under surface of the previous year's growth. The thin, rounded scales of the cone are thrust over conspicuous three-pointed bracts, and under each scale are two seeds, each with a single wing. The parent trees scatter these seed so effectively that they quickly take possession of burned forest areas. Trees may begin producing cones at twelve years of age, and continue with crops nearly every year.

The wood is usually yellowish to light red, with a narrow band of white sapwood. It is fairly light, strong, firm and works well. Compared with other American woods it is the strongest of all in terms of weight. The immense size of the trees permits the manufacture of timber remarkably free from knots and other defects. It is important in the lumber industry and building trade. When air dry a cubic foot weighs thirty-one pounds. It is used for all kinds of construction, railway ties, piles, etc., is resistant to decay, and can be attractively stained for interior trim. Recent estimates indicate that American forests contain 490,000,000,000 board feet of Douglas fir sawtimber, of which most is in Washington, Oregon and northern California. Douglas fir is second only to yellow pine in volume of annual production, and the present stand comprises about one-fourth of the remaining sawtimber in the United States. Before the war, the annual cut of fir was 6,500,000,000 board feet, with the State of Washington leading. During 1942 and 1943, the war demands for wood increased the fir cut to 8,528,709,000 feet.

Douglas fir may be grown from seed under nursery conditions, and successfully transplanted to forest plantations. Under natural conditions it grows from sea level where more than 100 inches of rain falls each year, to altitudes of nearly 11,000 feet where the annual precipitation is fifteen inches. In deep loam soils it develops widespreading root systems. In moist well drained soil trees will grow to a height of thirty-five feet in twenty-five years. The trees prefer northern and western exposures, but will withstand wind fairly well and endure considerable shade. The small trees are hardy and attractive for ornamental planting in the northern and northeastern states as well as in the West. Being moderately tolerant of shade, they hold their branches down to the ground unless heavily shaded.

The reddish brown deeply fissured bark of mature trees is sometimes a foot thick

Above:—The three-pointed bracts extending beyond the cone scales, the flexible bluntly pointed green needles, and dark orange-red winter buds combine to help identify Douglas fir

Below:—In their youth Douglas firs are dense-foliaged and symmetrical. They are planted over a wide area to decorate home grounds, for windbreak purposes and for future stands of timber

They may be planted close together and pruned for hedges. The symmetrical young trees whose soft rich green needles hang on long after the tree is cut down are being used in increasing numbers for Christmas trees and holiday decoration.

Douglas fir is particularly subject to fire damage during its early years, but as the bark grows thicker it becomes increasingly resistant. Not only does fire destroy many trees, but it also causes unfavorable soil conditions, and the fire scars furnish places where insects and fungi may enter. It may be attacked by a long list of insects, fungi and mistletoe but is little affected by most of them. The worst insect enemy is a beetle which bores between the bark and the wood, frequently killing the tree. Periodically the western hemlock looper destroys considerable merchantable timber, and eastern plantations have been threatened by a larch canker, but taken as a whole such losses are comparatively small.

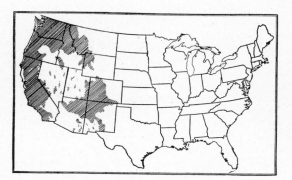

Natural range of Douglas Fir in the United States

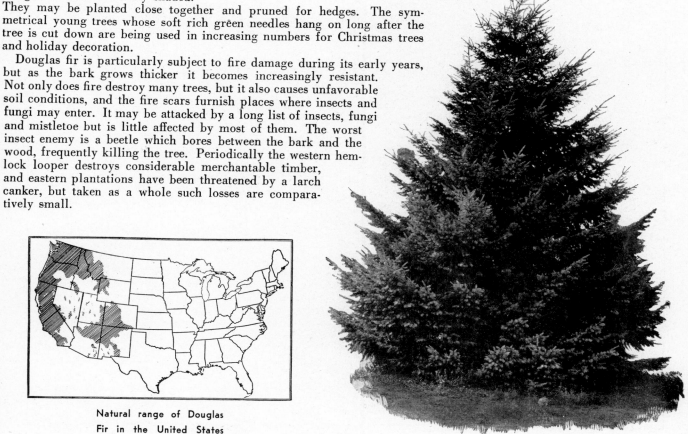

BALSAM FIR

Abies balsamea, (Linnaeus) Miller

TYPICAL of cold climates and well drained, moist situations, the arrow-headed spires of balsam fir add a note of deep green to the northern forests. Ranging from sea level to elevations of over 5,600 feet, it grows in New England and Labrador west and north across New York, the Lake States, and Ontario to a few degrees of the Pacific Ocean at the headwaters of the Yukon River. Most important of the two eastern true firs, *Abies balsamea* is one of ten *Abies* native to the United States and Canada. This large evergreen family is characterized by disk-like leaf scars and erect cones which break apart and leave a woody spike soon after the seeds ripen.

Often associated with red spruce, black spruce, tamarack, and hemlock, occasional pure stands are formed and on drier sites it is mixed with yellow birch, beech, and maple.

Perhaps the most symmetrical of all northeastern evergreens, it averages twenty-five to sixty feet in height and occasionally reaches eighty to ninety feet. The diameters range from ten inches to twenty-eight inches. With maturity, long slender branches develop in somewhat distant whorls and droop as they spread. At high elevations and on wind swept mountain summits dense, dwarfed mats are formed. Capable of enduring dense shade in early youth, it may grow rapidly but shows defects within ninety years and seldom lives beyond 150 years.

The deep blue-green, narrow leaves are about an inch long, and shiny on the upper side. The ends are blunt, frequently indented, conspicuously light colored on the under side and marked near the ends with rows of stomata. Arranged spirally on the twig, they usually part in two ranks like the teeth of a double comb to form a V-shaped depression on the upper side of the twig. The upper crown leaves are short, plump, incurved, and almost erect as compared with the longer leaves near the base. They adhere to the twigs about eight years and furnish winter food for deer and moose. The aromatic needles are widely used for stuffing balsam pillows. Oil of fir, sometimes used in pharmacy, may be distilled from either needles or bark. The young shoots are smooth with fine, grayish hairs, and the stout, blunt winter buds are resinous.

In early spring each tree produces male and female blossoms. Yellow catkin-like staminate blooms about one-quarter inch long emerge from the under side of the leaf axils over most of the past year's growth, but the erect, purple three-quarter inch cones containing the ovulate blooms are confined to the upper branches. These ripen in September as dark purple, slightly tapering, cylindrical cones two to four inches long and one to one and

Devereux Butcher

The deep blue-green spires of Balsam Fir reach heights of sixty feet and more a quarter inches wide. They stand erect like tapers on a candelabrum, and lose their overlapping fan-shaped scales soon after the seeds ripen. Each light brown, resinous seed is about a quarter inch long with a shining wing of about the same length. Heavy cone crops occur at intervals of two to four years. The winged seeds drift considerable distances, to germinate in moist exposed soil and on moss covered stumps, but many are eaten by grouse and small animals. Some natural reproduction occurs when the lower pendent branches become covered with soil and take root.

The dark purple cones stand erect amid the plump, upturned foliage of the upper crown

The bark of mature trees is dull, reddish brown with many thin scales and about half an inch thick. That of young trees and branches is thin, smooth, ash colored and underlain with many resin blisters. These are the source of Canada balsam — a greenish yellow, transparent, sticky fluid which dries into a transparent mass. It is used in pharmacy and as a medium in which to mount material on microscopic slides.

The wide-ringed, yellowish brown wood has a narrow band of white sapwood one to two inches thick, and weighs twenty-four to twenty-nine pounds to the cubic foot when air dry. It is soft, brittle, and quickly perishable. Its major use is for paper pulp, but considerable lumber goes into interior trim, crates, and packing boxes. It is often sold with spruce. The commercial sources of balsam fir are Vermont, Maine, Minnesota, Michigan, Wisconsin, New Hampshire, and New York from which 10,767,000 board feet were produced in 1941. In 1936, 365,200 cords of fir pulpwood were produced. Large numbers of small to medium sized, symmetrical Christmas trees are cut. Not only is their form attractive, but the rich green, blunt needles remain firmly attached and retain their color long after the tree is actually dry.

The ash colored bark of young trees is underlain with many balsam blisters

Balsam fir suffers comparatively little fire damage because of its moist locations, but when fire occurs the large number of resin blisters under the bark cause terrific heat. The shallow root system makes balsam fir easily wind blown and dangerous fire traps may result. Undoubtedly, its worst enemy is the spruce budworm, whose ravages extend from the Atlantic into Minnesota and central Ontario. Several fungi are also damaging.

This fir seldom prospers as an ornamental tree because of its susceptibility to city smoke and gases and its need for constant soil moisture. It has proved satisfactory in cool, moist, sheltered locations for about fifteen years before becoming ragged and unattractive.

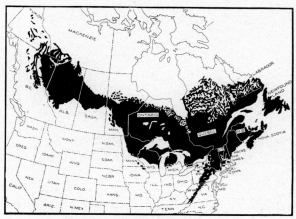

The natural range of Balsam Fir lacks little of being transcontinental

Abies lasiocarpa, (Hooker) Nuttall

ALPINE fir, whose slender spires supported by dense blue-green whorls of flat foliage sprays are a characteristic feature of large areas of high country in the western mountains, is found as far south as the San Francisco Mountains of northern Arizona and the Mogollon Mountains of New Mexico. Although relatively small and unimportant, this tree is the most widely distributed fir in western North America and is common in Colorado, Montana and Idaho, westward through the mountains of Oregon and Washington into the high ranges of British Columbia and northward beyond all the other western firs to sixty degrees latitude in Alaska. True to its name, it grows in cool, moist situations at elevations of 3,500 feet to 10,500 feet and occurs commonly at timberline as well as in protected valleys at the heads of streams, about mountain lakes and on moist meadows. Trees of largest dimensions are found growing on fairly deep, loose, moist soil at elevations of 5,000 to 8,000 feet. It does not thrive on heavy, clay soils. Within its range it is frequently associated with Engelmann spruce, lodgepole pine, mountain hemlock, western white pine, white bark pine and toward the South with aspen and cork fir.

The long, slender, narrowly-conical crown terminating in a conspicuous spire distinguishes Alpine fir from its associates. In the open, the narrow crowns of old as well as young trees extend down to the ground, while in dense forest stands the trunks of old trees are occasionally free from branches for twenty to forty feet. The dense, tough branches at the base of the crown droop and are often sharply curved or bent down upon the trunk. The twigs are commonly covered with tiny rusty brown hairs for two or three years.

Ordinarily, alpine fir attains heights of sixty to ninety feet with trunk diameters at breast height of fourteen inches to twenty-four inches. Occasionally, trees 175 feet high with diameters of three to five feet have been reported. While moderately long-lived, the largest trees are probably not older than 250 years, while trees ten inches to twenty inches in diameter are frequently 140 to 210 years old.

Two types of deep blue-green leaves or needles ranging from less than an inch to one and three-quarters inches long are commonly found on each tree. The leaves occur singly and are arranged alternately on all sides of the twigs. Those of the lower branches are relatively long, flat, blunt and all are distinctly upward pointing. On the higher limbs and branches the leaves are thicker, somewhat shorter, pointed and retain the feature of being distinctly massed and upward pointing. Each new season's growth of foliage has a silvery tinge.

Flowers of both sexes are borne on twigs of the previous year, on different parts of the same tree. The solitary staminate or pollen-bearing flowers are dark blue, later turning violet, and occur abundantly on the lower branches in the axils of the leaves. The scaly ovulate flowers are fewer in number, a violet-purple and stand erect on the upper branches of the crown. These mature during a single season into downy, deep purple cones whose cylindrical form is contracted toward the tip. They are from two and one-quarter to four inches long, about one and one-half inches in diameter, and stand erect on the upper branches

The slender dark blue-green spires of Alpine Fir are striking features in many areas of the western mountain region

Devereux Butcher

to form a purple cluster in the top of the tree. During warm weather they frequently drip with silvery resin.

The scientific name *Abies lasiocarpa* is derived from the Greek words *lasius*, meaning hairy or woolly, and *carpous*, meaning fruit. Literally translated, this would mean the fir bearing a hairy, pubescent fruit and compares with the common name, "downy-coned" fir.

Beneath each rounded cone scale are two ivory-brown seeds about one-fourth of an inch long with a large lustrous purplish or violet tinged wing. The cones swell when they ripen, releasing the scales as well as the winged seeds, so that the central axis remains on the tree for one or more seasons. The seeds retain their life but a short time, but during that period their capacity for germination is relatively high. Trees produce cones as early as the twentieth year and continue to bear abundant crops of seed at intervals of about three years. During some seasons, however, cones over large areas may fail to mature.

The rounded winter buds, consisting of light orange-brown scales more or less covered with resin may be a quarter of an inch thick.

The flinty bark of the trunk is usually gray, but sometimes a chalky white. It is relatively thin, seldom more than an inch and a quarter thick and is marked by the blister-like resin pockets characteristic of all the firs or "balsams." Even on large trees the bark is little broken except for occasional narrow shallow cracks near the base of the trunk.

Alpine fir is of little commercial importance and probably constitutes a minor part of the total estimated volume of 122,000,000,000 board feet of standing timber credited to the seven species of western fir. The pale, straw-colored wood is fine-grained, soft, and except for frequent small knots works easily, but is not durable in contact with the soil. Weighing only about twenty-one pounds to the cubic foot of dry wood, it is the lightest of all the firs. Dead timber is used locally for fuel, house logs and corral logs, while standing timber is occasionally cut and sawed into rough lumber for local use. It is primarily important as a protection forest on steep slopes at high elevations where few other conifers can live.

Natural reproduction is usually abundant in the open on exposed mineral soil and on moist duff under light or comparatively heavy shade. Seedlings grow thickly on the north sides of groups of trees and under the branches of mother trees.

Fire is the chief enemy of alpine fir. The dry lower branches are highly inflammable and when ignited quickly lead to dangerous crown fires. Even ground fires seriously injure the thin bark and make openings which harbor wood-destroying fungi. Insects seldom threaten the lives of these trees, but aphids or "plant lice" sometimes kill the lower branches.

Although naturally subjected to a rigorous climate with forty degrees below zero in winter and heat of ninety degrees in summer, alpine fir has not proven hardy for planting in the northeastern states where it is subject to winter injury.

George C. Stephenson

Purple cones, dripping with silvery resin, stand upright near the treetops on twigs of the previous year's growth

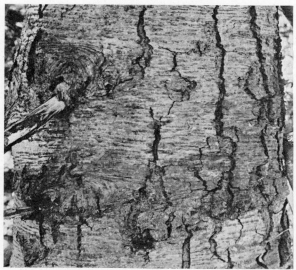

Devereux Butcher

The hard, flinty, ashy-gray bark has the resin-filled blisters characteristic of all balsams

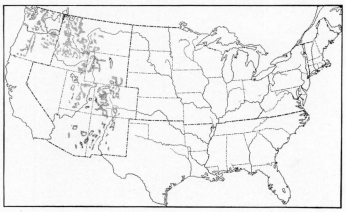

Natural range of Alpine Fir in the United States

***Abies grandis*, Lindley**

Downward sweeping limbs with upcurved ends characterize the Lowland White Fir, which attains heights of 250 and occasionally 300 feet

LOWLAND white fir, so called in contrast to some of the other true firs that occupy the higher mountain areas, is found throughout the coast region from Vancouver Island to Sonoma County, California, and east through Washington and Oregon into northern Idaho and Montana. It also grows in British Columbia to the northern end of Vancouver Island.

It thrives from sea level to 7,000 feet above the sea, where it seeks moist situations along alluvial stream bottoms and their border valleys, and on gentle mountain slopes. Best and most abundant growth is on stream bottoms at low levels along the coast. The deep root system favors fairly deep, porous, well drained soils. Best known of all the western firs because it is common in the valleys as well as on the mountains, it is a stately, narrow crowned tree rising to heights of 150 to 200 feet. Exceptional trees are 250 to 300 feet tall, with a trunk three to four feet, or rarely six feet, in diameter. It so fully lives up to its name *Abies grandis* that it is known to many as "grand fir." This is particularly true if the word *Abies* is derived, as some authorities have suggested, from the Latin word *abeo,* and used in an ascendant or upreaching sense. Certainly, of the eleven North American firs this is probably the tallest, but it does not attain the large dimensions of some of its western relatives. On less favorable sites the tree may be only eighty to 125 feet tall, with trunk diameters of eighteen to thirty inches, but in the high mountains it may be small.

Standing alone or in the open forest, trees hold their long, graceful downward sweeping branches to within a few feet of the ground, while in close grown stands the straight, gradually tapered trunk may be clear for sixty to 100 feet or more. The strongly drooping side branches, with upturned ends, frequently make the narrow, rather open crown appear widest in the middle. With advanced age, height growth becomes less rapid, and the side branches continue to extend so that the narrow tapering point develops into a rounded top. All except the topmost branches have a distinct downward and upward swing.

Ring counts on the stumps of felled trees have shown a diameter of thirty-four inches in 196 years, indicating this fir to be only moderately long lived, but capable of attaining an age of 200 to 250 years.

The dark, yellow-green leaves are shiny on the upper surface and so silvery white below as to be partly responsible for the name of white or silver fir, which confuses it with *Abies concolor.* The leaves are one to two inches long, about one-eighth of an inch wide, thin, flexible, deeply grooved on the upper surface, marked with two parallel lines of white stomata below, and the rounded end is usually distinctly notched. Arranged spirally, they appear to be on opposite sides of the twig with alternate long and short leaves. They spread out flat, like a comb on the lower branches, and are probably the most conspicuously flat and glossy of any of the native firs. Those in the upper crown, and especially on cone-bearing branches, are shorter, more densely crowded and curve upward, while the scattered leaves of the leader are distinctly pointed. They persist for five or ten years before being shed.

The round, resin covered buds as well as the twigs are pale russet brown, and the latter are covered with fine hairs through the first season. Like all the true firs of the genus *Abies*, male and female flowers are borne on branches of the previous year's growth, on different parts of the same tree. The female flowers, which mature in one season into seed-bearing cones are short, scaly, yellow-green bodies which stand erect in the upper branches of the tree. In contrast, the pale, yellow, pollen bearing male flowers hang singly among the leaves from the lower side of branches beneath those which bear female flowers.

The mature cones are bright yellow-green, roughly cylindrical and slightly indented in the end. They stand upright in clusters on the twigs of the upper crown. Each one is two and a half to four and a half inches long, and one to one and a third inches in diameter, consisting of many, closely packed scales concealing broad, squarish-ended bracts. The cones break apart soon after maturity to release the pale yellow, resinous seeds whose broad wings may carry them a hundred feet or more from the parent tree. Only the central core remains through the winter and early spring to stand up like a sharp pointed spike in the upper branches. Trees may begin to bear cones after the twentieth year, and heavy seed crops are produced at intervals of two or three years. Under ordinary conditions the seeds do not retain their vitality longer than one year, and seldom are more than half of them capable of germinating.

Chalky areas on the smooth, ashy brown bark of the young trees and branches contribute to the common name White fir, while the deeply but narrowly ridged bark of old trees is a pale red brown with an ashen tinge. It is hard, close, and horny, rarely more than two inches thick, but scarcely an inch thick on trees up to twenty inches in diameter. Like all true firs the young bark carries many blisters or resin pockets filled with clear, aromatic resin, which with the aromatic odor of the crushed leaves, accounts in part for the earlier name *Abies aromatica* given the tree by Rafinesque in 1832.

Few uses other than for pulpwood have been developed for the soft but firm, moderately wide ringed and straight grained wood, which varies in color from pale yellowish brown to a very light brown. A cubic foot of dry wood weighs about twenty-eight pounds, but is heavier than that of the other firs. Although easily worked, its brittleness and lack of strength or durability has limited its use largely to box boards, packing cases, slack cooperage, interior trim, and rough construction lumber.

Lowland white fir occurs only rarely in pure stands, but usually in mixture with Douglas fir, western red cedar, western hemlock, Pacific yew, and vine maple. At low levels in Oregon and Washington silver fir and Noble fir, broadleaf maple, and black cottonwood are added to its associates. In the low coast region it is found with Sitka spruce, and in California with redwood.

Since 1850 this tree has been planted for ornamental purposes in the British Isles and eastern Europe and under favorable circumstances has proved hardy as far north as New York.

George C. Stephenson

Green cylindrical cones stand erect on the upper branches, whose thin flexible leaves have a silvery white under-surface

The hard, narrowly furrowed bark of mature trees is pale red-brown with an ashen tinge and barely two inches thick

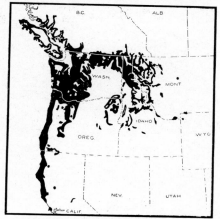

Natural range of Lowland White Fir

WHITE FIR

Abies concolor, Parry

WHITE FIR is the most important of seven true firs inhabiting the forests of the Pacific slope and of the Rocky Mountains. It grows generally on north slopes at moderate altitudes from southern Oregon through California into lower California, and from Nevada, Utah and southern Colorado through Arizona and New Mexico. It reaches greatest growth in northern California on the north and east slopes and at the heads of streams. While thriving best on fairly deep, rich, moist loams, white fir does well on all moderately moist soils, except heavy clays, and frequently grows on dry, coarse, disintegrated granite. It is a massive tree whose dense, heavily-foliaged crown may extend to the ground in open-grown trees or from a third to a half the way down the straight, ashy gray, gradually tapering trunk of forest-grown trees. The lower and middle crown branches droop conspicuously, while the upper branches are upright. With great age, growth slows down and the trees develop a rounded top. Occasional trees grow to a height of two hundred feet and measure six feet or more in diameter. Such trees may be three hundred and fifty years old, but trees forty inches in diameter are considered large.

Young trees have comparatively smooth, ashy gray bark with a brownish tinge, whose conspicuous resin blisters like those of the other true firs give rise to the popular name, "balsam." This clear material has several medicinal and scientific uses. With age the bark thickens to four or six inches, takes on a distinctly ashy gray color, breaks into deep, longitudinal furrows, and becomes hard, horny and fire resistant.

The flat, plump, blunt-pointed leaves form a yellow-green foliage with a bluish cast in the first few months of growth. With maturity this becomes more pale and takes on a whitish cast, which, with the light-colored bark, gives rise to the name, white fir. The leaves are arranged spirally on the branches and remain five to ten years before dropping. They stand out distinctly from two sides of the branch and those on the lower part of the tree are frequently longer, less curved and more sparse than those on the upper branches. Leaves of lower branches may be one to three inches long, while the upper leaves are seldom more than an inch long. Leaves from the middle branches of the crown may also differ slightly from those above and below them.

Both male and female flowers are borne on the same trees on branches of the previous year's growth and the cones develop to maturity during a single season. The short, rounded, scaly cone and seed-bearing ovulate flowers stand erect and singly on the uppermost branches of the crown. Be-

White Fir is a massive tree, is tolerant of shade and frequently holds its branches to the ground

low them, from the underside of the lower branches, hang the elongated, scaly, pollen-bearing, staminate flowers which drop soon after releasing their pollen. The cones, like those of other true firs, maintain an erect position and in early September mature as close-packed cylinders of cone scales, three to five inches long and range in color from ashen-tinged olive-green to purple. The seeds, which develop at the base of the scales, are a dingy yellow-brown with shiny, clear, rose-tinged wings. They are released to be carried fifty to one hundred feet by the wind as the thin, close-packed, overlapping cone scales gradually fall away from the central spike-like axis. Good seed crops occur at irregular intervals of two or three years, and, while most abundant during rapid height growth, continue to maturity. The erect, woody spikes of the cones remain attached to the branches for several years. In no cone-bearing trees except the eastern bald cypress does the cone break up as does that of the firs.

White fir wood is white, straight-grained, and fine-textured. It has no resin ducts and only a slight distinction between sapwood and heartwood. Unseasoned lumber has a disagreeable odor which is so entirely lost with seasoning that it has been successfully used for butter tubs. Its slight resistance to decay makes treatment necessary wherever the wood is to be used in contact with the soil or where termites are prevalent. The wood weighs about twenty-six pounds to the cubic foot when air-dry, or 1,550 to 1,600 pounds for every thousand board feet of sawed lumber. It compares favorably with eastern hemlock, spruce and ponderosa pine in strength and is used largely for the construction of small houses and for boxes and crates. It holds paint well and is successfully used for cupboards and interior trim. Pulp material suitable for newspaper and wrapping paper can be produced, but there is small prospect of any immediate market within its range.

The lumber of white fir is comparatively little known in lumber markets and is sold with that of lowland white fir (*Abies grandis*), red fir (*Abies magnifica*) and the other true firs. The lumber trade makes little effort to distinguish one from the other. The virgin stand of *Abies concolor* was estimated in 1931 to contain 35,340,000,000 board feet, of which nearly all was in California and Oregon. In 1941 the lumber cut of all the western true firs was 209,-326,000 board feet, while the greatest year's production was in 1926 with 349,984,000 board feet. About two-thirds of this came from California.

While the seeds have a relatively low percentage of germination, they grow readily on almost any seed bed. The tree reproduces naturally on exposed denuded lands as well as under its own shade. The seeds will grow under cultivation and the small trees are readily transplanted.

White fir is widely used as an ornamental tree, and is growing successfully in many eastern states from Virginia north into New England. Its dense symmetrical crown and ability to survive under heavy shade render it especially suitable for landscape planting.

The mature cone is three to five inches long and stands erect on the topmost branches

With age the resin pockets or "balsam blisters" disappear and the ashy gray bark becomes deeply furrowed, hard, horny, and fire-resistant

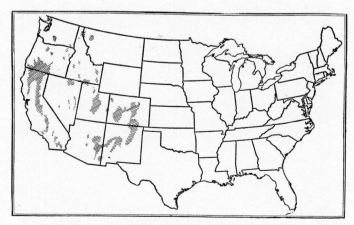

Natural range of White Fir in the United States

NOBLE FIR

Abies procera, Rehder (*A. nobilis,* Lindley)

AS ITS name suggests, this tree is an aristocrat among the true firs. In its native forest environment and growing at its best, it is a magnificent specimen, lifting its crown on a clean and symmetrical trunk a hundred and fifty to two hundred feet into the sky. On rare occasions, its topmost leader will touch the two hundred and fifty foot mark and its trunk girth at the base will exceed twenty feet.

In its crown too there is character that helps to distinguish it from other firs within its range. Standing out rigidly and somewhat sparsely, its branches grow at right angles to the trunk in widely spaced whorls or groups to form a round-topped cone, which at distant view often marks its identity. In the dense mature forest, its straight and symmetrical trunk is often clear of branches for a hundred feet. Open grown, however, branches may clothe its stem to the ground, the lower ones tending to droop.

Locally, noble fir is also known as feather-cone red fir, bracted red fir, larch and Tuck-Tuck, the last an Indian given name. Lumbermen have given it the name "larch" for marketing reasons. Wood of noble fir is superior to that of the other true firs and to offset the market prejudice against the latter, the trade name of larch has been used. *Abies procera,* referring to height, is now applied in place of *Abies nobilis*—a name previously given a fir of Central Europe.

Noble fir grows from the slopes of Mt. Baker in northern Washington southward along the Cascade Mountains to central Oregon, and in the coast mountains of Washington and Oregon, with the chief commercial range located in the central part of the Cascades in southern Washington and northern Oregon. It is seldom reported south of Latitude 40° 30'.

While demanding an abundance of soil moisture, the tree grows on many kinds of soil, but reaches its best development on deep, rich soil. It occurs on gently sloping ridges, valleys, and plateaus at elevations from 1,400 to 6,000 feet above sea level through a zone of uniformly mild, damp climate.

Growth of noble fir is fairly rapid, offering equal competition with its associates, which are usually Douglas fir, western white pine, western hemlock, and less frequently mountain hemlock, lodgepole pine, and silver and alpine firs. Pure stands of noble fir are rare and small in area. Little is known about the age of this species, but probably it is the longest lived of the firs.

The bark of noble fir is thin, averaging one or two inches thick on older trees. Grayish brown

The trunk of noble fir is straight and symmetrical, while the sparse, short branches arranged in whorls, form a round-topped conical crown

in color, it is broken by narrow grooves into irregular, soft plates covered with closely pressed scales that flake off, revealing a ruddy-colored underbark. On young trees the bark is gray and has the resin blisters common to the bark of young trees of other firs. The rounded reddish winter buds are about an eighth of an inch long, coated with resin, and the twigs are slender, hairy and reddish brown.

The curved needles of noble fir vary in color from pale to dark blue-green and appear to grow in a crowded mass along the upper sides of the branches. Needles of the lower branches usually are notched at the tip, and are about one or one and a half inches long, while those of the upper branches, noticeably four-angled, are about five-eighths to three-quarters of an inch long, and nearly always sharply pointed. All needles are grooved on their upper surface. In the vicinity of Davis Lake, Oregon, where the ranges of noble fir and red fir overlap, this groove characteristic offers a means of distinguishing the two species. Needles of red fir, instead of being grooved, are ridged on the top.

Flowers are borne on twigs of the previous season. The purple staminate or pollen-bearing ones hang singly from the branches of the lower crown, while the reddish or yellowish green ovulate ones with broad rounded scales and long bracts stand erect and scattered on the topmost branches. The erect, oblong, round-tipped cones are four or five inches long and are strikingly different from the cones of other firs, in that they have sharply pointed bracts which entirely cover the scales and give them a shingled appearance. Ripening early in September, the cones start to drop their scales and liberate the seeds in October.

Pale reddish brown, the seeds measure about a half inch in length, and are blunt and slightly rounded at the tip. The species is a fairly prolific seeder, some seed being produced every year, with abundant crops occurring at irregular intervals. Trees up to sixty years of age produce seed, but the largest crops are produced by older trees. The rate of germination is low, and seeds do not long retain their vitality. Seedlings grow best on mineral soil and humus in the open or in partial shade, but will not develop in continuous shade. Forest clearings or burned areas soon support an abundant growth of seedlings when parent trees are present.

A cubic foot of noble fir wood when dry weighs twenty-eight pounds. It is hard, strong, very close-grained, firm, and in color is light brown marked with reddish brown streaks which add to its beauty. Sapwood is darker than the heartwood. It is low in fuel value, but works easily and takes a good polish. Recent scientific developments have opened opportunities for noble fir timbers in airplane manufacture. Other uses include flooring, interior finish, doors, window sash, boats, crates, and boxes.

The thin bark makes the tree subject to injury by fire, but as it usually grows in moist locations, this danger is lessened. There is some loss in old trees due to fungus decay, but little in younger ones, while attack by insects is almost unknown.

In Europe noble fir has been successfully planted as an ornamental tree. In eastern United States, it will survive the winter cold as far north as central New England, but has not proven as satisfactory for ornamental purposes as some of the other firs.

Asahel Curtis

The erect, oblong cones have sharply pointed bracts covering the scales like shingles

The thin grayish brown bark is broken by narrow grooves into irregular, soft, scaly plates

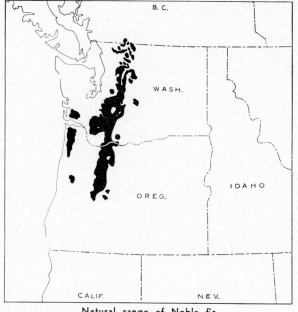

Natural range of Noble fir

Abies magnifica, Murray

RED FIR, also known as red-barked fir, Shasta fir and golden fir, is found on high mountain slopes and meadows from southern Oregon and northern California southward on the western slopes of the mountains to the divide between the White and Kern Rivers. It grows at elevations from 4,800 to 9,000 feet above sea level, and forms extensive forests in the Sierra Nevada and on Mt. Shasta at altitudes of 7,000 to 9,000 feet where it is associated with western white pine, Douglas fir and Jeffrey pine. Its largest size is attained on moist, sandy or gravelly loam soils, where deep snows frequently cover the ground from November to June but where the temperature seldom falls to zero.

True to its name, *Abies magnifica* becomes a magnificent, symmetrical tree commonly sixty to 125 feet high and occasionally 175 feet high with trunk diameters from one to five feet. The narrow, cone-shaped crown is composed of numerous horizontal strata of fan-shaped sprays. Too little is known regarding the longevity of red fir, but trees are known to have lived 350 to 370 years. The scientific name is credited to the botanical studies and descriptions of Andrew Murray, who as Secretary of the Oregon Botanical Association of Edinburgh, Scotland, sponsored the botanical expedition of John Jeffrey into northern California in 1852. The specimens and field notes of this expedition are in the Herbarium of the Royal Botanical Garden at Edinburgh.

There are some twenty-five species of fir distributed over the northern hemisphere. Eleven of these are native within the United States and seven are peculiar to the western mountain region.

In close stands the trunks of red fir are clear of branches for sixty to eighty feet. The central and lower branches droop, while those near the crown have an upward trend. Only in the densest stands are medium sized trees clear of branches for as much as half of their length.

The deep purplish brown or dark red bark of mature trees is two or three inches thick, hard, rough, with deep furrows and narrow, rounded ridges which give a peculiar diagonal or zigzag trend. In youth the bark, like that of many larger branches, is relatively smooth and conspicuously chalky white. As with other true firs, balsam blisters are evident under the thin bark of young trees and branches.

The dark blue-green, four-angled, flat leaves have wide blunt ends, are five-eighths of an inch to a little over an inch long without a twist, and are densely incurving so as to hide the upper side of the branch. The leaves frequently have a whitish tinge and the new growth is light green. They are arranged spirally on the branches and persist for five to ten years. Branches from which the leaves have fallen are marked by conspicuous circular scars, where the leaves were once attached. The twigs divide in a horizontal plane, developing numerous fan-shaped sprays of foliage which give the tree an appearance of being stratified. The leaves on the lower branches differ slightly from those in the middle and upper parts of the tree. The light, chocolate-brown leaf buds are sharp-pointed and without resin.

The greenish red ovulate catkins are about three inches long and stand erect and singly on branches of the uppermost part of the tree. They develop from buds formed during the previous season on twigs of that year, and grow during a single season from dull purple objects to erect deep purple or occasionally brown cones. They are broadly oval, four to eight inches long, two and one-half to three and one-half inches in diameter, with broad scales whose edges are upturned and

Harry H. Haworth

At elevations of 7,000 to 9,000 feet above sea level in Oregon and California, Red Fir develops into a tall symmetrical tree with dark blue-green foliage

partly conceal the irregular tongue-like points of membranous bracts. The dark reddish purple pollen-bearing flowers hang like long cylindrical cones from the under side of branches of the previous year's growth, and on the same tree with the ovulate catkins. They occur most plentifully in the upper half of the tree, but below the cone-bearing catkins. The cones mature in August of the first year and maintain their erect or nearly erect position, which is characteristic of all firs. They break up during September, liberating numerous seeds with large shiny purple or rose-colored wings. Only an erect spike, or central axis, three to seven inches long is left through the winter. The baldcypress of the South is the only other native cone-bearer whose mature cones break up as do the firs. Good crops of seeds are produced every two or three years. Seeds may be carried by the wind two hundred feet or more from the parent tree and germinate abundantly on exposed moist mineral soils, or in light shade. Seedlings grow rapidly and frequently cover high slopes or openings cleared by fire or storm. As the tree grows older it is less tolerant of side shade.

The wood has a reddish tinge, is soft, light, rather brittle and with a straight, fine grain. It is more durable in contact with the soil or exposure to the weather than the wood of any of the other native firs. Weighing twenty-nine pounds to the cubic foot when air-dried, it ranks as the heaviest of all firs. No separate estimates exist regarding its commercial stand, but it forms a considerable part of the 122,000,000,000 board feet of standing timber credited to the seven species of western fir, of which 107,453,000 board feet were cut in 1935 as compared with 67,253,000 board feet in 1933. The heaviest production is reported from California and Oregon. It is used largely for rough lumber, packing boxes, bridge floors and mine timbers but as yet has no definite place in the lumber market.

The blisters on the bark are the source of an oleo-resin known as Canada balsam, used for mounting microscopic specimens, for medicinal purposes and in the manufacture of some varnishes. An essential oil used in pharmacy is also obtained from the leaves, which give off a turpentine-like odor when bruised.

The dense foliage and frequent exudation of balsam on the bark make young stands of red fir susceptible to fire, but with increasing age, the thicker bark resists damage from the heat of ground fires. Dense young stands are also seriously weighed down and bent by heavy snow storms.

Small woolly sucking insects known as adelgids sometimes cause extensive injury to the leaves and buds of this and other firs. No satisfactory control measures have been developed for forest trees but soapy solutions containing nicotine are usually effective when sprayed on infested ornamental trees during late winter or early spring.

The handsome regular habit of red fir together with its ability when young to grow in crowded, shady stands makes it desirable as an ornamental tree. It has proved successful on cool moist sites in the eastern states and in northern Europe but is generally less hardy than Noble fir or some of the local species. The leaves are injured by smoke or other atmospheric impurities, so that this tree is unsuitable for planting in cities or in the vicinity of factories using soft coal.

National Park Service

The deep, purple, four to seven-inch cones stand singly and erect on twigs of the previous year's growth

National Park Service

Deep zigzag furrowings in the hard, rough, dark red bark are characteristic of Red Fir

Natural range of Red Fir in the United States

GIANT SEQUOIA

Sequoia gigantea, **Decaisne**

Gabriel Moulin

A Giant Sequoia, over a thousand years old, lifts its rounded crown above a massive trunk, and shows its size in contrast to neighboring pines and firs

GIANT SEQUOIA or Big Tree, oldest and most massive of all living things, links our civilization with the dim records of the past. John Muir called it "king of all the conifers of the world, 'the noblest of a noble race.' " Flourishing trees now standing in the California groves were swaying in the Sierra winds when Christ walked the earth. These trees of the Sequoia group are remnants of an ancient race which flourished as far north as the Arctic Zone during Tertiary and Cretaceous times. All but two species—Giant Sequoia, *Sequoia gigantea,* and the Redwood, *Sequoia sempervirens,* have disappeared since the Glacial Period. These two continue growing in the California coast mountains and western slopes of the Sierra Nevada, at elevations of 4,000 to 8,500 feet above sea level. The older trees grow on high land from which the glacial ice apparently melted long before it did in the intervening canyons. Here the snow gathers six feet deep for three to six months each year, and the temperature may drop below zero. In contrast to the redwood, the Giant Sequoia grows at higher elevations and cooler sites farther back from the coast, and out of the fog belt. They are found in some seventy groves of five to 1,000 trees in an area extending from the North Grove, east to Lake Tahoe in the Tahoe National Forest, southward for 260 miles to the Deer Creek Grove, east of Porterville in the Sequoia National Forest. The annual precipitation in this area varies from forty-five to sixty inches, much of which is in the form of heavy snowfall.

The nearest relative of the Sequoia on this continent is the baldcypress, *Taxodium distichum,* of the southern states, but the name of these westerners perpetuates that of Sequoyah, otherwise George Guess of Georgia, a talented Cherokee Indian chieftain, who, between 1770 and 1843, invented the Cherokee alphabet.

Giant Sequoia thrives in shallow grassy basins where the soil is deep and sandy to gravelly, and in draws near the headwaters of streams where soil moisture is abundant. While occasional pure stands of Giant Sequoias are found, they usually tower among a forest of sugar pine, incense cedar, white fir, Douglas fir, or ponderosa pine. The trunk may rise eighty to 225 feet before the first limb, and be surrounded by a crown rounded at the summit, or much broken, depending upon the age of the tree. The trunk of young trees is clothed to the ground with slender up-curved branches, and is highly ornamental.

Trees attain heights of 300 to 330 feet, and one in the Calaveras Grove is estimated to have once been 400 feet high. This grove of about one hundred trees was first reported in 1841. Ten feet from the ground and above the stump-swell trees may be twenty-seven to thirty feet in diameter, but more frequently they are twelve to seventeen feet in diameter, 200 to 280 feet high, and from 1,200 to 2,000 years old. The stump of one tree recorded 3,400 rings of annual growth, and John Muir counted the rings on another which he believed to be over 4,000 years old.

Giant Sequoia has bright, deep green foliage in the form of scale-like, sharp-pointed leaves closely overlapping one another on the branches, after the manner of cedars. They are "evergreen" and remain on the branches three to four years.

Tiny flowers of both sexes, borne singly at the tips of different twigs on the same tree, appear in February and March, when snow is on the ground. The pollen-bearing flowers are about a quarter of an inch long, scaly, and in large numbers over the tree. Clouds of pollen from these fertilize the small, pale green seed-producing flowers, which mature in two seasons into woody, yellowish brown, egg-shaped cones varying from two to three inches long. Under each thick cone-scale are five to seven brown, flat, wing-margined seeds with a kernel about the size of a pin head. The seeds are released in the late autumn, when the wind carries them relatively short distances from the parent tree, but the empty cones may remain on the tree. Unlike the redwood, the Giant Sequoia does not produce sprouts, but depends entirely upon seeds for reproduction.

The red-brown bark is twelve to twenty-four inches thick, spongy and in two layers. The outer is composed of fibrous scales, while the inner is thin, close and firm. Vertical breaks extending the length of the trunk give it a fluted appearance.

The heartwood is dull purplish red-brown, lighter and more brittle than that of Redwood. The straight grain varies from very fine in the later growth of old trees to coarse in the wood produced during the first 400 to 500 years while the tree growth is rapid. The wood contains much tannin and when freshly cut the heartwood is a brilliant rose-purple surrounded by a thin layer of white sapwood. Like redwood, its uses are various but the loss in felling is so great, the logs so difficult to handle and the wood so brittle that it is now practically off the market.

With the rosy purple drops of Giant Sequoia sap, John Muir wrote letters, and reported that the Indians drank it in the hope of gaining some mystical power.

The most imposing Giant Sequoias are within the General Grant National Park and the Sequoia National Park. Between the Kings River and the Kerns River are many trees twenty-five feet in diameter containing upwards of 500,000 board feet, and probably 3,000 years old. The largest of these trees probably weighs over a thousand tons.

Giant Sequoia owes its long life in no small measure to its freedom from destructive fungus and insect enemies. This may be due to the high tannin content of the wood, and also because there are no pitch tubes, as in the case of the pines, through which fungi may progress through the wood. Most destructive are the results of fire or other more or less natural causes which undermine the roots, causing the tree to settle and tip over. Occasionally, also, huge limbs may grow so as to over-balance the tree.

Giant Sequoia seeds germinate best on bare exposed soil in sunny places and in spite of the small amount of stored food within the seed, seedlings are fairly common in favorable places. The seedlings will not grow naturally in the dense shade of the forest where thick layers of litter cause plants to die before becoming rooted in soil. Favorable conditions for natural reproduction frequently follow fires, floods, or where the ground has been disturbed by logging or road building operations. While ground fires help prepare the soil for seedlings to start, subsequent fires are disastrous to the young trees.

Seedlings are successfully grown in nurseries and can be transplanted. Giant Sequoia has been extensively planted in California, and will grow in parts of the eastern United States, and also does well on the British Isles and in Central Europe.

Woodbridge Metcalf

Sharp pointed, scale-like evergreen leaves overlap one another as with the cedars, while the dull yellow-brown cones are two to three inches long

The natural range of Giant Sequoia, Sequoia gigantea, is confined to a small area in California

National Park Service

Deep fissures in the thick red-brown bark give the Giant Sequoia trunk a fluted appearance

Sequoia sempervirens, (Lambert) Endlicher

THE redwood, whose family covered most of the northern hemisphere before the glacial periods, is now confined to an area of less than 1,500,000 acres. It grows in an irregular strip scarcely thirty-five miles wide and 500 miles long, extending along the west slope of the Pacific Coast from the Chetco River in southwestern Oregon to Salmon Creek Canyon, about one hundred miles south of San Francisco in Monterey County, California. The trees grow from sea level to approximately 3,000 feet above the sea, on flats and seaward slopes subject to frequent, heavy fogs.

The redwood and its close Sierra relative the Big Tree, *Sequoia gigantea,* are the largest, and probably the oldest, examples of life in North America, if not in the world. Lambert, of London, published the first description of redwood in 1803, under the name *Taxodium sempervirens,* in the belief that it was related to the southern cypress. In 1847, believing it to be a distinct genus, the name *Sequoia* was given by a German botanist, Endlicher, to honor the half-breed Cherokee chief Sequoyah who formulated an alphabet for his tribe, and *sempervirens* is from the Latin, meaning "always green," sometimes interpreted "ever living."

Although not as longlived as the Big Tree nor as great in girth, it grows to a greater height than any other American tree. On flats under good conditions it grows to be 350 feet high and from twenty to twenty-seven feet in diameter. The oldest redwood found during investigations by the Forest Service was twenty-one feet in diameter and 1,373 years old. Another tree fifteen feet in diameter and 270 feet high, described by Prof. W. R. Dudley was 2,171 years old. Accurate ring counts cannot be secured without destroying the tree, but it is assumed that redwoods 300 feet high and twenty feet or more in diameter may approach an age of 2,000 years. Most of the redwoods cut in commercial operations are from 400 to 800 years old. These are from three to ten feet in diameter, and 200 to 275 feet tall. The tallest measured tree is 364 feet high and stands on Dyerville Flat.

The larger trees have a straight, slightly tapered, heavily buttressed trunk, clear for more than one hundred feet, with an open round-topped crown of relatively short horizontal branches spreading with a downward tendency. The crowns may occupy a third to a half of the total length. Those of young trees ten to fifteen inches in diameter are narrowly conical and may extend to the ground.

The sharply pointed, flat, bright, deep yellow-green leaves of the lower branches and young saplings stand out stiffly on opposite sides of the twigs and vary from one-third of an inch to an inch in length, while on the main stem of the branches they may occur as several overlapping lines of closely pressed scale-like forms. The leaves of each season's growth may remain on the tree for three or four years, and then cling to the branches for another one or two years after they are dead.

Tiny male and female flowers are on different branches of the same tree. The flower buds form in the autumn near the ends of the previous year's shoots. In the late winter or early spring the staminate flowers develop as small greenish yellow bodies in the axils of the leaves, while the more broadly egg-shaped ovulate flowers are terminal.

By early September of the same year the ovulate flowers mature into dull, purplish brown, egg-shaped cones about an inch long, and half as broad. Closely packed under each cone scale are four or five small russet brown, wing-margined seeds which are shed slowly, and carried comparatively short distances by the wind. They are about one-sixteenth of an inch in diameter and when clean will run about 123,000 to the pound. The cones remain on the trees several months after losing their seeds.

Rearing its crown to heights of over 300 feet, the coast Redwood of California is the taller and more graceful of the two species of Sequoia

The dull red-brown bark of old trees has a grayish hue and is longitudinally fissured. It is very dense and tight, may be a foot thick, and is highly resistant to fire. Beneath this is a firm, thin, cinnamon-red layer of more closely pressed bark.

Redwood is named for the soft, straight - grained, moderately strong heartwood which varies in color from a light cherry to a dark mahogany, and also for the color of the bark. The narrow sapwood is almost white. Air-dry heartwood weighs twenty-four to twenty-six pounds to the cubic foot. This is similar to the weight of the wood of northern white pine, to which it compares favorably in strength and stiffness. The wood is several pounds heavier than that of the Big Tree and is stronger. It is easy to work, shrinks and swells but little, takes paint well, and resists decay and insects. Railroad ties, bridge timbers, tanks, flumes, silos, bee keepers' supplies, posts, grape stakes, shingles, siding, ceiling, doors, general mill work, caskets and furniture are among its many uses.

Recent estimates indicate the region contains about thirty-nine billion board feet, although in 1909 there was estimated to be over one hundred billion board feet. In 1941, the commercial cut of redwood was reported as 455,519,000 board feet, but from 1900 to 1930 the average annual cut was close to 500,000,000 board feet. Individual acres yielding over 100,000 board feet of sawtimber are very common, and some acres of unusually large trees are reported to have produced a million board feet.

Although many seeds are produced nearly every year only fifteen to twenty-five per cent are perfect and the germination is low. Even so, millions of seed germinate and supplement the many vigorous sprouts which are produced from the stumps, root collar and roots of old as well as young trees. The "Muir Woods" near the base of Mt. Tamalpais, about 38,000 acres in state parks, and a growing sense of public responsibility among redwood timberland owners give assurance that considerable areas may be saved for future generations.

None of the ordinary wood-rotting fungi grow in redwood timber and the tree is singularly free from fungus diseases. A so-called brown rot takes heavy toll of the standing timber. This causes portions of the butt to assume the properties of charcoal and to crumble into a fine powder. Another stringy type of fungus does some damage. Similarly, few insects cause material harm and the wood is highly resistant to attacks of termites. Even fire does relatively little damage to trees which have acquired a thick bark, but the young growth is killed or seriously injured. The frequent "goose pens" in the larger trees are evidence that persistently repeated fires will make inroads upon them, and at the same time, of the amazing ability of the tree to maintain life, by healing over injuries wherever living tissue remains.

Redwood requires a moist, cool climate of high humidity as shown by its dependence upon the Pacific Coast fogs. It seldom thrives in a dry or warm climate, but will stand temperatures ranging from 15 to 110 degrees Fahrenheit. The best stands are on protected flats and benches along streams or on moderate west slopes opening toward the sea. Thirty to sixty inches of rain falls in the autumn and winter and sea fogs bathe the region in summer. It grows in mixture with Douglas fir, tanbark oak, Sitka spruce, Port Orford cedar, western red cedar, white fir, and western hemlock. Where conditions are favorable the redwood leads all of these in the struggle for growing space. Efforts to grow redwood in the eastern states have met with little success.

The bright yellow-green leaves of the lower branches stand out stiffly on opposite sides of the twigs and remain on the tree three or four years. Those on the main branches are scale-like. The egg-shaped cones are scarcely an inch long, about half as broad, and mature in a single season

Redwood bark is reddish gray in color, fibrous in texture and gives a fluted appearance to the tree

The natural range of Redwood is limited to a narrow strip extending along the Pacific Coast from southwestern Oregon to about 500 miles into California

BALDCYPRESS

Taxodium distichum, (Linnaeus) Richard

THE baldcypress, equally at home on land or in the water, lifts a massive, buttressed, tapering trunk, surrounded by curious cone-shaped knobs, above the stagnant water of southern swamps or river bottoms to carry a crown laden with drooping locks of Spanish moss. This remnant of ancient times, when similar trees were distributed over North America and northern Europe, is making its last stand in the southeastern states where it grows along the coast from southern Delaware to southern Florida, westward along the Gulf Coast into Texas, and northward up the river valleys through Oklahoma and Arkansas to southern Illinois and southwestern Indiana. Usually it occurs along low bottomlands in saturated, or seasonally submerged soil. Thousand year old trees may become 150 feet high and twelve feet in diameter, but more often they approach 120 feet in height and three to five feet in diameter. In youth the crown is narrow and pyramidal, but with age the branches spread to form a broad irregular crown.

Although a conifer it is not evergreen, for its leaves and small immature twigs are shed each fall. The only other deciduous conifer, the larch, sheds only its leaves.

The scientific name *taxodium* comes from its resemblance to the yew or *taxus*, while *distichum* is from two Greek words meaning twice or double ranked, and refers to the two-ranked arrangement on the twigs of the long, narrow, rather flat leaves. These are one-half to three-quarters of an inch long, light yellow-green, arranged spirally on the twigs, and feathery in appearance. They turn yellow or brown before they drop in the autumn.

In the spring each tree may carry male and female flowers which develop on twigs of the preceding year's growth. The male flowers are slender, purplish, three to six inches long, tassel-like clusters, while the female or ovulate flowers are scattered singly on the ends of the branchlets. These develop in a single season into spherical, purplish cones about an inch in diameter. Thick rhomboid scales fit closely together and under each may be two light brown, winged, somewhat pyramidal, horny seeds. Cypress also sprouts freely from the tree stumps during the first fifty to one hundred years.

Small, brown and more or less egg-shaped leaf buds appear on light green, slender twigs, which by winter become light red-brown and lustrous.

The reddish brown, fibrous ridged bark of old trees peels off in long strips, and is one to two

The massive, buttressed trunk of the Baldcypress supports a broad irregular crown of light green feathery foliage

86

inches thick. On younger trees the bark is light brown, less deeply ridged and thinner.

Shallow serpentine roots spread out from the buttressed base of the tree. Where water stands during part of the year these develop sharp, elongated cones or "knees" which rise a few inches to five or six feet above the mud surface, corresponding to the high water level of the locality. They are covered with thin bark, are hollow, and usually die when water is permanently drained or when the parent tree is cut. They help anchor the tree and are believed to furnish air to the roots. In spite of the unstable soils in which cypress thrives, even the tallest trees are seldom thrown by the wind.

The soft, narrow-ringed, pale brown to reddish wood weighs twenty-two to thirty-seven pounds to the cubic foot when air dry, averaging about twenty-eight pounds. It is easily worked, has no resin ducts, feels slightly greasy or waxy, and has a peculiarly rancid odor. The heartwood is so durable in contact with the soil, or when exposed to the weather, as to be known as "the wood eternal." Cypress is used for structural purposes, for flooring, water tanks, ships, cross-ties, shingles, coffins, laundry appliances and greenhouse equipment.

More than half of the present stand of about 11,500,000,000 board feet is located in Florida and Louisiana. During 1941 the cut of 349,610,000 board feet was chiefly from Florida, South Carolina, Louisiana, Arkansas, Georgia, Mississippi, Virginia, North Carolina, Tennessee and Alabama. In 1930 the cut was 490,857,000 board feet, while in 1913 it exceeded a billion board feet.

Baldcypress trees may grow in relatively pure stands in swampy areas or in mixture with tupelo gum, green ash, willow, overcup oak, red gum, the soft maples and elms. Single acres with over 100,-000 board feet have been measured, while forty-acre tracts have yielded 1,500,000 board feet. Usually, however, stands do not exceed 8,000 to 10,000 board feet to the acre.

This last representative of an ancient race resists most insect enemies, but is subject to a heart-rot fungus which fills the wood with holes to be known as "pecky" cypress. This has many uses where strength or ability to hold water are not essential. The thin bark offers little protection against fire and during years of drouth when swamps are dry great quantities of timber are burned.

Cypress is successfully planted throughout its range for ornamental and roadside purposes and individual specimens are proving hardy in central New York and over much of Indiana and Illinois.

Purplish, woody, spherical cones about an inch in diameter are borne on the twigs of the previous year's growth. Each cone may yield eighteen to thirty light brown, winged seeds

The fluted, buttressed trunk and the "knees," which often protrude above the mud and water, are covered with fibrous, reddish brown bark. The "knees" are hollow and are part of the shallow roots. They are believed to furnish air when the base of the tree is submerged

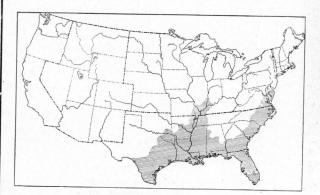

Natural range of Baldcypress

CALIFORNIA INCENSE CEDAR

Libocedrus decurrens, Torrey

California Incense Cedar attains heights of 150 feet in the coast ranges of Oregon and California

THE tall, compactly columnar crown of incense cedar, consisting of flattened frond-like branches, and reared on a rapidly tapering cinnamon-red trunk is frequently seen growing singly or in small groves over the western slopes of the mountain ranges from northern Oregon to lower California. Confined largely to elevations of 4,000 to 8,000 feet above sea level, it ranges for a thousand miles from the basin of the Santiam River in Oregon, southward along the Cascade Mountains and the western slopes of the Sierra Nevada, over the California coast ranges to the mountains of southern California and lower California. Eastward it is found in a few scattered mountain areas in Nevada.

Mature trees range from seventy-five to 110 feet in height and from two and a half to four feet in diameter. Trees 150 feet in height occur throughout the Sierra and one tree 186 feet high has been recorded. The younger trees with trunks up to twelve inches in diameter maintain a narrow, columnar form with branches reaching to the ground. The larger branches have a distinct upward turn. With age and maturity, the crown flattens out and becomes more open. Incense cedar is a relatively slow-growing tree reaching an average diameter of about thirteen inches in 100 years and frequently attaining ages of 300 to 500 years. One tree measuring 51.2 inches in diameter at stump height was 542 years old, and trees may reach ages ranging from 800 to 1,000 years.

The yellowish green evergreen foliage consists of small, pointed, scale-like leaves adhering closely to slender branchlets and capable of remaining on the tree from three to five years. They form flat sprays. Each leaf extends from one-eighth to one-half inch along the branch and has a characteristically long base to which the technical name *decurrens* refers. A small resin gland on each leaf is responsible for the pungent, aromatic odor so apparent when the leaf is crushed.

Libocedrus is the name of a widely distributed family of trees closely related to the true cypress and not far distantly to the *thuja*. *Libocedrus decurrens* is the only one of the nine species of the genus which is native to North America. Eight other species are found from Chile to Patagonia in South America. China, Formosa, New Guinea, New Zealand, and New Caledonia. *Libocedrus* is derived from two Greek words and may be translated as "the cedar tree, the wood of which was burnt for perfume or to scent ointment."

Flowers of the two sexes are found on parts

of the same tree, or occasionally upon different trees. In January the quarter-inch long, golden yellow, pollen-bearing male, or staminate flowers shower the tree with gold and mingle with the snow as it lies on the branches. The female flowers develop on the ends of the past year's growth, as small light yellow-green cones with two to six pairs of leaf-like scales.

By late summer, following the appearance of the blossoms, small urn-shaped cones, from three-quarters to one and one-half inches long, develop and hang pendent on the extreme ends of the branchlets. These cones somewhat resembling those of *thuja*, or white cedar, but with fewer scales, consist of six leaf-like scales in pairs, and enclose one or two tiny, winged seeds. By September the cones open and great numbers of seed drift down in the wind in such quantities as to form a red-brown carpet beneath the parent trees. The dry, yellow-brown cones cling to the trees for several months thereafter.

The widely buttressed bases of mature incense cedar trees are clothed in thick, shreddy, cinnamon-red bark which is deeply grooved and ridged. On young trees the bark is purplish red, flaky, and has a silver sheen on the loosened scales. Later it takes on a reddish brown hue which glows in the sunlight. The upper bark of old trees is two or three inches thick, while along the base it may be six or eight inches thick.

The soft, light brown wood is frequently tinged with red, although the sapwood is cream colored. It has a compact, fine, straight grain, splits readily and evenly, and does not check or warp in seasoning. The wood weighs, when air dry, about twenty-five pounds to the cubic foot, is aromatic, takes a good polish and is extremely durable when seasoned. It is widely used for fence posts, railroad ties, shingles, and to an increasing extent for pencil slats, cedar chests, so-called moth proof linings for the interiors of wardrobes, and for door and window frames. It is sometimes used for cigar boxes. The entire stand of incense cedar is estimated at 11,000,-000,000 board feet, with 9,000,000,000 in California and the remainder in Oregon and Nevada. The average annual cut of incense cedar for the ten years from 1926 to 1935 was approximately 17,000,000 board feet, which with unrecorded amounts which went into fence posts and railroad ties would place the annual cut roughly at 20,000,-000 board feet, but in 1941 the production was reported as 40,392,000 board feet.

Under the most favorable conditions it may form half of the stand in mixture with ponderosa pine and sugar pine. It is also found in mixtures with the California Big Tree, California black oak, Jeffrey pine, and occasionally with white fir, lodgepole pine, and limber pine. Best development is found on the west slope of the Sierra at elevations of 5,000 to 6,000 feet above sea level.

The thick, fire-resistant bark makes mature incense cedar trees relatively immune to fire damage, but heavy losses are sustained when fire runs through young growth and reproduction.

There are no insect enemies of any importance, but practically one-half of all incense cedar trees as they stand in the woods are defective, and most of the loss is due to a dry-rot fungous which attacks the heartwood, excavating parts throughout the length of the trunk.

Incense cedar has been extensively planted for ornamental purposes in the eastern states where it prospers as far north as Massachusetts. The tree lends itself to unusual landscape effects, does well on well drained, loamy soils, and is highly tolerant of shade.

George C. Stephenson

Light brown cones develop in one season and hang from the ends of the branchlets

The deeply furrowed, shreddy, cinnamon-brown bark is two to three inches thick, or even heavier at the base of old trees

Natural range of California Incense Cedar

NORTHERN WHITE CEDAR

Thuja occidentalis, **Linnaeus**

IN COOL swamps, or beside streams or lakes from Nova Scotia and New Brunswick west to southeastern Manitoba, and from New England and New Jersey west to central Minnesota and southward through the Appalachian mountains, with the possible exception of Pennsylvania, the narrow, pyramidal crowns of northern white cedar, or arbor vitae, make a familiar sight. Sometimes growing in pure, almost impenetrable stands, it also flourishes in company with spruce, larch, alder, and balsam. In moist fields and shallow, rocky pastures, it may grow in scattered picturesque clumps, the taller trees thrusting their conical crowns above the center of the group, while smaller trees crowd close around the outer edge.

Under favorable conditions in the north, this tree occasionally attains seventy feet in height and three to six feet in diameter. Ordinarily, however, northern white cedar trees are considered large when fifty to sixty feet tall with diameters of two to three feet. Southward, the tree becomes less abundant and smaller, so that in the mountains of western North Carolina and eastern Tennessee it is found only at high elevations and reduced to the proportions of a shrub.

A slow growing tree, most of whose wood is added during early years, it may reach ages of 250 to 300 years.

The smaller twigs and branchlets are so densely covered by scale-like leaves that they appear to be the leaves themselves. Actually, each dark green leaf is scarcely a quarter of an inch long, and with its fellows is arranged in overlapping rows of alternating pairs on the flattened branchlets. The under surface is light green, and when bruised gives off a tansy-like odor.

In April or May small liver-colored flowers are borne on the ends of the branchlets, the two sexes being separate and distinct from one another. The solitary elongated s t a m i n a t e cones are about one-sixteenth of an inch long, entire, and composed of three to six pairs of stamens, while the purplish ovulate cones are similar in size and consist of four to six pairs of thin, elongated scales. By late summer the fertilized cones mature. They are a light yellow to cinnamon red from one-third to one-half inch long and stand erect on the twigs. The seeds which form beneath the scales are light brown about an eighth of an inch long and nearly en-

Devereux Butcher

Northern White Cedar has a shapely pyramidal crown of feathery dark green foliage

circled by thin wings as broad as the body. These help carry the seeds considerable distances by the wind, but the empty cones remain on the twigs through the winter.

The trunk may be lobed and buttressed at the base, tapering and often divided into two or more secondary stems. It is frequently distorted and twisted; similarly the thin fibrous light brown bark may seem to spiral around the trunk. It is a quarter to a third of an inch thick. On the larger branches the bark is dark orange marked with shallow fissures.

The wood of northern white cedar, or arbor vitae, is pale yellow-brown, aromatic, soft, brittle, coarse grained, and durable in contact with the soil. A cubic foot when air dry weighs about nineteen pounds. Surrounding the heartwood is a thin layer of nearly white sapwood. The wood is easy to work and has little tendency to shrink or warp. It splits easily, and the annual growth rings will separate from one another when the wood is pounded. This quality permitted the Indians to separate thin splints for use as canoe ribs. The same feature, however, reduces the value of this wood for many modern purposes and is characterized in many trees as "ring shake" or "wind shake." Because of its durability in contact with the soil and moisture, it is used for shingles, railroad ties, poles, fence posts, buckets, stave cooperage, tanks, cisterns, boats, and canoe frames. Because of its light weight as well as durability, it is also used for fish net floats and imitation minnows for fishermen. An aromatic oil is distilled from the leaves and twigs which is sometimes used to relieve chest colds and for other medicinal purposes.

Thuja occidentalis is not a true cedar, but is more strictly speaking an arbor vitae. *Thuja* is a Latin name for a conifer tree, while *occidentalis* refers to the fact that it is native to the western hemisphere and thereby distinct from the oriental cedar. There are seven species of *Thuja*—two native in North America, and the others in China, Japan, and Formosa. American Indians referred to this tree as Oo-soo-ha-tah, meaning, "feather leaf."

Northern white cedar was once of great importance in the Lake States, but those stands of saw-timber are now reduced to an estimated 157,000,000 board feet. In New England the stand is estimated to contain 1,826,000,000 board feet, most of which is in Maine. Some 31,000,000 board feet are scattered through the Middle Atlantic States with the bulk in New York. On the basis of these figures the present stand of northern white cedar saw-timber has been estimated as something in excess of 2,000,000,000 board feet. During recent years the average annual cut has been less than 5,000,000 board feet.

This tree begins to bear seed when ten to fifteen years old. Seed producing years follow frequently thereafter. The seed germinate readily and may take root wherever the moist soil is exposed. Because of its trim, somewhat artificial appearance, it is frequently used for hedges and windbreaks. It is also planted for ornamental purposes on lawns and in parks. Nursery men recognize some forty-five varieties of northern white cedar, all of which are propagated by means of cuttings rather than from seed. Small trees are also easily raised from seed and lend themselves to successful transplanting. Best results are achieved in a seed bed containing considerable peat, but partial shade must be provided. Except as protected naturally by its moist environment, it is easily injured by ground fires, but has few serious insect or fungus enemies.

George J. Baetzhold

The small scale-like leaves are in overlapping rows on the branchlets. The cones are urn shaped and grow erect near the ends of the leafy twigs

Deep fissures break the thin orange-brown bark into narrow, interlacing ridges

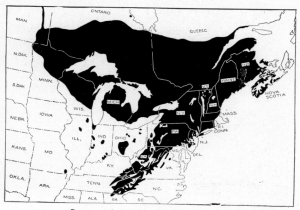

Range of Northern White Cedar

WESTERN RED CEDAR

Thuja plicata, Don

WESTERN red cedar ranks among the large trees of the Pacific Coast and is found from southern Alaska to northern California, on sites where the soil is moist. It grows at elevations ranging from sea level in the far north to 7,000 feet in the northern Rocky Mountains, where the magnificent proportions of the coastwise tree are reduced to those of a small wind blown bush. Heavily buttressed trees 150 to 175 feet high and five to eight feet in diameter are fairly common, while exceptional trees attain heights of 190 to 200 feet with occasional diameters of ten to sixteen feet. The center of large trees is usually hollow.

In densely crowded stands the trees have long clear trunks, frequently with branches below the main crown. The narrow conical crown of young trees reaches to the ground, and even in dense stands the lower branches are retained until the tree reaches heights of fifty to eighty feet. In old trees the crown extends in width, becoming short and blunt. On young trees the slender limbs curve upward, but with age they swing downward in a long graceful curve. While diameters of twenty-four to forty inches are reached in 200 to 500 years, some of the largest trees are believed to be 800 to 1,000 years old.

Small scale-like, bright green leaves form flat, lacy sprays after the manner of the eastern white cedar, *Thuja occidentalis*. They are glossy above, distinctly darker and with frequent white, triangular spots beneath, remain on the tree about three years, and have a pleasant odor.

Thuja plicata is derived from the Greek and Latin, and refers to a tree having sweet smelling wood whose leaves are plaited or folded.

In April small inconspicuous flowers of the two sexes appear usually on different branches of the same tree. The flowers are about one-twelfth of an inch long and develop singly at the ends of the twigs. The staminate ones are yellowish and the ovulate are pinkish at pollination. From the latter, leathery brown cones about one-half inch long comprised of six fertile scales, mature by the end of August. Each fertile scale may bear two tiny double - winged

Western Red Cedar grows in densely crowded stands to heights of 175 feet and more

Devereux Butcher

seeds which are shed in the fall of the same year. The upturned empty cones remain on the tree until the following summer. The cinnamon-red, stringy, fibrous bark is seldom over seven-eighths of an inch thick and so tough that the Indians peel strips twenty to thirty feet long from young trees for making baskets and even for rope or fish line. The strongly aromatic wood is reddish brown when freshly cut, but becomes dull brown with exposure. It is free from pitch, of medium to coarse grain, very soft and brittle, weighs twenty-four to thirty pounds to the cubic foot when air dry, and is unusually resistant to decay or insect attack. Probably two-thirds of all western cedar goes into shingles of which it forms the bulk of our supply. Other uses include lumber, poles, posts, piling, boats, pattern stock, laundry machinery, cigar boxes, and greenhouse equipment. Paints, varnishes, and lacquers adhere well and it glues readily. Because it works easily and scarcely warps or shrinks it is favored for the exterior of houses. The Indians of the Pacific Northwest used it for totem poles, canoes, and lodges.

The reported production of western red cedar for lumber was 181,230,000 board feet in 1941, which represented a steady drop since 1905 when the production was approximately 290,000,000 board feet. The manufacture of western red cedar shingles consumes 500,000,000 to 800,000,000 board feet, while an additional 100,000,000 board feet is cut for poles, posts, and piling. The annual cut for all purposes, accordingly, approximates 700,000,000 to a billion board feet. The commercial stand within the United States is estimated to approximate 35,000,000,000 board feet, of which the bulk is in the Pacific Coast region.

Western red cedar does not grow in pure forests, but forms three to twelve percent of the total growth in company with Douglas fir and western hemlock.

The moist character of the sites where western red cedar grows is an important factor in protecting the tree against fire. The thin bark offers little fire resistance, so that when fires do occur the trees are usually fatally injured. In contrast, however, neither insects nor fungi are major sources of damage.

Although few efforts have been made to use it for reforestation, it is recognized as a conifer of unusual promise for ornamental planting on the West Coast as well as in the eastern states as far north as Massachusetts. It assumes a graceful pyramidal outline and prospers in fertile well drained soil.

Flat, lacy sprays of scale-like, bright green leaves and up-turned leathery brown cones characterize this tree

The cinnamon-red, fibrous bark is less than an inch thick

Natural range of Western Red Cedar in the United States

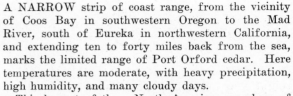

PORT ORFORD CEDAR

Chamaecyparis lawsoniana, (Murray) Parlatore

A NARROW strip of coast range, from the vicinity of Coos Bay in southwestern Oregon to the Mad River, south of Eureka in northwestern California, and extending ten to forty miles back from the sea, marks the limited range of Port Orford cedar. Here temperatures are moderate, with heavy precipitation, high humidity, and many cloudy days.

This largest of three North American members of the genus *Chamaecyparis* has three other relatives in Japan. Heights of eighty to 175 feet, and occasionally of 200 feet, with diameters of twelve feet, belie the Greek word *"chamai"* meaning "on the ground," which combined with *"kyparissos"* or *"cypress"* makes *Chamaecyparis.* The specific name, *lawsoniana,* honors Sir Charles Lawson, a Scottish economist in whose nursery were raised the first seedlings from seeds which William Murray gathered in the cañon of the Sacramento River in 1854. The larger stands of timber were reported in 1855 from the Coos Bay area.

Diameters of three to seven feet are probably attained in 300 to 350 years, while the largest trees may be 600 years old. Best growth is attained on moist hillsides or canyon bottoms, but the dry, sandy ridges on the western slopes of the coast ranges support trees up to 5,000 feet above sea level. A narrow crown terminating in a nodding spirelike head, with its main portion comprised of horizontal or somewhat pendulous branches with fine, flattened, lacy sprays, takes up a quarter to a third of the full height of forest grown trees. Heavy buttresses mark the base of the larger trees but these rapidly contract to form round, full stems. The trunks of forest trees may be clear of branches for 150 feet but the drooping branches of open-grown trees extend to the ground.

Bright green scale-like leaves about one-sixteenth of an inch long pressed flat, one overlapping another, thickly clothe the branchlets. Each leaf becomes nearly a quarter of an inch long and more loosely spreading near the ends of the leading shoots. Each leaf is glandular on the back, with white stomatiferous lines below. They turn bright red-brown and fall during the third year.

The pollen-bearing catkins of Port Orford cedar are bright red and appear in early spring. Small reddish brown ovulate cones of about seven scales appear at the same time. By early autumn these mature as clear, dark russet brown, berry-like cones about one-third of an inch in diameter. Each cone is composed of three pairs of shield-shaped scales overlapping one another to form a series of x-like markings. The erect cones release their two to four small wing-margined seeds late in September or early October.

After about twelve years trees begin bearing seed crops during alternate years and continue into advanced age. The seeds have a high percentage of germination but must encounter suitable conditions soon after their release. They are seldom carried far from the parent tree. Seedlings can grow in shade or full sunlight, and so take over available open sites,

Fine lacy sprays droop from the short conical crown of tall forest-grown Port Orford Cedar trees

Ray I. Kimmey

regardless of whether they are burned over. Exceedingly dense cover suppresses the seedlings and eventually kills them.

The reddish brown, fibrous bark may become six to ten inches thick, and is divided into broad ridges marked by loose, thin shreds and separated by deep irregular longitudinal fissures.

The even grained wood of Port Orford cedar is moderately soft, durable, and weighs about twenty-nine pounds to the cubic foot when air dry. Its nearly white sapwood is scarcely distinguishable from the yellowish white heartwood. It is easily worked, capable of a high polish, holds paint well, and is easy to season. Because of its resistance to the action of acids, the most important use is for storage battery separators.

Other commercial uses include Venetian blind slats, millwork, deck and boat construction, plywood for aircraft, railway ties, mine timbers, flooring, broom handles and blocks for sulphur matches. An abundance of resin gives an aromatic gingerlike odor which causes the wood to be sought for mothproof box and closet linings. An oil is also distilled from the wood for use in soap.

In 1933, the stand of Port Orford cedar over sixteen inches in diameter was estimated at 1,450,000,000 board feet, of which nearly 1,200,000,000 is in an area of less than 400 square miles in southwestern Oregon. Only recently have statistics distinguished the lumber production of Port Orford cedar from other "cedar" lumber produced in Oregon and California. In 1941 the reported production was 72,706,000 board feet. Of this amount some 16,000,000 board feet were exported in 1936, and 5,400,000 board feet in 1938. The bulk of the exports were logs to Japan, with smaller quantities to Italy and Germany.

Limited pure stands of Port Orford cedar occur in the vicinity of Coos Bay, Oregon. It usually constitutes less than one-fourth of the stand, being associated with Sitka spruce, Western red cedar, Douglas fir, Western hemlock and Lowland white fir. In its southern range this tree invades areas occupied by redwood, red fir, California laurel and occasionally ponderosa pine and sugar pine. Stands of 20,000 board feet to the acre are common, with occasional acres measuring 100,000 board feet.

The thick bark protects mature trees—but heavy losses result when fire runs through young growth. It has few insect enemies and the wood is highly resistant to decay. Fire-killed trees have proved sound and usable after standing forty years or more.

In the ornamental trade, this tree is known as Lawson Cypress. Since its introduction, shortly after 1854, some seventy varieties and forms have been planted in Northern Europe, New Zealand, and America, and it is hardy as far north as Massachusetts, though sensitive to sudden temperature and humidity changes, and does not thrive in a dry climate.

Devereux Butcher

Three pairs of shield-shaped scales combine to form the small cones which stand erect among the feathery sprays of scale-like foliage

The reddish brown fibrous bark is six to ten inches thick

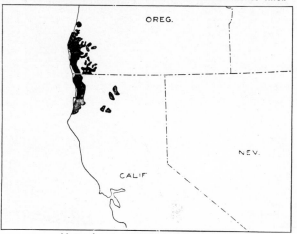

Natural range of Port Orford Cedar

SIERRA JUNIPER

Juniperus occidentalis, Hooker

THE burly, time enduring Sierra juniper occupies exposed slopes and canyon sides in dry, gravelly, or rocky soils of high mountain regions from southeastern Washington through Oregon, Nevada, California, and into lower California. Scattered stands extend eastward into high elevations in Idaho, Montana, Utah, Arizona, and New Mexico. It is widely distributed from 2,000 to nearly 10,000 feet above sea level. The open, round-topped, stocky crown extends within a few feet of the ground, and trees twenty to thirty feet tall are common, but more frequently it is scarcely more than a bush. Under favorable conditions they attain heights of sixty to eighty feet, but the short, abruptly tapering trunk is seldom clear for more than four to eight feet. Huge lower branches often rise from the base and middle of the trunk to extend horizontally, and the trunk often divides into two or more thick forks to form a low, broad crown. Many trees reach diameters of sixteen to thirty inches at breast height, exceptional ones three feet to six feet, and a few of nine to ten feet have been reported.

Enormously large surface roots ramify into the dry, rocky soil and rock crevices to anchor the tree against the fierce winds. On sheltered flats the crowns may be symmetrical with densely conical, round tops.

This true juniper is commonly referred to as juniper or Sierra juniper. There is no record of its earliest discovery, although doubtless members of Lewis and Clark's expedition saw it sometime during 1804 to 1806. The name *occidentalis* was given by Sir William Jackson Hooker in 1839, and distinguishes it as of the Western Hemisphere.

Two types of pale, ashy green foliage are borne on each tree. The larger portion are scale-like leaves, about one-eighth of an inch long, which overlap one another in groups of three as they closely clasp the stiff twigs to form a rounded stem with six longitudinal rows of leaves. Contrasting these, and usually on young growth, are longer, more needle-like leaves whose points stand out and make the twig harsh to the touch. A glandular pit, whitish with resin, marks the back of each leaf, and when

The broad open crown of Sierra Juniper, supported on a short chunky trunk, stands firm against the high mountain winds

viewed against the light with a strong lens, minute teeth may be seen on the leaf margins. The twigs of the Rocky Mountain juniper, *Juniperus scopulorum*, are four-sided, with leaves arranged alternately in pairs. The crushed foliage of these junipers gives off a pungent, aromatic odor, and a decoction is sometimes used as a remedy for malaria, kidney trouble, boils, headaches, and coughs. The leaves begin to die during the second year and are gradually forced off by the growth

Pale, ashy green, scale-like leaves press close against the twigs, near whose ends are borne the bluish black berry-like fruits

to expose the smooth, red, new bark. There are no distinct or definite winter buds.

Like all junipers, the tiny, pollen-bearing male flowers are usually borne on different trees from those which bear the fruit developing female flowers. From the latter there mature in September of the second year bluish black berries about one-fourth to one-third of an inch long. A whitish bloom covers the rough skin, and the outer ends are slightly marked by the tips of the female flower scales, indicating that they are not true berries but modified cones whose scales have become fleshy and united. Within and thinly surrounded by dry flesh are two or three pitted or deeply grooved bony seeds whose large resin cells give the berry a sweetish, pungently aromatic flavor. They are relished by birds and by the Indians. The tree reproduces scatteringly in pure mineral soil.

Wide shallow fissures divide the fibrous, clear cinnamon bark, which is half an inch to an inch thick

The firm, stringy bark is a clear cinnamon-brown, a half inch to an inch and a quarter thick. Wide, shallow furrows extend vertically over the trunk to divide the bark into long, flat ridges connected at long intervals by narrow, diagonal ones.

The fine grained wood is pale brown tinged with red, slightly aromatic, and of great durability when exposed to weather or soil. It is soft and brittle, splits easily, and is one of the heaviest of all the cedars, for a cubic foot weighs about forty pounds when air dry. The thin outer layer of sapwood is nearly white. Because of its close similarity to the wood of the eastern cedars, there is some demand for it as a pencil wood. Usually, however, the trunks are short and knotty, so the distinctly local uses are for fence posts, railroad ties, fuel, and novelties.

Known as a slow, persistently growing tree, it is chiefly recognized for its ability to grow as an advance guard where few other trees can exist. The open groves are frequently without mixture of other trees. Sometimes, however, the stand includes a few such trees as lodgepole, Jeffrey, ponderosa pine and the nut pines.

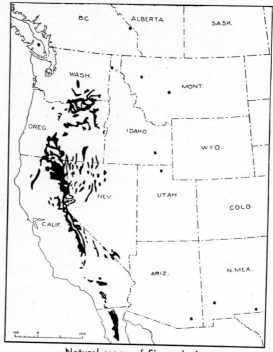

Natural range of Sierra Juniper

97

EASTERN RED CEDAR

Juniperus virginiana, Linnaeus

The slender columnar form of Eastern Red Cedar is most frequently seen, but with age the crown becomes broader and more open

FENCE ROWS along pastures and abandoned fields, dry gravelly slopes, rocky ridges, limestone outcroppings, and even swamps and lake borders over most of the eastern half of the country from the Atlantic seaboard to the Great Plains are frequently punctuated with the dense evergreen pyramids or columns of eastern red cedar.

Ordinarily a tree twenty to fifty feet high with a short trunk one to two feet in diameter, on alluvial soils in the southern states it may attain 120 feet of height and produce a deeply fluted trunk four feet in diameter. On poor soil in the north red cedar may live for years becoming scarcely larger than a bush. Growing slowly, trees sixteen inches to two feet in diameter may be 130 to 150 years old, but the larger ones live 300 years or more.

A juniper rather than a true cedar, this *Juniperus* was distinguished by the name *virginiana* because the first botanical specimens were from the Virginia colony. The family is one of great antiquity, and the early forms of some thirty-five known species are found in glacial deposits throughout the world. None occur or were ever found south of the equator. Of the eleven species native to the United States, red cedar is the most widely distributed and most important.

Each tree bears two forms of tiny evergreen leaves. Those on seedlings and vigorous twigs are sharp pointed and awl-shaped, while closely overlapping scale-like ones clothe the major portion of a tree and press hard against the twig in opposite pairs. They remain five or six years on the branches growing browner with each year.

From February to May small inconspicuous male and female flowers appear on different trees, and occasionally on the same one. From the ovulate bloom a dark blue, fleshy, highly aromatic, berry-like cone develops, with one or two, and rarely three or four tiny chestnut-brown, wingless seeds. By early autumn of the same season that the tree blooms, the green berries mature to a dark purplish blue covered with a white powdery bloom. Not only do these furnish food for birds and small mammals, but they possess medicinal values and are used to flavor gin. Crops of berries are abundant every two or three years, but only one-third to two-thirds of the seeds are capable of germination. Natural reproduction of red cedar is only by seed, which are often scattered by birds.

The shreddy, light reddish brown bark is scarcely more than one-eighth to a quarter of an inch thick. The trunk is often so grooved as to suggest hardship, and the bark peels off in narrow fibrous strips. The reddish bark and wood led the French of Canada to call this cedar *baton rouge*, meaning red stick. Finding the same tree in Louisiana, they gave its name to their capital, Baton Rouge.

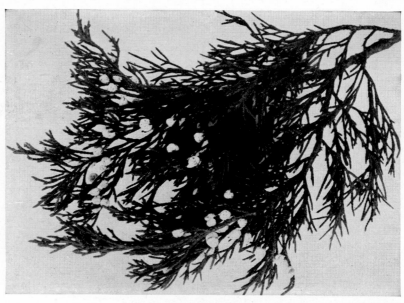

Dark purplish blue berries grow on the sprays of tiny evergreen leaves of Eastern Red Cedar

The slow-grown, fine-grained, brittle wood of highly aromatic quality is bright pinkish red to deep reddish brown, surrounded by a thin layer of nearly white sapwood. A cubic foot when air dry weighs only thirty-one to thirty-three pounds and because of its soft texture, easy working qualities, fragrance, ability to take a high polish, and durability finds an active demand for lead pencils, lining for clothes chests and closets, cigar boxes, canoes, and a wide variety of wooden-ware. Cedar oil is distilled from the leaves and twigs. The scattering stands prevent any satisfactory estimate of the existing volume of red cedar, and for the same reason the commercial production is largely in the form of small lots of short logs which farmers haul to local markets. Including white cedars, the reported cedar cut in 1941 was slightly under 38,-000,000 board feet, of which the bulk came from Tennessee, Virginia, North Carolina, South Carolina, and Kentucky.

A few destructive boring insects feed on living and dead trees and bagworms occasionally eat the foliage. The chief enemy, however, is fire, for the thin bark and shallow root system leaves red cedar an easy victim of relatively light surface fires. In mixture with other trees such as the ashes, maples, oaks, hickories, beech, loblolly pine, black gum, and cypress, it is less seriously affected by fire. Wood rots do considerable damage to southern trees, and as the alternate host of the cedar apple rust it is considered a menace wherever apple growing is of first importance.

Extensively used for ornamental planting, over thirty horticultural forms of red cedar are recognized. It will grow on almost any soil except that which is distinctly swamp.

The shreddy, light reddish brown bark is from an eighth to a quarter of an inch thick

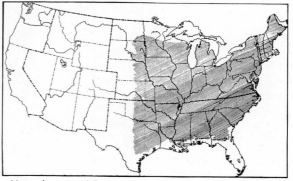

Natural range of Eastern Red Cedar in the United States

99

BUTTERNUT

Juglans cinerea, **Linnaeus**

BUTTERNUT, or white walnut, grows from southern New Brunswick and Maine through the upper peninsula of Michigan to eastern South Dakota, thence southward into northern Arkansas and the mountains of Alabama and Georgia. It is usually a short-trunked spreading tree seldom more than thirty to fifty feet high and one to three feet in diameter. Occasionally when grown in the forest it attains a height of eighty to one hundred feet and diameters of three to four feet. Butternut closely resembles its relative, the black walnut, but the general form of the tree is lower and more spreading. Furthermore, it prefers greater moisture, adapts itself more readily to poor shallow soils and will grow under greater extremes of temperature. The name *cinerea* is derived from the Latin word *cinerarius* meaning "of ashes" and probably refers to the ashen color of the bark. The entire scientific name as given by Linnaeus might be translated as "ashen walnut."

The alternate compound leaves are fifteen to thirty inches long with eleven to seventeen leaflets. These have unequally rounded bases, are pointed, have small marginal teeth and are covered with fine sticky hairs. The leaves and fruit drop early, revealing large, conspicuous three-lobed leaf scars on the twigs, each of which is surmounted by a pale gray, raised, downy pad, or "eyebrow." This feature, together with the long downy terminal bud and the sticky leaflets, the sticky leaf stalk and the elongated nut, help distinguish the butternut from the black walnut.

Inconspicuous flowers of both sexes appear on the same trees along with the new leaves in May or early June.

Butternut trees are frequently found in old pastures where they take on the spreading, many-branched form of a short-trunked orchard tree. The large compound leaves are lighter green than those of black walnut, have fewer leaflets, and are sticky to the touch. The crown appears thin and lacking in vigor

Leaves and nuts fall almost simultaneously in the late autumn, revealing the characteristic "Y"-like branching of the smaller twigs. The tree is seldom symmetrical because of the tendency of side limbs to break during the wind and snow storms. The tendency to develop the under buds on each twig gives the limbs a horizontal rather than upright trend

Mrs. J. G. M. Glessner

100

Long, drooping, yellow-green pollen-bearing catkins hang from the previous year's growth, while the globular pistillate flowers are in groups of three or five on the new growth. These develop into pear-shaped sticky fruits whose pulpy covering or husk encloses a deeply ridged, oblong nut with a rich, sweet, oily kernel which gives the tree its name. The nuts ripen in October. Butternut kernels are widely recognized as a food product and the immature nuts are occasionally pickled.

The light brown, soft, coarse-grained wood may be polished to a satiny lustre, and weighs only twenty-seven pounds to the cubic foot. It is lighter in color and not as strong or durable as walnut. Small amounts are used for cabinet work, interior finish, boat trimming and furniture. No authentic figures of the present stand or annual output are available, but it is doubtful if more than a million board feet of butternut lumber were ever produced in a single year and much less in recent years.

Butternut is more valuable for its nuts than for lumber or shade. The tree is short-lived and seldom attains ages of more than seventy-five or one hundred years. The large spreading limbs are frequently broken by wind or snow and few trees reach maturity without serious injury from insects or fungus diseases. The annual litter from the nuts, the heavy fall of leaves, the low crown and the brittle limb-wood discourage its use as a shade tree, but it is a pleasing addition to a spacious lawn. Several strains of rapid-growing trees capable of producing large quantities of easily cracked nuts have been reported, so that butternut may find a real place among food crop trees.

Above: The yellow-green compound, highly aromatic leaves are fifteen to thirty inches long, with eleven to seventeen taper pointed leaflets. The pear-shaped nuts are covered with a sticky green husk and mature in the autumn after one year's growth. The oily, highly flavored kernel is used in cooking, and the immature nuts are often pickled in vinegar, sugar and spice

Right: The gray to black bark with broad flat whitish ridges and narrow criss-cross furrows may become three-quarters of an inch to an inch thick. The yellow inner bark is bitter, has mild cathartic properties and furnishes a brown dye once used to color cloth

Lower Right: Natural range of Butternut in the United States

Left: A greenish gray winter twig revealing the chambered pith, typical of the walnut family, the alternately arranged triangular, three-lobed leaf scars, the downy side buds with the elongated terminal bud, and the raised downy pad or "eyebrow" between the leaf scar and the bud. These are all characteristic of the Butternut

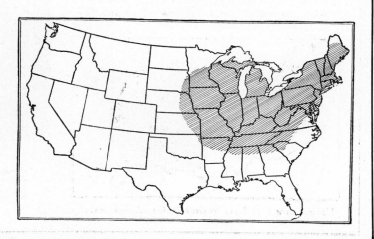

BLACK WALNUT

Juglans nigra, Linnaeus

BLACK walnut is common to the eastern half of the United States, and southern Ontario. In the deep alluvial soils from Maryland, Pennsylvania, and Virginia, west into eastern Iowa and Missouri, trees have grown 150 feet high and six feet in diameter with clear lengths of fifty or sixty feet, while trees with a breast high diameter of three feet and 100 feet high are fairly common.

Juglans is a contraction of *Jovis glans*, a Latin name designating the nut or acorn of Jupiter, while *nigra* may refer to the black bark, the rich brown wood, or the dark outer shell of the nut. The Indians in central New York called it "Dent-soo-kwa-no-ne," or round nut.

Closely related to the butternut or white walnut, *Juglans cinerea*, it has two relatives in California and the southwest, and belongs to the same genus as the Persian walnut, whose nut is marketed as English walnut, and lumber as Circassian walnut.

The compound leaves are one or two feet long with fifteen to twenty-three lance-shaped, sharply-toothed leaflets attached to a slightly hairy stem. The globular, light green fruits are an inch and a half to three

Black Walnut forms a round-headed tree with relatively scant foliage that reveals the sturdy branches

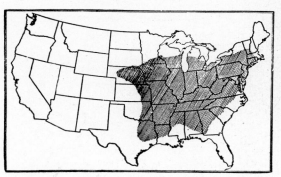

Natural range of Black Walnut in the United States

The leaves begin to drop in the early fall exposing a sharply divided trunk and a sturdy framework of heavy alternate branches. The dark brown, occasionally black bark is broken into prominent, rounded ridges, becoming two to three inches thick on older trees

inches in diameter, consisting of a thick pulpy hull surrounding a single nut whose hard, deeply grooved shell protects a kernel of unusual flavor. Each tree bears staminate or pollen-bearing catkins on the previous year's growth, and pistillate flowers in groups of two to five at the ends of the new growth, during April or May.

In winter, walnut trees may be distinguished by the sturdy crown, dark deeply grooved bark, stout twigs, and the large gray, downy, terminal buds. The smaller, downy side buds are alternate, and above a heart-shaped, three-lobed leaf scar, with three V-shaped bundle scars. The diaphrams of the chambered pith of black walnut are thin and pale buff while those of butternut are dark and coarse.

The soft brown, coarse-grained, easily worked wood weighs about thirty-nine pounds to the cubic foot, when air dry. For many purposes it is stronger than white oak, and has been used since earliest American history for fine furniture and interior panels as has Persian walnut in the Old World. It ranks as America's foremost cabinet wood. Walnut's ability to resist blows without splintering, to withstand strains under extremes of heat and cold, and the ease with which the finish may be restored, explains its wide acceptance for gun stocks and, during World War I, for airplane propellers. It is durable when used in contact with the soil. The stand in 1920 was estimated to be 820,000,000 board feet.

Upper right: Two walnuts in their green husks maturing on the end of a current year's leafy twig

Center: Pistillate or nut-producing flowers, and a catkin of pollen-bearing flowers in April or May

Lower left: The compound leaves of Black Walnut have fifteen to twenty-three leaflets. A slanting cut across the twig reveals the chambered pith

The nut or seed has a hard deeply chiseled shell (Natural size)

Because the trees grow singly or in small groups, there are no reliable estimates of the present stand. The 1941 production was 44,-181,000 board feet. The leading states in order of production are Missouri, Kentucky, Indiana, Kansas, West Virginia, Tennessee and Ohio. Total production in 1929 was 71,-523,000 board feet.

The nuts mature in a single season, during September and October, and frequently remain on the trees a week or two after the leaves have fallen. They are prized by squirrels. The kernels are used by confectioners, bakers and makers of ice cream, because the distinctive flavor and texture is not lost in cooking. The nuts may be planted during the autumn or husked and stored in a cool cellar, embedded in sand or in a pit a foot or more underground, preparatory to being planted in early spring. They do best when spaced twenty-five to thirty feet apart, and prove satisfactory along roadsides and on lawns, because the comparatively light shade cast by the leaves interferes little with the growth of grass. Black walnut trees prosper best in deep, rich, well drained soil where moisture is plentiful. They grow readily from seed and for two or three years are easily transplanted so that trees have been set out in every state.

Walnut is relatively resistant to fungus and insect attacks. Tent and walnut caterpillars are sometimes disfiguring but rarely kill the trees, and the leaves are subject to leaf spot diseases which are unsightly but not particularly harmful.

Under desirable conditions black walnut ranks among the rapid-growing American hardwoods, attaining heights of thirty to forty feet and breast-high diameters of five to nine inches in twenty years. It will stand little shade from other trees, and drops the lower branches early so as to develop a relatively high crown.

PECAN

Carya pecan, (Marshall) Britton

ALTHOUGH belonging to the hickory family, and known for its excellent wood, pecan lays claim to commercial importance through its delicately flavored nuts. The name is of Indian origin and refers to the nuts which have since been developed to form an important article of commerce. It is a large tree with a massive trunk and stout, spreading branches which, under forest conditions, form a narrow, symmetrical, inverse pyramidal crown, and in open-grown trees form a broad, rounded crown. Occasionally trees are found having heights of a hundred and sixty or seventy feet, and with trunk diameters of six or seven feet, but usually the pecan is ninety to a hundred feet high with trunk diameters of two and a half to four feet.

The range of pecan has been greatly widened by cultivation. Its natural range extends southward from eastern Iowa through southern Illinois and southern Indiana, western Kentucky, western Tennessee, central Mississippi and Alabama to Louisiana, and west to Missouri, southeastern Kansas, eastern Oklahoma through Arkansas to central Texas and Mexico. It is a tree of

Bureau of Plant Industry

Ripening in September or October, the thin shelled, clustered nuts have tasty kernels which are high in food value

F. W. Besley

Largest member of the hickory group, the stout spreading branches of open-grown Pecan trees form broad rounded crowns

bottomlands demanding the rich moist soils along streams and rivers. It reaches its greatest size in the Ohio basin. Never found in dry locations, it will thrive, however, when planted on drier sites.

Pecan is the largest of the hickories, as well as the longest lived, and trees three hundred and fifty years of age or over have been found. In its early stages pecan grows rather rapidly, and faster than any other hickory.

Bark on the mature trunk is light brown or gray, about one to one and a half inches thick. It is deeply and irregularly broken into narrow perpendicular ridges that are cracked into small, thick, appressed scales.

Twigs are rather slender. When young they are somewhat tinged with red and loosely covered with hair, later occasionally becoming smooth and marked with lenticels or pores. The sharply pointed, hairy terminal winter-buds measure a half inch in length, while those growing along the twigs are smaller, less pointed, and are sometimes borne on stalks.

Leaves are pinnately compound, measuring twelve to twenty inches in length. They are arranged alternately on the twig, and have nine to fifteen short-stalked, finely toothed, sharply pointed leaflets varying from four to seven inches in length. Appearing in April or May, the slender, pendulous staminate or pollen-bearing catkins are about five inches long, and are borne near the ends of twigs of the preceding year, or occasionally on the young shoots of the current year. The small, inconspicuous, greenish pistillate or seed-producing flowers occur in spikes at the ends of twigs.

Ripening in September or October, the dark brown nuts, which measure from one to two and a half inches in length, are borne in clusters of three to eleven, and are covered with thin husks that break into four sections to release the nut. Husks frequently remain on the tree during the winter.

Pecan is the most important nut tree native to North America, and several varieties have been developed which produce nuts of larger size and improved quality. Although grown in commercial plantations, large quantities of the nuts on the market come from wild trees. Pecan nuts are remarkable for their high food value.

Wood of pecan weighs forty-six pounds to the cubic foot when dry, and is ring-porous, heavy, hard, brittle, not strong, compact, and has many inconspicuous medullary rays. Heartwood is light brown, tinged with red, and the sapwood paler. It is chiefly used for fuel, occasionally for agricultural tools which do not require special strength and for furniture.

Pecan reproduces by seed and by sprouts from younger stumps. Never forming pure stands, it occurs in groups or singly in mixture with gum, oak, and ash. Because of its moist habitat, it is seldom damaged by fire. It is, however, subject to attack by the hickory bark beetle and to injury by frost. It is frequently used as an ornamental and shade tree in the coastal areas south from Maryland.

Another name for this tree is *"pecanier"* given to it by the Acadians. The scientific name *carya* comes from the Greek word *"karua"* which means walnut tree.

Pollen-bearing flowers appear in early June on the twigs of the preceding year, and the leaves, which resemble those of other hickories, have more leaflets than other species

The thick bark of mature trunks is light brown or gray, and is broken into perpendicular ridges that are cracked into small scales

Natural range of Pecan

105

BITTERNUT HICKORY

Carya cordiformis, (Wangenheim) K. Koch

THE tall sturdy, straight-trunked bitternut hickory with its well-rounded top, grows from southern Maine and Quebec to Minnesota and southward in all the states to western Florida and eastern Texas.

Bitternut, sometimes called swamp hickory, thrives best in low moist soil near the borders of streams and swamps, but it is also found on rolling uplands.

Ordinarily a stout-branched tree reaching a height of one hundred feet with a trunk diameter of two or three feet, it attains its largest size in bottomlands of the lower Ohio River where occasionally it develops a trunk diameter of four feet, and a height of 120 feet.

There are several species of hickory. Four of them are commercially more important than the others, and these are known as the true hickories. The pecan hickories comprise a larger number of species, and it is to this group that bitternut belongs. All the hickories are members of the walnut family *Juglandaceae*, and all are slow-growing trees, but bitternut grows more rapidly than the rest. It is also the shortest lived of the hickories, reaching maturity at about two hundred years.

The most striking characteristic of the bitternut hickory is its bright yellow winter buds, which offer a means of identification. Those at the ends of the

The stout spreading branches with slender branchlets form a broad handsome head when bitternut grows in the open

George J. Baetzhold

The crown of dark green foliage is usually well-rounded and is broadest at the top. The trunk is straight and column-like

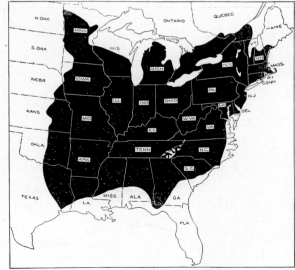

Natural range of Bitternut Hickory

branchlets are one-third to three-fourths of an inch long, obliquely blunt-pointed, and enclosed in two pairs of rough scales. Buds at the sides of the branchlets are only one-eighth to three-quarters of an inch long, somewhat four-angled, sharp-pointed, nearly egg-shaped, and are often stalked.

The compound leaves are six to ten inches long, alternate on the branchlets and smallest of all hickory leaves. Each slender hairy stalk carries five to nine leaflets shaped like lance heads and margined with coarse, thick-pointed teeth. The leaflets, four to six inches long and three-fourths to an inch and a quarter wide, grow directly from the stalk, and usually have an uneven base. They are dark yellow-green, shiny on the upper side and paler and hairy beneath, and turn yellow in the autumn.

The green staminate or pollen-bearing flowers appear in May or June. They are three to four inch catkins borne on the twig of the preceding season in clusters of three and hang from a common stem about an inch in length. The pistillate or nut-producing flowers, one or two to a stalk, are a half inch long, slightly four-angled, and covered with a yellow, scaly wool.

The nut, ripening in October, is almost round, abruptly contracting into a point at the end and is enclosed in a thin scaly husk which splits about half way down in four lines of division. It is smooth and gray with a reddish brown, very bitter kernel from which the tree gets its common name, bitternut.

Early settlers pressed oil from the kernel which some used as a remedy against rheumatism, while others used it to feed the flame of crude lamps.

Bark on the lower trunk of mature trees is one-third to three-quarters of an inch thick, and is shallowly fissured into close, flat ridges so interwoven as to give it a net-like appearance. The slender twigs, bright green and somewhat hairy at first, soon become smooth or nearly so, and finally turn pale gray. They are marked by many small, pale, corky growths and small leaf-scars.

The dark brown wood is hard, strong, tough, and close-grained. It is heavy, a cubic foot of air-dry wood weighing forty-seven pounds. Although somewhat inferior to the wood of the true hickories in strength and shock-resisting qualities, it is used for tool handles, agricultural implements, hoops, and vehicle parts. It also makes excellent fuel.

In common with other hickories, the bitternut is susceptible to attack by a number of insects and diseases. The insect responsible for killing many trees is the hickory bark beetle. After the trees have been cut, the green wood is often seriously damaged by pinhole borers. Unless carefully stored, powder-post insects attack the seasoned sapwood of all kinds of hickory products.

Young bitternut hickory in the open is readily injured by frost. It is capable of enduring fairly dense shade for a number of years without losing vitality, and when freed by an opening in the forest, will recover and develop rapidly. This and its persistent sprouting ability when young enable it to survive many unfavorable conditions, but repeated burning or constant pasturing reduces the growth and causes the trees to become stag-headed; gives little resistance to insect attack and is ultimately followed by death.

Hickory smoke has long been considered best for curing hams and bacon. Even now thousands of cords of wood are burned in farm smoke houses. The wood

The thin husk of the inch-long nut is four-winged and coated with yellow, scurfy hairiness. The compound leaves of five to nine leaflets are relatively small

The light brown bark is tinged with red, scarcely three-quarters of an inch thick, and broken into thin interlacing ridges which never become shaggy

is also sought by those who enjoy an open fireplace because it forms firm glowing embers and relatively little ash.

Hickory is a specialty lumber, the use of which is largely limited to the places where weight is secondary to the need for strength and elasticity. It is, therefore, handled in comparatively few lumber yards. With the passing of the "horse and buggy days" when hickory was important in the manufacture of vehicles, the annual cut has declined from 333,929,000 board feet in 1909 to 37,759,000 board feet in 1939.

SHAGBARK HICKORY

Carya ovata, (Miller) Britton

SHAGBARK hickory is a distinctly American tree. Only one hickory species exists beyond our continent, and this in eastern China, but during pre-glacial periods they covered Europe and the Mediterranean countries. Of all the hickories, however, none are so important or widespread as shagbark.

Its irregular, round-topped crown reaches heights of 120 to 140 feet, and the trunk which is frequently divided attains diameters of twenty to thirty inches. It is a common feature of bottomlands and pastures of all the eastern states from southern Maine to southeastern Minnesota, south as far as eastern Texas with the exception of Florida and portions of the Georgia and Carolina coastal plain. Pure stands are rare and best growth is achieved in mixture with oaks and other broad-leafed trees in the Cumberland Mountains and Mississippi River bottoms. Under forest conditions the straight trunk may be clear of branches for fifty to sixty feet.

The compound leaves arranged alternately on the stem have five or seven leaflets whose narrow base is attached directly to the leaf stalk. The three outer leaflets are four to six inches long while the lower ones are smaller. Narrow at the base, wide at the top, the margin of each leaflet is toothed and the shape described as obovate.

In May or June while the leaves are developing, separate male and female blossoms appear at the base of new shoots. The drooping spikes of staminate flowers are four to six inches long, while the two to five flowered pistillate ones—one-third of an inch long—are covered with a rusty wooly growth. Those which are fertilized develop during the summer into green semispherical fruits one-fourth to two and a half inches in diameter. This is described as ovate and is responsible for the name *ovata* to distinguish this *Carya* from other hickories. The thick outer husk splits into four sections when ripe and reveals a single, white, thin-shelled nut whose sweet kernel is edible. These fruits ripen with the frosts of October.

When the leaves drop conspicuous, slightly elevated, roughly heart-shaped leaf scars are left on the twig to persist two or more years. At the base of the leaf stalk and in the curve of the leaf scar a blunt-pointed, broadly ovate bud is completely formed before fall. The terminal bud is one-half to three-fourths of an inch long, blunt-pointed, and covered with slightly downy, dark brown scales. A cross section of the twig reveals an obscure five-pointed star of dark colored pith.

Regardless of season, Shagbark Hickory is a rugged, picturesque tree with a strong, frequently divided trunk. Heights of 120 to 140 feet are attained, with trunk diameters of twenty to thirty inches

The long, flat plates of gray bark of mature trees, loose at one or both ends, gives the name "shagbark." On young trunks, the bark is smooth, firm and light gray.

The reddish brown heartwood was long considered inferior in strength and toughness to the surrounding two to four inches of white sapwood, but laboratory tests show no material difference. No other commercial wood has the combination of strength, toughness, and elasticity, and no other American hardwood could adequately substitute for hickory in case of shortage of supply. Not durable in contact with the soil, it is subject to attack by boring insects.

Hickory lumber having no more than twenty rings to the inch is generally the strongest, and is used for handles of axes, picks, hammers, and hatchets. Until recently large amounts were used in making spokes and rims of wheels, singletrees, and buggy shafts. Increasing quantities are used in athletic equipment. Hickory wood weighs about sixty-three pounds to the cubic foot when air dry and is admirable for fuel.

Nearly half the present stand of about 6,000,000,000 board feet grows in the lower Mississippi Valley. The production of hickory lumber has declined from 334,000,000 board feet in 1909 to 78,508,000 board feet in 1941.

Hickory is reproduced from seeds and sprouts. Two to three bushels of shelled nuts may be produced by thrifty, open-grown trees. Trees of seedling origin grow slowly, but may reach ages of 150 to 200 years. The hickories are attacked by various insects, but suffer greatest harm from the hickory bark beetle.

Drooping spikes of staminate flowers   George J. Baetzhold

Charles F. Steiger

Long, loose plates of gray bark give shagbark hickory its name

Above—Hickory nut enclosed in husk. Below—The compound leaf has five and rarely seven leaflets

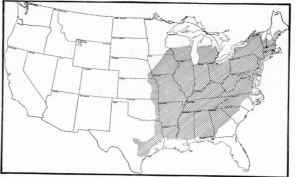

Natural range of Shagbark Hickory

MOCKERNUT HICKORY

Carya tomentosa, K. Koch

MOCKERNUT HICKORY with its coarse leaves and twigs grows from Central New England across southern Ontario to southeastern Nebraska and all the eastern states from east Texas to Maine. It is found on dry slopes and ridges, but attains best development on rich uplands and deep fertile soil in the lower Ohio basin and in Missouri and Arkansas. Mockernut is the

In winter the large, stout twigs, the ascending upper branches and drooping lower ones are characteristic

most abundant of the hickories in the South and is the only one found in the southern coastal pine-belt.

Attaining maturity at 250 to 300 years, mockernut hickory sometimes reaches a height of ninety or a hundred feet with a trunk three feet in diameter, but is usually much smaller, with upright rigid upper branches and gracefully pendulous lower ones.

The fragrant leaves, eight to twelve inches long, have flattened, grooved hairy stems and occur alternately on the twigs. Each leaf is composed of five to nine toothed leaflets which taper to the base. The upper leaflets, five to eight inches long and three to five inches wide, are two or three times the size of the lowest pair. The leaves are shiny dark yellow-green above, pale green and more or less finely hairy beneath, with a stout softly-hairy midrib below. They turn yellow in autumn.

The dark reddish brown hairy winter buds at the ends of the twigs are broadly egg-shaped and nearly three-quarters of an inch long. The side buds are similar in shape and color but are only one-half or one-third as large. The stout angular twigs are brown with conspicuous lenticels, and thickly covered with pale hairs in the first year, but become nearly smooth and dark gray in the second year. The wooly hairiness of leaf under surfaces, twigs and buds is recognized in the specific name *tomentosa*.

The flowers appear in May when the leaves are half grown. The long stalked slender, green, hairy staminate catkins are at the base of the new growth and the pistillate ones, in two to five crowded spikes, are narrowly bell-shaped.

The nearly round reddish brown nut is smooth, slightly flattened, usually four-ridged with a pointed tip and a slightly rounded base. It is enclosed in a thick, red-brown husk which is one and a half to two inches long and readily splits nearly to the base. The name mockernut hickory is given this tree because the sweet kernel is small and difficult to extract.

L. W. Brownell

The strong, rigid branches and dull green coarse foliage form a wide, irregular rounded crown

Never scaly, the dark gray bark of the mockernut hickory is about one-half to three-quarters of an inch thick and furrowed into flat ridges.

The close-grained wood is heavy, a cubic foot weighing over fifty-one pounds when dry. The brown heartwood is surrounded by nearly white sapwood which is often three inches wide. The strength, hardness, toughness, and flexibility of hickory has made it the foremost wood for shock resisting handles of such

The hairy terminal buds are a half to three-quarters of an inch long, while the lateral buds, though similar in color and shape, are much smaller

The dark, shiny leaves turn clear or rusty yellow in autumn, and the smooth reddish brown nut is enclosed in a thick, usually hairy red-brown husk

tools as axes. Nearly three-fourths of all hickory lumber goes for this purpose. It is also used for vehicle parts and furniture, and makes an excellent fuelwood.

Mockernut hickory in company with three other commercial hickories comprises a stand of some 16,-000,000,000 board feet, which together produced 78 - 508,000 board feet of lumber in 1941. More than half the production was from West Virginia, Mississippi, Kentucky, Arkansas, Ohio, and Tennessee. It is subject to injury by frost and fires, but young hickory is persistent and will come up in spite of repeated burning and cutting.

G. B. Sudworth

The hard, irregularly furrowed bark is broken into broad, close ridges

The flowers appear in May, and the pollen-bearing ones shown here are hairy catkins borne in stalked clusters, while the seed-producing ones are in crowded spikes

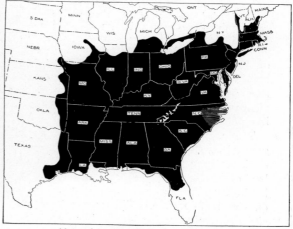

Natural range of Mockernut Hickory

111

Carya glabra, (Miller) Swee:

ON dry ridges and open pastures in woodlands and fertile coves from Vermont to Michigan and south through Illinois to the highlands of Mississippi, Alabama, and Georgia, pignut hickory trees rear their compact, narrow oblong crowns and scatter disappointing nuts. With advancing age the crown becomes increasingly broad and round. The slender, more or less contorted branches droop slightly at the ends, and the trunk is usually short. Normally, it is a tree fifty to 100 feet high, with a trunk two or three feet in diameter, but sheltered trees in secluded fertile coves

Courtesy Arnold Arboretum

Gnarled, up-reaching branches, with drooping ends are revealed in the fall and winter

of the Appalachian Mountains may reach a height of 120 feet and a trunk diameter of five feet. While pignut hickory normally matures at 200 to 300 years, the largest trees live 350 to 400 years.

Three, seven, or rarely nine dark yellow-green leaflets arranged pinnately along a common stem or petiole, comprise the compound leaf of this hickory. Each lance-shaped leaflet is three to six inches long and grows directly on the leaf petiole. The entire leaf may be eight to twelve inches long. They are arranged

alternately on slender gray to reddish brown twigs. At the base of each leaf stem is a small blunt, reddish brown bud which becomes fully formed by late summer. The oval terminal bud, although larger than the side buds, is scarcely three-eighths of an inch long, and like the lateral ones is protected by several smooth or finely downy scales.

The scientific name, *carya,* comes from the Greek word, ''karua''—which means walnut tree, while *glabra* refers to the smooth twigs and buds.

With maturity the dark gray, narrow flattened bark ridges form irregular diamond-shaped areas. The hard, tough bark is one-half to three-quarters of an inch thick, and usually tight to the trunk.

In May drooping clusters, or aments, of staminate flowers appear with the limp new leaves, and hidden near the end of the previous year's growth are small pistillate blooms. By early autumn these develop into brown, pear-shaped fruits the hard shell of which splits back along four sutures to reveal a smooth,

In summer the dark yellow-green foliage fills in the oblong to broadly oval crown of Pignut Hickory

brown, slightly angled nut. The kernel is generally difficult to extract, and the flavor varies from bitter, or astringent, to insipidly sweet.

The close grained, light brown to creamy white wood, like that of shagbark hickory is very hard, tough, and resilient. It is the heaviest of all the commercial hickories, weighing about fifty-three pounds to the cubic foot when air dry. As a shock-resisting wood, hickory is without equal, and is widely used for tool handles and athletic equipment where strength and toughness are required. The best hickory shows an oily or glossy side grain surface when smoothly finished, and gives a clear ringing tone when dropped on end on a hard surface. Wide-ringed, fast growing, heavy hickory having about six to ten growth rings to the inch is generally strongest. Buyers are frequently prejudiced in favor of the white sapwood over the darker colored heartwood. This results in giving special value to the wide-ringed white wood from second growth stump sprouts. Careful studies, however, reveal that weight for weight, sound hickory has the same strength, toughness, and resistance to shock, regardless of whether it is red heartwood, white sapwood, or a mixture of the two. Pignut hickory is marketed with the wood of the other true hickories, and timber from this tree contributed substantially to the 78,508,000 board feet of hickory lumber produced in 1941.

The wood of all the hickories is admirable for fuel, and for years green hickory has been singled out as best for smoking meats. It is the standard against which all other woods are compared when fuel values are considered —a cord of hickory being approximately equal to a ton of coal.

The deep tap roots cause this and other hickories to be exceedingly windfirm, but surface fires frequently burn through the thin bark to cause serious injury and open the way for subsequent attacks by wood destroying fungi. Leaf-eating insects are common sources of damage, but of all its enemies the hickory bark beetle is undoubtedly most destructive. They can be discouraged by keeping the trees in a state of healthy vigor.

Pignut, in company with other hickories, is slow growing, and not to be recommended for street or roadside planting, but is an admirable addition to parks and broad landscapes. It grows naturally in mixture with other trees, and has unusual sprouting ability.

Thin shelled pear-shaped nuts borne on the ends of the previous season's growth are partially hidden by large compound leaves whose seven to nine leaflets are dark green and narrowly lance-shaped

The dark gray bark with flattened interlacing ridges surrounds the trunk with a tight covering

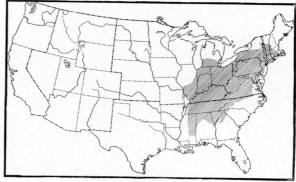

Natural range of Pignut Hickory

QUAKING ASPEN

Populus tremuloides, Michaux

FROM Labrador and the southern shores of Hudson Bay, northwest to the valley of the Yukon within the Arctic Circle in Alaska, south through the mountains into northern Mexico and Lower California, scattering across the northern plains states, and more dense from northeastern Missouri and northwestern Nebraska to New England and the Southern Appalachians, grows the white trunked, fluttering-leaved quaking aspen. It thrives on moist sandy soils and gravelly hillsides from sea level to elevations over 10,000 feet in the California mountains.

Quaking Aspen frequently reaches forty or fifty feet in height and eighteen to twenty inches in diameter, but in the southern Rockies it attains one hundred feet with diameters up to three feet. It matures at sixty or seventy years, and seldom lives beyond eighty years. Inability to withstand heavy shade causes rapid thinning of dense young stands, but except as man interferes, quaking aspen usually mantains its ground against all coniferous competition.

It is a true poplar of the family *Salicaceae,* and the genus *Populus.* Of eleven members of the poplar or cottonwood group found in the United States, *tremuloides* is distinguished by almost incessant trembling of the small broadly egg-shaped leaves, whose slender,

In winter Quaking Aspen makes a colorful picture with its central stem of blotched white supporting innumerable slender, reddish brown twigs

Aspen lifts its narrow, round-topped crown of shimmering leaves forty feet or higher

one and a half to three inch long stems are pinched flat from the sides. Each leaf ends abruptly in a short point, is two to three inches broad and edged with small regular teeth. The upper surface is shiny green and the back a pale dull green. In autumn the leaves turn golden yellow some days before dropping.

Staminate and pistillate flowers appear as drooping gray catkins, the two sexes being on different trees, and the seeds maturing before the leaves are fully formed. The fruit is about four inches long, and composed of many light green capsules like quarter inch long Indian clubs. Packed within each capsule, the tiny brown seeds are so small that two million scarcely make a pound.

The yellowish green or nearly white powdery bark of young trunks and branches is marked with dark scars. Bark near the base of old trees is nearly black, one or two inches thick, roughened by bands of wart-like growths and divided into flat ridges. Branchlets are red-brown and shining, roughened by large elevated leaf scars, and they gradually turn dark gray.

The soft, close-grained light brown heartwood merges into a broad band of nearly white sapwood. A cubic foot when air dry weighs about twenty-five pounds. Aspen wood is used for paper pulp, boxes, excelsior, matches, and small quantities for furniture and vehicle parts. Several million board feet are cut annually, but no separate record is kept of lumber cut.

Aspen is so subject to heart rot that many trees are useless before reaching fifty years. Fungus often enters through fire scars as well as in tunnels cut by aspen borers.

Aspen is easily killed by fire, but its vigorous sprouting permits it to return quickly. Seeds travel long distances on the wind, germinate quickly in moist soil bared by fire, and the small plants which grow rapidly in exposed situations help prevent soil washing.

Charles F. Steiger

The one-and-a-half to two-inch, dark green leaves are attached by narrow, ribbon-like stems

Horizontal creases and scars mark the thin white or yellowish green bark

George J. Baetzhold

Staminate and pistillate flowers appear before the leaves as drooping catkins, and on different trees

Natural range of Quaking Aspen

115

EASTERN COTTONWOOD

Populus deltoides, **Marsh**

THE BROAD spreading crown of eastern cottonwood is common from Quebec to northern Florida and west along the upper streams leading into the Great Plains. Most frequently found along water courses, it often forms extensive groves in the north and west.

Developing first a narrow, conical crown, with maturity it becomes broad and open, supported by a massive trunk often divided near the ground. Under forest conditions the bole may reach fifty to sixty feet to the main limbs. Ordinarily, eighty to 100 feet tall and three to four feet in diameter, under favorable conditions west of the Mississippi, trees attain heights of 150 feet and diameters of seven to eight feet.

The poplars are of ancient origin and the name *populus* may refer to an early Roman expression *arbor populi,* the people's tree. Of some twenty-five species recognized throughout the world, eleven are found in North America. Of these *deltoides,* with its delta shaped leaf, is the most important eastern representative.

The bright green, glossy, leathery leaves are broad and triangular, with coarse, rounded, marginal teeth and a flattened stem or petiole about as long as the leaf blade. Together they are four to seven inches long. The shiny brown terminal buds are resin-covered and like the crushed leaves have a pleasant balsamic odor.

Flowers of both sexes are borne separately on different trees and appear in March or April before the leaves unfold as three to five inch drooping catkins. By May the more loosely flowered pistillate catkins are six to eleven inches long, with scattered, pointed capsules which expel the tiny, fragile seeds whose attached fibres of fluffy white down carry them long distances. A few hours must bring them to some place of exposed mineral soil such as that on recently flooded banks and river islands or their vitality is lost. Cottonwood also reproduces from stumps and root sprouts and may be readily grown

Cottonwood with its wide spreading open crown is familiar to the open plains and prairies

The bright green, leathery, broadly triangular leaves, together with the stems, are four to seven inches long

Winter reveals the short trunk and vigorous growth of limbs and branches from cuttings. The deeply fissured bark of mature trees is a dull gray to brown, two to three inches thick, with rather wide ridges. On young trunks and branches it is smooth, thin, and grayish yellow tinged with green.

The wood is of varied shades of brown with a thick white margin of sapwood. It is close grained and porous, with a dull luster, soft, weak, usually easy to work, but warps badly in seasoning. A cubic foot when air dry weighs about twenty-four pounds and is almost devoid of taste or odor. It is used largely for boxes, crates, packing cases, excelsior, core for veneers, paper pulp, and locally for poles, posts, and fuel.

In 1932 the stand of eastern cottonwood and aspen saw-timber was estimated to be 4,437,000,000 board feet, but the steady reduction of annual output indicates a failing supply. Production in 1939 was 130,-000,000 board feet with Mississippi, Arkansas, Louisiana, and Minnesota responsible for nearly two-thirds of the cut.

Cottonwood is remarkable for its rapid growth, but height growth declines soon after forty years. Thereafter trees may remain sound and vigorous, but growing slowly, for 100 years or more. Trees have been observed to grow four to five feet in height each year and with diameters increasing two-thirds of an inch for the first twenty-five years. Others reached 100 feet in height in fifteen years.

Frequently planted for shelter and ornament in the treeless plains and prairies west of the Mississippi. the wide spread, shallow root system which helps make the tree wind-firm, often upheaves sidewalks. Moreover, the tiny rootlets fill drain pipes in their search for water. Accordingly, many towns and cities prohibit the planting of cottonwood within their boundaries.

Fire is destructive until after the young trees are fifteen or twenty years old and the bark thick enough to resist the heat. The low overflow lands on which most cottonwoods grow is their chief source of protection. Various fungus diseases are more to be feared, and during the first few years the young shoots are eagerly eaten by field mice, rabbits, and cattle.

The densely flowered, pollen bearing staminate catkins are three to five inches long

The mature bark is dark gray to brown with deep fissures and rounded ridges

Long strands of capsule fruits cause the name "Necklace" poplar

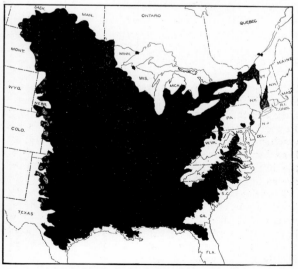

Natural range of Eastern Cottonwood

EASTERN HOPHORNBEAM

Ostrya virginiana, (Miller) Koch

THE Eastern hophornbeam is a small, shapely tree with bark of narrow scales and a broad head of slender branches. It is seldom found in large groups but usually grows scattered singly on well-trained gravelly ridges and slopes in the shade of oaks, maples, and

Eastern Hophornbeam is a small tree with long, spreading branches that form an ir-regular, broad crown, often as broad as high

other larger trees. It is found from Nova Scotia westward through southern Canada to the lower slopes of the Black Hills of South Dakota in all the eastern states from the Atlantic to Nebraska, eastern Kansas and east Texas. It also extends to the highlands of southern Mexico and Guatemala. It is most abundant and reaches its largest size in Arkansas and Texas.

The Eastern hophornbeam tree is usually not more than thirty feet tall with a short trunk eighteen or twenty inches in diameter, but occasionally is fifty or sixty feet tall with a trunk nearly two feet in diameter. In most cases it develops a broad top, sometimes as much as fifty feet across, of many small spreading branches, the lower ones sometimes drooping, but with the branchlets tending upward. Twigs and branches are so tough that they are rarely injured by wind.

Though easily mistaken for young elm, this hophornbeam is one of four species belonging to the *Ostrya* group of the family *Betulaceae.* It is the more widely known of the two species that are native to North America. The single other American hornbeam is limited to the southern slopes of the Colorado River canyon about seventy miles north of Flagstaff, Ari-

zona. The common name comes from its fruit, which closely resembles that of the common hop-vine, and from its wood, which has a horny texture. *Ostrya* is the classical name of this tree and is from the Greek meaning a kind of tree with hard wood.

The leaves, three to five inches long and one and a half to two inches wide, are alternate and have short, slender, hairy stems. They are egg-shaped in general, with more or less rounded or slightly heart-shaped bases, tapering pointed tips, and irregularly saw-toothed margins. When full grown the leaves are thin and extremely tough, with the upper surface dark yellow-green and the lower surface pale yellow-green. Prominent on the under side are the light yellow, slender, hairy midrib and the numerous parallel, slender, primary veins. In the autumn the leaves turn a clear yellow.

During most of the year the twigs are tipped with slender, cylindrical buds of the staminate or pollen-bearing catkins, which are about one-half inch in length. These develop in April and May at the same time as the leaves, becoming about two inches long, loose and drooping. The pistillate flowers are slender, pendent catkins about one-quarter inch long with thin hairy stems and pale green or reddish leaf-like scales. The hop-like fruit is one to two inches long,

Eastern Hophornbeam is a tree of high, dry ridges with scaly bark, long slender branches, and very tough, upturned branchlets

L. W. Brownell

The leaves are thin, papery and tough, turning pale yellow in autumn, while the bladder-like scales of the fruit are pale green or reddish

L. W. Brownell

Pendent staminate catkins, green tinged with red and about two inches long, develop in April or May to fertilize the pistillate catkins growing from the sides of the twigs

Bark of Eastern Hophornbeam is thin, flaky and grayish brown broken into flat scales that are loose at the ends

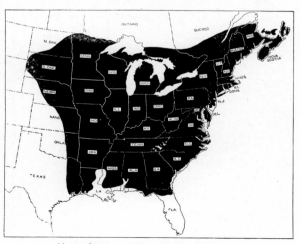

Natural range of Eastern Hophornbeam

two-thirds of an inch to one inch wide and borne on a short, slender, hairy stem. It consists of a number of small sacs each containing a little flat nut about a third of an inch long.

The light chestnut-brown winter buds are a quarter inch long and slightly hairy. No terminal buds are formed and the branches lengthen from upper lateral buds. The slender, light green twigs turn a shiny light orange by midsummer. Retaining their luster, they become red-brown during the first winter and gradually grow darker brown with age.

The bark on the trunk is about a quarter inch thick, grayish brown, and rough with narrow elongated plate-like scales.

The strong, hard wood is light brown tinged with red, with an outer layer of nearly white sapwood a few inches wide. It is tough, close-grained, and heavy, a cubic foot weighing 52 pounds when dry, is durable in contact with the soil but, while it is capable of taking a fine polish, it commands no special attention in commerce. The trees are so small and scattering as to have no place in lumber records. The wood is used largely for fence posts, tool handles, mallets and other small articles which demand hardness and strength.

The eastern hophornbeam is a slow-growing tree that can easily be raised from seed. The seeds usually take two years to germinate after they are planted. A very hardy tree, it is not seriously injured by disease, rots, or insect enemies.

BLACK BIRCH

Betula lenta, Linnaeus

L. W. Brownell

In the open the trunk is short, and the branches long and spreading, but in the forest, black birch is tall and slender and clear of limbs for a great height

THE gracefully symmetrical round-topped black birch with its nearly black bark, slender branches, and dark green foliage is found on rich well-drained uplands from southern Maine through New York to eastern Ohio, southward to Delaware and in a narrowing area along the Appalachian Mountains to northern Georgia and Alabama. It is a common forest tree in the north but reaches its largest size in eastern Tennessee on the western slopes of the southern Appalachians.

Black birch belongs to the birch group of the family *Betulaceae,* which also includes the hornbeams, the alders, and the shrubby hazel. *Betula* is the Latin name for birch. The word is supposed to have come from the old Gallic name for these trees, the wood of which the Gauls carbonized to obtain birch tar. *Lenta* means tough, pliant, bending, and applies well to the slender whip-like branches which grow out almost at right angles to the trunk and droop at the ends. Black birch is also called sweet birch from the fragrant wintergreen flavor of the inner bark.

Black birch reaches a height of seventy or eighty feet with a trunk diameter of two to five feet. The bark on old trunks is one-half to three-quarters of an inch thick, dark reddish brown or almost black, furrowed, and broken into thick irregular plates. On young stems and branches it is smooth and shiny, marked with long horizontal narrow corky lenticels or pores. The twigs, pale green at first, change to dark reddish brown. As with all the trees in this family, no terminal buds are formed at the ends of the branches. The branches are prolonged by the uppermost slender sharp-pointed lateral buds. The leaves, growing alternately, often in pairs, on the sides of the twigs, are more or less oval with an uneven, rounded or heart-shaped base, a tapering tip, and numerous sharp, slender, incurved teeth on the margin. They are two and a half to six inches long and one and a half to three inches wide. The upper surface is dark dull green and the under surface is pale yellow-green with conspicuous hairy primary veins and yellow midrib. Supported by stout, hairy stems, approximately an inch long and deeply grooved on top, the leaves turn a clear, bright yellow in autumn.

The staminate catkins, about three-fourths of an inch long, form in the late summer, and remain on the tree through the winter. In

The lower branches are horizontal and the upper ones steeply ascending to form a wide spreading crown in open-grown trees

L. W. Brownell

April, before the leaves come out these catkins open to three or four inches in length and are bright yellow at first, and later, when the pollen develops, greenish yellow. The pistillate catkins are pale green and little more than half an inch long, maturing into erect small-scaled cones, one to one and a half inches long.

The wood of black birch is strong, hard, heavy, close-grained, has high shock-resisting ability, and a cubic foot when dry weighs forty-eight pounds. The dark reddish brown heartwood is enclosed in pale yellow sapwood that is several inches thick. Its principal uses include general millwork, boxes, crates, spools, bobbins, novelties, wooden-ware, fuel, motor vehicle parts, and, because it takes a fine polish, it is also used for furniture. In smaller quantities it is used for pulpwood.

Devereux Butcher

The leaves grow in alternate pairs along the sides of the twigs or singly near the tips, and the cone-like fruits grow from the base of the leaf stems

Black birch is one of the most important hardwoods for distillation in the production of wood alcohol. Distillation of the wood, bark and twigs also produces oil of birch, a substitute for oil of wintergreen used for flavoring, while birch beer is made from the sap.

The worst enemy of black birch is the bronze birch borer which tunnels between wood and bark and frequently kills trees by girdling. This pest is usually not prevalent in healthy stands of forest-grown black birch, but prefers old trees, trees on poor sites, and open-grown trees. Young trees are sometimes attacked by fungus.

Devereux Butcher

Bark on the lower trunk of old trees is cracked into irregular scales, and on young trunks and limbs it is smooth, and has horizontal pores

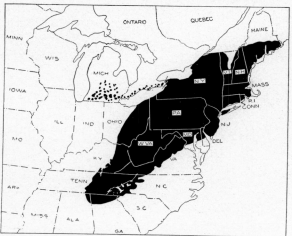

Natural Range of Black Birch

Devereux Butcher

Seed-producing catkins are pale green and grow erect from the sides of the twigs, while the pollen-bearing, staminate ones, shown at the right, are yellow and hang from the tips of twigs

YELLOW BIRCH

Betula lutea, Michaux

A LUSTROUS, silvery yellow bark on limbs and young trunks makes yellow birch easy to identify. Except on very young trees, the bark peels into thin, papery strips that give a ragged appearance. Marked

ond growth forests sometimes contain limited areas of pure yellow birch, with straight, gleaming trunks.

In the open, trunks are usually short and divide into numerous large ascending limbs with slender, somewhat pendulous branchlets that form a broad open head. Under forest conditions trunks are tall and clear of limbs. Mature trees average sixty to seventy feet in height with trunks two or three feet in diameter. On preferred sites trees reach ninety or a hundred feet in height with trunk diameters of four feet.

The range of yellow birch extends from Newfoundland, Nova Scotia and the north shore of the Gulf of St. Lawrence west across Minnesota and eastern Iowa, and southward along the mountains to Georgia. A tree of rich, moist woodlands, its preferred sites are val-

Often attaining large size, the straight, slender trunk and oval crown are characteristic of the forest-grown yellow birch

by horizontal lenticels or pores, the bark on old trunks is gray or blackish, deeply and irregularly grooved and about one-half inch thick.

Yellow birch grows in mixture with beech, maple, ash, red and white pine, spruce and balsam fir. Sec-

During the winter, before developing into pendent catkins, the staminate aments are shiny chestnut-brown, and about three-quarters to an inch long

Each scale of the cone-like fruit contains three winged seeds. Seeds and scales drop away in autumn leaving a central, erect core on the twig

leys and stream banks, although it adapts itself to higher ground, as in the mountains of New England where it reaches elevations of 3,000 feet. It is most abundant and largest in Canada, northern New England, northern New York and northern Michigan.

The twigs resemble those of black birch, but lack the strong wintergreen flavor of the latter. They are green and hairy at first, turning light orange-brown during the first summer, later becoming smooth and dark. Covered with three to eight scales which are downy on the margins, the winter buds are found only along the sides of the twigs—the terminal bud being absent. At the tips of the twigs the pendent staminate or pollen-bearing catkins are borne in clusters of two to four. At the sides of the twigs the solitary, stemless pistillate or seed-producing flowers appear, and by autumn develop into scaly seed-bearing cones about an inch in length.

Attached by short, grooved stems, the leaves are pointed, with sharply double-toothed margins, and have a wedge- or rarely heart-shaped base. Dull dark green above, they are yellow-green beneath with hairs on the veins, and measure three to four inches long and one and a half to two inches wide.

Yellow birch wood weighs forty pounds to the cubic foot when dry. It is hard, strong, and takes a satiny polish. Heartwood is light brown tinged with red, and the sapwood nearly white. Most abundant of all North American birches, it furnished the bulk of 214,100,000 board feet of lumber produced in 1941. It is used for furniture, packing boxes, button molds, wheel hubs, flooring, veneer, interior finish, woodenware, agricultural implements and many other purposes. Areas of greatest commercial abundance are Wisconsin, northern Michigan, New England, and New York.

The lustrous, silvery yellow bark on limbs and young trunks peels into thin papery curls

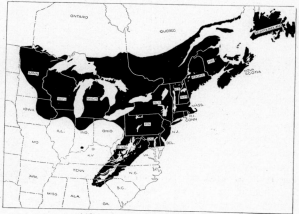

Natural range of Yellow Birch

RED BIRCH

Betula nigra, Linnaeus

Red Birch attains heights of eighty or ninety feet, with a trunk sometimes five feet in diameter

Devereux Butcher

reddish brown or blackish and deeply broken into thick irregular scales.

The slender, lustrous, chestnut-brown twigs are hairy and covered with lenticels. The winter buds are pointed, smooth, or slightly hairy and encased with three to seven reddish brown scales.

Throughout the world there are thirty species of birch, and, of these, twelve are native to North America with their distribution reaching from the Arctic Circle south to Texas and Florida. Three of the North American species are dwarfs.

Red birch is also called river birch, water birch, blue birch, and black birch. The scientific name, *Betula nigra*, was given this tree by Linnaeus. While this means black birch, it is in some degree a misnomer. The Latin word *nigra* probably refers to the blackish bark on the lower trunk of mature trees, but since the bark on upper trunk and branches is pale cinnamon to even a silvery gray, the name does not strictly apply. Cherry birch, named *Betula lenta,* by Linnaeus, is more truly a black birch, for its bark is black from base of trunk to branches.

The alternate, angularly ovate leaves of red birch are borne on short, slender, hairy, slightly flattened stems, and measure one

STREAM and river banks, the shores of ponds, and swampy forest land in the eastern third of the United States are the natural habitat of the red, or river birch. A mature tree usually has a short trunk that divides into several large ascending limbs which compose an open, irregular crown of slender drooping branchlets. Under favorable conditions, particularly in the bayous of the lower Mississippi Valley, red birch attains a height of a hundred feet with a trunk diameter of five feet, but normally it is fifty to eighty feet tall, with trunk diameters of two or three feet. Red birch grows as far north as New Hampshire and Massachusetts and westward through Pennsylvania to southern Minnesota. Southward the range extends into northern Florida and west into eastern Texas. Like other birch species, this one is graceful in form, but its chief distinguishing characteristic is the cinnamon-colored bark with its somewhat metallic sheen which separates into ragged, papery scales. On young trunks and the upper limbs and branches of old trees, it is marked by narrow, longitudinal lenticels, or breathing pores. On older trees, especially those growing in drier sites, the bark on branches may be smooth, shiny, and gray. On mature trunks it may be an inch thick. It is dark

Devereux Butcher

Two or three slightly diverging limbs divide into many branches and branchlets to form the irregular crown of Red Birch

124

and a half to three inches in length. They are unevenly double toothed, pointed at the outer end, and are distinguished by their broad, wedge-shaped base. The newly opened, light yellow-green leaves are hairy on both sides and accompanied at the base of their stems by pale green stipules, or leaf like appendages. These drop off after the leaves are fully developed. The mature leaves are thin and tough, deep green and lustrous above, paler beneath, and smooth except on the midrib and primary veins. In autumn they turn dull yellow before falling.

The pollen-bearing, staminate catkins form during the preceding season and are clustered at the ends of twigs. By April or May they are two or three inches long. The pistillate or seed-producing catkins appear when the leaf buds begin to open and they are borne singly and erect on the short, two-leaved lateral twigs.

Cone-like cylindrical fruits mature in May and June while the undersides of the deep green double-toothed leaves are still coated with fine hairs

Unlike the fall-ripened seeds of other birches, those of the river-loving red birch mature in late spring or early summer. The small, winged, nut-like seeds are driven by the wind or carried by water and germinate readily in the moist, deep, rich, alluvial soils of bottomlands which are the natural habitat of this tree. Though a fast growing tree when young, red birch is comparatively short lived, and will tolerate little shade at any stage of its life. Young stumps produce vigorous sprouts.

A cubic foot weighs about thirty-five pounds when air dry. It is strong, close-grained, rather hard, and more durable in contact with the soil than other birch woods. The heartwood is light brown and the sapwood pale buff in color. It is of relatively small commercial importance because of its scattered distribution and is used largely in the locality where it is grown. When cut, the wood may be marketed with beech and maple, as well as with other birch species. It is used locally in the manufacture of cheap furniture, turned articles, shoe lasts, wooden shoes, yokes, berry baskets, and wagon hubs. Hoops for peach baskets in Maryland and for rice casks farther south are made from the branches. There are no estimates concerning the volume of merchantable red birch lumber available, and no record is kept of the lumber manufactured and sold from this single species. The species is well equipped to reproduce itself, and the supply is not being heavily drawn upon.

Red birch is not particularly susceptible to disease or to attack by insects, but it is frequently severely injured and even killed by the action of heavy cakes of ice which are carried down stream with the flood during early spring thaws. On such occasions, young trees may be pushed down and stripped of their bark as the ice passes over them.

Because of its graceful form, this tree is well suited for ornamental purposes. In the northeast it is often planted in parks and on estates, preferring soil which is relatively deep, moist, and well drained.

The bark on old trunks is dark, red-brown and nearly an inch thick, deeply furrowed, and broken into closely pressed scales

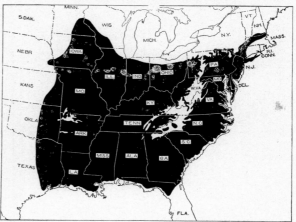

Natural range of Red Birch

125

PAPER BIRCH

Betula papyrifera, Marshall

SINGLY or in clusters, the creamy white stemmed and open crowned paper birch—bright green in summer and lacey in winter—prefers moist, rich soil but grows on a variety of sites from northern New Jersey to Iowa, through Minnesota, and north to the limit of tree growth below the shores of Hudson Bay, into Labrador and Newfoundland. It is the most widely distributed of the world's thirty varieties of birch. Trees reach sixty to eighty feet and two to three feet in diameter, but are usually smaller. With age the crown becomes broad and open with few large limbs, many horizontal branches and flexible twigs.

The simple, irregularly double toothed, abruptly pointed, oval leaves with broad bases grow alternately from smooth reddish brown twigs. They are two to

Devereux Butcher

Gleaming white bark and an open crown with small branches and many flexible twigs distinguish Paper Birch throughout the seasons

three inches long, one and a half to two inches wide, bright green above and lighter beneath with warty glands along the main veins.

Slender brown, tassel-like male flowers three to four inches long hang in twos and threes from the twig ends in April or May. Back from these and nearly erect are short greenish female cones. By autumn these ripen into cylindrical, short stalked, loose, cone-like

A. H. Ballantine

Devereux Butcher

The irregularly toothed leaves are two to three inches long, while the short stalked seed cone is an inch or more long

In early spring twigs bear long dangling staminate blooms with shorter nearly erect pistillate cones

Devereux Butcher

Horizontal lenticils and dark blotched scars mark the fraying white bark with under layers of orange

fruits packed with thin heart shaped discs to which tiny, oval seeds are attached. Millions of seed are released annually to germinate on exposed mineral soil such as old burns. Thus many available openings are captured and paper birch is one tree that covers more area than when America was discovered.

On young trees and older branches the chalky lustrous white bark peels easily and may be separated into paper-thin layers marked with horizontal lentice's or breathing pores. On the copper colored inner bark these raised slits are bright orange. With age the outer bark rolls back in irregular, frayed, horizontal sheets and the blotchy blackened lower trunk develops increasingly deep fissures. Early explorers adopted the arts of the northern Indians by using this bark for canoes, as well as for receptacles in which to store or carry food. The modern tendency to strip it is often fatal to the trees and always disfiguring.

The scientific term *papyrifera* describes the paper like bark, while *betula* is the Latin name for birch. It closely resembles European birch, *Betula alba*. With its pendulous variety this is hardier than *Betula papyrifera* and was adopted as the "Mothers' Tree" in 1923. So named it is increasingly planted throughout the northern and central states on Mothers' Day in May.

The close grained, hard, fairly tough heartwood is light brown tinged with red, while the thin sapwood is nearly white. When air dry a cubic foot weighs about thirty-seven pounds. It works readily but is not durable in contact with the soil. It is used for spools, clothes pins, tooth picks, shoe pegs, shoe lasts, novelties, turnery, and for wood pulp and fuel.

Some 3,000,000,000 board feet of commercial paper birch supply an annual cut of approximately 50,000,000 board feet. "Red heart" frequently reduces the usefulness of one-sixth the mature stand. Trees may reach sixty to eighty feet with diameters of nine or ten inches in sixty-five years, but seldom live beyond 150 years. Occasionally in pure stands, paper birch is usually in mixture with white pine, red pine, red spruce, aspen and yellow birch.

Especially attractive when planted in combination with evergreens, those grown south of its natural range are usually killed by borers. The thin bark is easily penetrated by grass fires, but stump sprouts often temporarily restore the burn.

Natural range of Paper Birch

127

Fagus grandifolia, Ehrhart

Devereux Butcher

BEECH is native from southern Canada, northern Michigan and eastern Wisconsin to the Atlantic, and south to eastern Texas and northern Florida. Preferring deep, rich, well-drained soils, it grows wherever moisture is in the upper layers. It attains largest size, however, in the rich, alluvial bottomlands of the Ohio and the lower Mississippi River valleys, and along the western slopes of the Southern Appalachian Mountains. Here trees with trunks over four feet in diameter reach heights of 120 feet and are clear for sixty to seventy feet.

The glossy, blue-green, straight-veined leaves are simple and alternate on the twigs. They are three to five inches long and rather coarsely serrate with a vein terminating in each tooth.

Each tree bears separate male and female flowers. These appear in early spring when the leaves are half grown; the yellow-green staminate ones being about an inch in diameter, hanging from

Open grown beech trees have a low wide spreading crown comprised of many long horizontal branches. The smooth tight fitting bark is silvery gray touched with irregular dark blotches and bands

long stems, while the pistillate ones are usually in pairs covered with many pointed bracts and supported on a short hairy stem.

By early autumn the short-stalked bur is ripe. Within, surrounded by a downy lining may be found two or three small triangular, highly polished, brown, sweet-meated nuts. These edible nuts are responsible for the classical Latin name *fagus,* from the Greek, *phagus,* to eat; while *grandifolia* refers to the beautiful leaves. This tree reproduces by root sprouts as well as by seeds.

The smooth, close-fitting, blue-gray bark covers the trunk and branches like a skin. Seldom more than half an inch thick, it is frequently mottled with dark blotches and bands.

Beech wood is light red in color, heavy, hard, strong, close grained, and difficult to split. A cubic foot when air dry weighs about forty-five pounds. It shrinks considerably in drying, is not durable when left in contact with the soil, but takes a high polish and wears well when subjected to friction under water. The wood is used for chairs and other furniture, flooring, railroad ties, woodenware, handles, novelties, and because of its clean odor for barrels and boxes in which to hold foods.

Roughly about eight and a half billion board feet of beech timber are growing in the United States, of which the bulk is in New England, New York, and Pennsylvania. Beech lumber produced in 1941 amounted to 228,344,000 board feet. West Virginia and Ohio were the largest producers.

Of relatively slow growth, it may attain ages of 300 to 400 years. It is subject to several injurious insects and fungi, and the thin bark makes it an easy victim to ground fires.

W. M. Harlow

The yellow-green staminate blooms appear when the leaves are still limp. Each leaf is three to five inches long with parallel veins terminating at the marginal teeth. The tapering bud is an inch long and polished brown.

W. M. Harlow

George J. Baetzhold

The shiny triangular nuts are encased in a small prickly bur

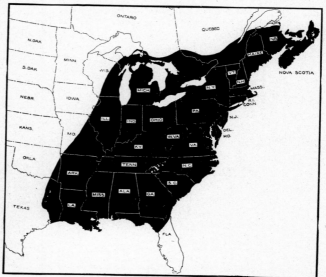

Natural range of Beech in North America

129

AMERICAN CHESTNUT

Castanea dentata, (Marshall) Borkhausen

THE American chestnut, which has given joy to so many people, is practically doomed by a disease, but continues sufficiently important to command attention among American trees. Before the chestnut blight gained its present headway, chestnut was found from southern Maine through-

out the northern states to the foothills of the southern Appalachian Mountains and west as far as southern Michigan through Indiana to northern Mississippi. Suited to a variety of soils, chestnut attains its greatest size on well drained slopes in western North Carolina and eastern Tennessee. Here trees a hundred feet high with trunks five and six feet in diameter are found, and trees sixty to eighty feet high are not uncommon. The tapering trunk divides into several horizontal or ascending branches to form a broad, somewhat pyramidal head.

Commonly called American chestnut, and sometimes sweet chestnut because of the nut, the Indians of central New York called it "O-heh-yah-tah," or prickly bur. *Castanea dentata,* the scientific name, includes the Latin name for chestnut and refers to the tooth-like notches on the margins of the bright green leaves.

The long catkins of male flowers appear during late June and early July as buff-colored streamers over the trees. Less conspicuous fruit-bearing flowers develop simultaneously on the new wood of the same trees, and in a few

Open-grown American Chestnut develops a broad, somewhat pyramidal crown, supported on a short thick trunk

The leaves fall in October and November to reveal the tapering trunk and sturdy horizontal or ascending branches

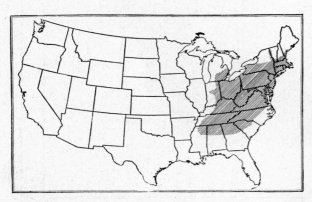

Natural range of American Chestnut in the United States

weeks prickly green burs appear. These become two to two and one-half inches in diameter by the end of August, and ripen during October and November, when the prickly covering splits open and reveals one to five dark brown sweet-meated nuts within a velvety case.

The dark grayish brown bark of mature trees is one to two inches thick, hard and deeply cleft to form broad flat ridges. That of young trees is smooth, often shining, and of a purplish brown color. It is an important source of tannin for the leather industry.

The buds are bluntly pointed, chestnut brown, alternate on the branches, and are borne singly at the ends of the twigs rather than clustered as with the oaks. The leaves are simple, five to ten inches long, narrow, toothed, and smooth on both sides. A cross-section of a twig reveals a star-shaped pith.

Chestnut reproduces from sprouts as well as from seeds. When cut or killed by fire or blight, chestnut trees sprout vigorously from the stump, which results in groups of two or more trees. In blight infested areas the roots and stump of dead or felled trees annually produce sprouts which live for a year or more before they in turn are struck down by the disease.

The wood is reddish brown with light colored sapwood. Although coarse, light, soft and relatively weak, it is useful for structural purposes, for interior trim, for fence posts, ties, pulpwood and fuel, as well as for furniture, packing cases, and crates. Superficially resembling oak but without prominent medullary rays, a cubic foot air dry weighs only about thirty pounds. Similarly it lacks the strength of oak. The ability of chestnut wood to resist attacks of wood-destroying fungi encourages its wide use for fence posts, fence rails and railway ties.

Had it not been for the chestnut blight this tree would still rank among the more important commercial and horticultural trees of the eastern states. But it has been decimated. In 1941, the total cut of chestnut lumber, most of which was blight-killed, was 93,171,000 board feet. The sweet chestnuts had long been used for food and were a source of income to many farmers, while tannic acid, used for tanning leather, was secured from the wood.

The chestnut blight, a fungus disease imported from Asia before this country had enacted plant quarantine laws, was first recognized in New York City in 1904. Since then it has spread rapidly over New England, New York and along the eastern slopes of the Allegheny Mountains and into the southern Appalachians.

There are other enemies of the chestnut but in comparison with the blight they are all of secondary importance. No adequate method of control has been developed, and in spite of constant search, no strain of blight-resistant American chestnut has been discovered.

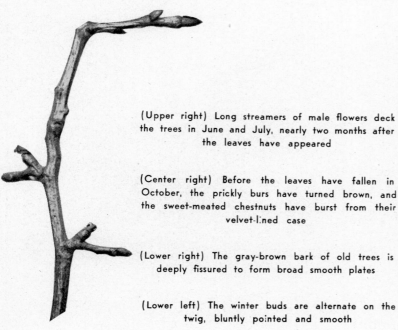

(Upper right) Long streamers of male flowers deck the trees in June and July, nearly two months after the leaves have appeared

(Center right) Before the leaves have fallen in October, the prickly burs have turned brown, and the sweet-meated chestnuts have burst from their velvet-lined case

(Lower right) The gray-brown bark of old trees is deeply fissured to form broad smooth plates

(Lower left) The winter buds are alternate on the twig, bluntly pointed and smooth

NORTHERN RED OAK

Quercus borealis, **Michaux**

THE OAKS are naturally divided into two groups—white oaks and black oaks. Of the latter red oak is easily the largest, most

Louis Boeglin

The broad, symmetrical crown of dark green foliage and the thick, short trunk combine grace and strength in the Red Oak

widely distributed, and commercially most important.

The broad symmetrically spreading crown of dense dark green foliage is a conspicuous part of the landscape throughout the entire northeast—as far west as central Minnesota, southern Wisconsin, Iowa and Arkansas, and south into northern Louisiana, Mississippi, Tennessee, and northern Georgia. The trunk of open grown trees often separates at fifteen or twenty feet from the ground into several

The trunk of open grown trees is relatively short, dividing into several stout branches which grow longer with increasing age

stout branches. In the forests, the trunk assumes greater length and carries a narrow, round-topped crown. Some trees in the Ohio Valley and the mountains of West Virginia, Kentucky, Tennessee, and North Carolina reach 150 feet in height and six feet in diameter, but more ordinarily it is seventy to ninety feet high and two to three and a half feet in diameter.

This description combines the two more important and frequently confused red oaks of the north — *Quercus borealis* and the larger *Quercus borealis maxima. Borealis,* meaning northern, refers to the range of the species, while *maxima,* or largest, distinguishes this particular variety of oak, whose tree as well as acorn are the biggest of all the black oak group. *Quercus* is an ancient Latin name, probably of Celtic origin, meaning "beautiful tree."

The simple, alternate leaves

Louis Boeglin

have five to eleven unequal bristle-tipped lobes tapering from broad bases. They are five to nine inches long, four to six inches broad, dark green above, and paler green beneath. Appearing late in spring, by autumn they turn deep red or orange to hang on until late fall or winter.

Flowers of both sexes appear on different parts of the same trees in May or June with the unfolding leaves, when the long hairy staminate catkins seem to veil the entire crown. The less conspicuous, greenish pistillate blooms develop into single or pairs of short-stalked acorns. They are fertilized by wind-borne pollen from the staminate catkins of the neighboring trees, and take two years to mature into broadly oblong, reddish brown acorns, an inch or more long with a diameter only a little less. Each acorn rests in a flat saucer-shaped cup whose narrow border is covered with small closely fitting scales. The dark gray to reddish brown bark of mature trees is a half to three-quarters of an inch thick, and has a light reddish or flesh colored inner bark.

The strong close-grained wood is light reddish brown in color with a thin layer of lighter colored sapwood. A cubic foot weighs about forty-five pounds when air dry, being not only lighter but less strong than white oak. It is, however, used for many of the same purposes, including general construction, flooring, interior finish, cheap furniture, railroad ties, posts, poles, and fuel.

Red oak reproduces itself by stump sprouts or coppice, as well as from seeds. It grows in company with other oaks, sugar maples, elm, white pine, and the hickories, and is the most rapid growing of all the oaks.

George Baetzhold

Slender, pendulous catkins of pollen bearing flowers are borne late in the spring along with the unfolding leaves

The dark gray to reddish brown bark is broken into broad, flat topped ridges

Ernest Crandall

The dark green leaves are five to nine inches long with unequal bristle-tipped lobes, while the shallow-cupped, reddish brown acorns are broadly ovate

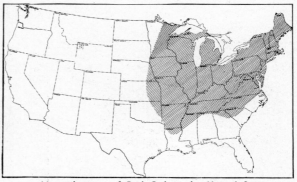

Natural range of Red Oak in the United States

133

PIN OAK

Quercus palustris, Muenchhausen

PIN OAK is more widely known as a street or ornamental tree than for lumber purposes, but grows naturally from southern Arkansas and north central Mississippi northward to southern New England and New York. The westward distribution extends to southern Michigan and Wisconsin, eastern Iowa, Kansas and the Oklahoma Ozarks. Pin oak usually occupies poorly-drained flats, low clay ridges, edges of swamps, and occasionally very moist upland sites. One common name, swamp oak, corresponding with the scientific name *palustris*, is derived from the Latin word *palus* meaning swamp. *Quercus* is reported in "Tree Ancestors" by Berry, to be derived from the Celtic *quer* or fine, and *cuez* or tree. So it may be said that this is the fine tree of the swamp. The common name, pin oak, refers to the great number of short, spur or pin-like branchlets on the main branches, or to the remnants of dead branches which extend through the wood to the center of the trunk.

Pin oak is a tree of moderate size, rarely exceeding eighty-five or ninety-five feet in height, and three feet in diameter. Occasional forest-grown specimens reach a height of one hundred

G. H. Collingwood

Pin Oak develops a single central trunk with relatively small side branches which support a dense crown of glossy green leaves. The same tree shown in winter reveals (lower right), the small, tough side branches. Below: Natural range of Pin Oak in the United States

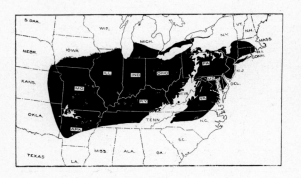

G. H. Collingwood

and twenty feet, with a trunk four or five feet in diameter. Its straight trunk extends well up into a symmetrical, pyramidal crown whose tough drooping branches frequently sweep the ground. With increasing age the crown loses its original pyramidal shape and becomes broad and rather open.

The bark is light to dark grayish brown, hard, so close as to appear tight, from three-fourths of an inch to one and one-fourth inches thick, and divided by narrow, shallow fissures into broad, low, scaly ridges. The five to nine-lobed narrow leaves are four to eight inches long, thin, firm, dark green and lustrous above, paler beneath, and perfectly smooth except for tufts of pale hairs in the axils of the larger veins. They have slender stems or petioles, one-half of an inch to two inches long, and the irregularly toothed lobes taper to narrow, pointed ends.

Male and female blossoms are borne separately on the new wood of the same tree. The male or staminate flowers appear with the leaves in early spring as brown tassels, while the less conspicuous pistillate flowers may be found at the angle where the new leaf joins with the main stem. The reddish brown acorns are broader than long and set close on the main stem in flat, saucer-shaped cups. They take two years to mature, and are set singly or in clusters on the two-year old branches.

Pin oak has no special commercial importance, but, although generally inferior, is cut and marketed as red oak wherever found in ordinary logging operations. The numerous small adherent limbs cause excessively knotty logs, and the heavy, hard wood checks badly in drying. Accordingly, only the best trees are cut for lumber. It is used for flooring, small fixtures, handles and for other purposes normally filled by red oak, and also for ties, car stock, piling and railroad material.

The upright pyramidal crown, lack of heavy side branches, clean trunk and rich glossy leaves make it one of the most desirable oaks for street and ornamental planting. A fibrous root system without a distinct tap root gives ease and security to transplanting. When planted in well drained moist soils it grows rapidly, produces a dense shade, and with relatively little pruning does not interfere with street traffic. Best results are secured when the trees are planted about forty feet apart.

Aside from attacks by the obscure scale, which resembles the San Jose scale, pin oak is especially free from injury by disease or insects, but fire frequently damages trees growing in the woods or on large estates. The obscure scale can be controlled by spraying with lime-sulphur or miscible-oil solutions in the early spring before the leaves appear and again in midsummer.

G. H. Collingwood

The deep-cut, glossy, dark green leaves have five to seven lobes terminating in irregular points. The small, brown acorns are set in shallow, flat cups and mature on wood of the previous year

G. H. Collingwood

Low, scaly ridges and an appearance of tightness help characterize the dark gray bark of mature Pin Oak trees

G. H. Collingwood

Before the spring leaves have reached full size, the tree is decked with tassels of pollen-bearing staminate flowers. The inconspicuous pistillate flowers are hidden within the axils of the leaves

135

SCARLET OAK

Quercus coccinea, Muenchhausen

Devereux Butcher

Scarlet Oak usually reaches heights of from sixty to eighty feet, with a trunk diameter of two or three feet and an open crown

of four feet. The crown is open and narrow with slender lateral branches which droop slightly at the ends. Intolerant of shade, the lower crown is often marked with persistent dead branches.

The thin, five to nine lobed, bristly pointed leaves occur alternately, are three to six inches long, three to five inches wide, and broadly oval in general outline. The sinuses between the lobes are deeper than those of the black oak, extending more than halfway to the mid-rib and are rounded at their bases. The midribs and primary veins are yellow. The slender leaf stems are one and one-half to two and one-half inches long and circular in cross section. Though members of the black oak group, to which scarlet oak belongs, usually have hairy leaves, only occasional tufts of reddish pubescence appear in the axils of the veins of scarlet oak leaves. First

SCARLET OAK occurs naturally from Maine and southern Ontario to eastern Virginia, westward through Michigan to southern Minnesota, southward into eastern Oklahoma and southern Alabama and throughout the Allegheny Mountains. Never forming pure stands, it frequently appears in the north with white pine, white oak and red oak, and in the south with shortleaf pine, post oak and white oak. Its best development is in the Ohio basin.

Known widely as scarlet oak, it is also called red oak and Spanish oak.

Favoring light sandy or gravelly soils, it grows well on various sites. Its large spreading lateral roots run so close below the ground level that they often break through the surface and become exposed. Generally sixty to eighty feet tall with a trunk diameter of two or three feet, the rapidly tapering trunk occasionally towers one hundred and fifty feet and reaches a diameter

Maryland State Dept. of Forestry

The trunk tapers rapidly, while the branches, drooping slightly, are comparatively small and spreading

The staminate flowers appearing in May or June, occur in clusters of catkins three or four inches long

Broadly oval in outline, the leaves are smooth and have yellow primary veins, while the short-stalked acorns are often striped

Bark on the mature trunk is rough, dark gray or nearly black divided into scaly ridges, and is almost one inch thick

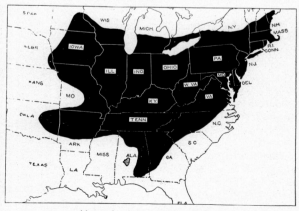

Natural range of Scarlet Oak

appearing bright red and finely matted with pale hairs, the leaves turn to a rich bright green. Again in the autumn, they turn bright scarlet and persist late into the season. The specific name *coccinea* comes from the Latin *coccum,* and refers to an oak gall used in making red dyes. It is applied to scarlet oak because of the striking leaf coloration.

Appearing in May or June, both male and female flowers occur on the same tree. The short-stalked, oval acorns ripen in September and October of the second season. They occur singly or in pairs, and are one-half to one inch long, with reddish brown surfaces often lined with thin light stripes. The mildly bitter kernel is nearly white while that of black oak is deep yellow.

The broadly ovate, blunt pointed buds are one-eighth to one-quarter inch long, dark reddish brown, and covered with pale, fine hairs. As compared with those of the red oak they are broader in proportion to their length.

The rough, nearly black bark is almost an inch thick, divided into irregular scaly ridges, and may be mottled with gray. On young stems and branches it is thin, smooth and grayish brown to light brown.

The heartwood is pinkish to light reddish brown, strong, hard, coarse and a cubic foot weighs about forty-six pounds when air dry. Although inferior to red oak it is manufactured and sold with red oak and black oak for use in furniture, interior finish and agricultural implements.

Reasonably rapid growing, scarlet oak has been planted widely in the United States and Europe as a tree for parks and streets.

BLACK OAK

Quercus velutina, La Marck

Devereux Butcher

An open-grown Black Oak develops an irregular and wide-spreading crown of large ascending branches

northern Florida, west to eastern Texas, eastern Oklahoma, eastern Kansas, southeastern Nebraska and Iowa. In upland cutover forest areas it is the most abundant species, and though it prefers rich, well-drained, gravelly soils, black oak is not usually found in great abundance in the better soils because it is very intolerant to shade, and unable to compete with other species. It is most often found on the poorer soils of slopes and ridges, the young trees developing long taproots that enable them to survive where many species would suffer for want of water. The most common associates of this tree are the other oaks, occasionally ash and yellow poplar.

Bark on the mature trunk is dark gray or almost black, often paler gray in the coastal regions, three quarters to one and a quarter inches thick. Bark on young trunks and on branches is warm gray and smooth; inner bark is deep orange, very bitter to taste and is rich in tannin. From the deep orange inner bark a yellow dye commercially known as quercitron is made.

ONE of the commonest and largest of the eastern oaks is black oak which varies greatly as to form in different localities. Average height is from sixty to eighty feet with trunk diameters from two to three feet, and under favorable conditions, particularly in the lower Ohio basin, sometimes a hundred and fifty feet with a trunk diameter of four or five feet. In general habit black oak is similar to scarlet oak, but the limbs are usually somewhat stouter. On good sites the bole is long with little taper, occasionally free of limbs for forty feet, while on less favorable soils the trunk tapers excessively and limbs grow closer to the ground.

The name, *Quercus*, is Latin for oak and means "beautiful tree"; *velutina* comes from the word *vellus* which means fleece and refers to the surfaces of the leaves which are velvety when young; also, perhaps, to the downy winter buds.

The range of black oak extends from southern Maine and northern Vermont westward through southern Ontario, southern Michigan to southeastern Minnesota, and south to

Devereux Butcher

J. B. Sudworth

Acorns measure one-third to three-quarters of an inch long, and are held by deep, thin-scaled cups

Black Oak leaves, more varied than those of any other oak, usually have seven lobes

The stout, smooth, or slightly hairy twigs of black oak are dull red brown, later turning dark brown, and have large lenticels or pores. The lateral buds are alternate, those near the ends of twigs clustered about the terminal bud; they are yellowish gray, measuring one quarter to one half inch, are sharply pointed, and usually five-sided. The down with which they are covered offers a means of identifying this oak from others in the black oak group.

The alternate leaves measure five to six inches in length and three to four inches in width. They are bristle-tipped as are the leaves of all oaks in the group. Their indentations are deep, rounded and wide, extending at least half way to the midrib. The mature leaf is thick, tough, smooth, dark green, and very shiny above, paler and somewhat hairy or smooth beneath, with brown hairs at the connections of the main veins. The yellow stout stems are two to six inches long.

In May or June, when the new leaves are half grown, the flowers appear. Borne on the growth of the preceding season, the pollen-bearing ones occur in hairy catkins, four to six inches long, while the seed-producing ones, growing at the bases of the leaf-stems of the season, are reddish and borne on short, hairy stems. Ripening from October to November of the second season, the acorns are either stemless or on short stalks. The yellow, bitter kernel is not edible. Crops of acorns are produced every two or three years. Black oak is fairly prolific and germination is frequently eighty per cent or over. The approximate maximum age of black oak ranges from a hundred and fifty to two hundred years.

Black oak wood is heavy, hard, strong, not tough, coarse-grained, checks in drying, and has fewer and smaller medullary rays than the wood of most other oaks. Heartwood is reddish brown, the sapwood narrow and pale. A cubic foot when seasoned weighs forty-four pounds. Most important of the black oak group, with an estimated stand of over eight billion board feet, it is used for cheap furniture, slack cooperage, flooring, construction, interior finish and fuel, it is not easily worked.

The healthy tree is not usually severely attacked by insects or borers. Black oak is seldom planted as an ornamental tree.

R. C. Brundage

Bark on large trunks is broken by deep furrows into ridges that are transversely cut into block-like strips

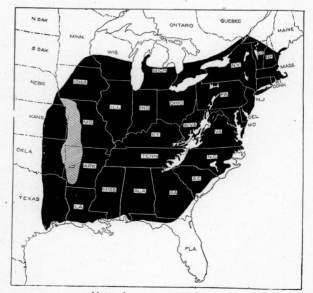

Natural range of Black Oak

SOUTHERN RED OAK

Quercus falcata, Michaux

L. W. Brownell

Forest grown Southern Red Oak is medium-sized with a long straight trunk, while in the open the trunk is shorter, and the branches wide-spreading

falcata. Accordingly, this is the name dendrologists have recently decided upon.

Usually a medium-sized tree, this species, when growing under forest conditions, has a long, straight trunk and upward-reaching limbs that form a high, rounded crown. In the open it develops a short trunk with wide-spreading limbs to form a broad, open, round-topped crown. Heights are usually from seventy to eighty feet, with trunk diameters of two to three feet, but trees one hundred feet high with diameters up to five feet have been recorded.

The dark gray bark on mature trunks is rough, with shallow fissures, and broad ridges. It may be three-quarters to one inch thick, but on limbs and on young trunks it is relatively smooth and lighter in color. Although rich in tannin, it has found no extensive use by tanneries.

The angular twigs are first dark reddish brown, covered with thick rusty down, and in their second year become dark red-brown or gray. Winter buds are an eighth to a quarter inch long and covered with chestnut-brown,

SOUTHERN red oak grows as far north as southern New Jersey and southeastern Pennsylvania, but is more common in the South Atlantic and Gulf States. Reaching into central Florida, it extends westward to the valley of the Brazos in Texas and northward into Missouri and the southern parts of Illinois and Indiana. The tree is also found in isolated portions of southern Ohio and western West Virginia.

Locally called Spanish oak, Spanish water oak, spotted oak, turkey oak and red hill oak, the confusion of names entered the field of botanists and dendrologists, some of whom followed Marshall and Sudworth in calling it Spanish oak, *Quercus digitata,* while others followed Linnaeus in calling it southern red oak, *Quercus rubra.* Later Sargent revealed that Linnaeus' type specimen was the same as Michaux had earlier described as *Quercus*

Maryland State Department of Forestry

Varying in shape more than those of other oaks, the leaves are of two types. Acorns are about one-half inch long held by a stemless or short-stalked saucer-shaped cup

Devereux Butcher

Opening in April with the leaves, the staminate flowers are arranged in pendant, hairy catkins

hairy scales. This oak belongs to the black oak group. Its leaves grow alternately along the twig. They are firm, dark green and glossy above, paler and downy beneath, and occur in a greater variety of shapes than do the leaves of most other oaks. In general there are two types. Both have a taperingly wedge-shaped or rounded base, but the finger type has slender, pointed or tooth-tipped lobes with the terminal lobe more or less curved after the manner of a scythe blade. This is referred to in the scientific name *falcata* which comes from the Latin word *falcatus,* meaning scythe. The other type of leaf resembles the outline of a bell, is less deeply cut, and the broader lobes are distinctly tooth-tipped. Both kinds may occur on the same or different trees—the finger-like leaves filling the bulk of the crown, and the broad-lobed, tooth-tipped ones of bell shaped outline on the lower branches. In autumn they turn dull orange or brown.

Flowers of both sexes appear on the same tree in April when the leaves unfold. The staminate or pollen-bearing ones are in clusters of drooping, hairy catkins, three to five inches long. The pistillate or acorn-producing flowers occur in pairs or singly on stout, hairy stems. Measuring about half an inch long, and maturing the second year, the rounded, bitter acorns occur singly or in pairs. They are about one-third covered by scaly, saucer-shaped cups.

Weighing about forty-three pounds to the cubic foot when air-dry, the coarse-grained, light red wood of southern red oak is hard and strong, has a few broad, conspicuous medullary rays, checks badly when drying, and is not durable in contact with the soil. It is used for general construction, slack cooperage, crates, furniture and fuel. Open pores extending with the grain of the wood render it unusable for barrels in which to store liquids.

The dark brown or blackish bark is broken by shallow fissures into broad ridges

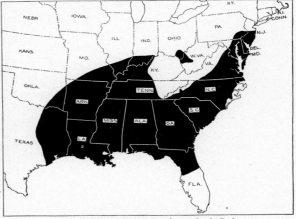

Natural range of Southern Red Oak

WILLOW OAK

Quercus phellos, Linnaeus

Willow Oak has a strong central trunk supporting numerous side branches from which grow many small spur-like branchlets, resembling those of the pin oak

knots in the wood and greatly reduce the clear merchantable length.

It thrives on poorly drained bottom lands that are normally covered each winter with shallow water, occurs in rich moist soil along the margins of streams and swamps, and also on higher land. It grows from southern Long Island and Staten Island in southeastern New York chiefly along the maritime plain to northeastern Florida, through the Gulf Region to the Sabine River Valley in eastern Texas and north through eastern Oklahoma, Arkansas, southeastern Missouri to central Tennessee, southern Illinois and eastern Kentucky. Reaching its largest size and greatest abundance in the lower Mississippi Valley, it grows in company with other oaks, hickory, tulip tree, maple and elm. It is so frequently found along wet margins of streams and swamps as to be erroneously known as swamp oak, or water oak. The abundant short spur-

WILLOW OAK lays no claim to size or majesty, but its round-topped symmetrical crown, rapid growth and long life place it among the most attractive of the red oak or black oak group. Occasionally, in the moist fertile portions of its southern range it attains heights of 100 to 120 feet and diameters at breast height of three to five feet. Over most of its range, however, it is usually forty to fifty feet high with a full clear trunk fourteen to twenty inches in diameter, frequently rising intact through the crown. The side branches are slender like those of the pin oak and the lower branches droop or dip down at the ends. The side branches persist except in dense shady stands.

Under forest conditions it develops a tall, straight trunk and a full symmetrical crown. The trunk prunes itself slowly, leaving many small live and dead branches which form

The full, round, slightly conical crown of Willow Oak is frequently forty to fifty feet high and may attain a height of one hundred feet or more

like branchlets on the lower branches have led to wide use of the name pin oak.

Willow oak gets its name from the long, narrow, lance-shaped or occasionally scythe-shaped vivid light green leaves, which in shape as well as color resemble those of a willow more than an oak. In texture, however, they are thicker and more leathery. They are pointed at both ends, two and one-half to five inches long, one-fourth to one inch wide with a short stem or petiole and a slender yellow midrib. The shiny light green of the upper side is mildly contrasted by a lighter green below. In the South the tree is nearly evergreen, and the leaves never attain the bright autumnal colors of the red, pin and scarlet oaks but turn a pale yellow before falling. The long narrow entire leaf, which is common to only a few other oaks, leads occasionally to the common name—peach-leaf oak. Willow oak may be confused with the true water oak, *Quercus obtusa* Ashe, the laurel oak, *Quercus laurifolia* Michaux, and with shingle oak, *Quercus imbricaria* Michaux. The leaves are smaller, narrower, without hairs on the under surface, and of almost uniform width. The acorns of laurel oak are larger and the cups not so flat as those of willow oak.

The flowers are each of a single sex and are found on all parts of the tree,—the male catkins on last season's growth and the female flowers in the axils of the new leaves. They appear in late March in the South. Farther north they appear in April or May and continue in evidence for two or three weeks. The pollen from the pistillate blooms, which are like yellow-green knots along the two to three inch stems, is carried by the wind to fertilize the pistillate flowers. These stand on short, slender, smooth stalks or peduncles at the base of the leaves. Characteristic of the red oak or black oak group, it is the fall of the second season before they mature into hemispherical, light yellow-brown acorns about a half inch long set less than a quarter of their diameter in a thin saucer-shaped cup. This in turn is covered with thin elongated scales, and the inside is lined with a mat of fine, white hairs. The acorn is held to the twig by a short stalk, and the meat is bitter with tannin.

Dark, chestnut brown, narrowly conical winter buds about an eighth of an inch long and without angles are borne alternately on smooth, slender, reddish brown twigs marked with dark lenticels or breathing pores. Each of the numerous, well defined bud scales is edged with pale gray or white.

The red-brown to steel gray bark is a half to three quarters of an inch thick, generally smooth and very hard. On large mature trees it is nearly black, broken into rough, hard ridges and irregular plates by narrow fissures. *Phellos* comes from a Greek word referring to cork and was used to refer to the oak long before the name was accepted by Linnaeus. It has no reference to any special corky quality of the bark.

The strong, heavy, close-grained wood is reddish brown and resembles that of red oak, with which it is most frequently marketed. In the Mississippi delta region it is of considerable commercial importance but there are no reliable estimates of the available stand of this species. It weighs about forty-five pounds to the cubic foot when air-dry. This is about the same weight as white oak, but its strength is only eighty-six per cent of that wood. It is used for interior trim, house frames, doors, floors, slack cooperage, and railroad ties.

Willow oak is hardy as far north as Massachusetts and in the South Atlantic and Gulf States is recognized as one of the best of the quick growing trees for street and ornamental planting. The comparatively shallow

The narrow light green leaves, two and one-half to five inches long and pointed at each end, resemble those of a willow more than an oak

The relatively smooth brown to dark gray bark is one-half to three quarters of an inch thick

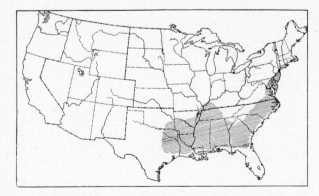

Natural range of Willow Oak in the United States

root system helps make it easily transplanted. Trees twelve to fifteen feet high may be dug from the woods and successfully grown but well rooted nursery-grown stock is more satisfactory for ornamental planting. Although with few enemies, trees are occasionally seriously retarded by scale insects which feed on the tender bark of twigs and small branches.

LIVE OAK

Quercus virginiana, Miller

THE massive live oak is one of the most impressive and majestic trees of the south Atlantic and Gulf Coast states. It is found on the coastal plain from southeastern Virginia to the tip of Florida and along the Gulf Coast to Mexico reaching inland as far as the Red River Valley, and the westernmost tip of Texas. It is also found in the mountains of Cuba, southern Mexico, and Central America.

The live oak in its best known form is a dense round-headed tree seldom more than fifty feet tall with a massive trunk three or four and rarely seven feet in main about thirteen months on the tree before being pushed aside to make room for new ones. The evergreen leaves are usually elliptical or egg-shaped, and are borne on short, stout stalks. They are two to five inches long, and a half to two and a half inches wide. Most of the leaves have entire margins slightly rolled under, wedge-shaped bases, and rounded tips; but occasionally leaves occur with a few teeth beyond the middle, and a sharp pointed tip. They are shining dark green above, whitish and downy beneath, and when the new leaves appear toward the end of winter

Live Oak is often much broader than high with long, spreading limbs, massive trunk and a rounded crown of small evergreen leaves

diameter above its swollen and buttressed base and divided a few feet from the ground into two or more large spreading limbs fifty to seventy feet in length. Though seldom attaining more than sixty feet in height, the width of branch spread is sometimes as much as three times greater. It reaches its best development and largest size on rich hummocks and ridges a few feet above sea level from the Atlantic to the east Gulf coast. In sandy barren soil near the seacoast and on the shores of salt water bays it attains the proportions of a shrub sometimes bearing acorns when only a foot high. Westward from the coast of Texas it often forms the principal part of the shrubby growth on low, moist soil.

The name live oak has been given this tree because it retains its leaves throughout the year. They re-

those of the previous season turn brown and drop off. A thick, and a thin-leaved form is recognized, although the thin-leaved form is the most widely distributed, and includes nearly all the large live oak trees. The leaves of this form are only slightly curled on the margins, while those of the thick-leaved form are conspicuously curled on the edges.

Flowers appear in March or April, the yellow pollen-bearing ones in hairy catkins two or three inches in length; the acorn-producing ones in spikes on slender, hairy stems.

Acorns of the live oak are egg-shaped, shiny, dark, chestnut-brown, about an inch long and one-third of an inch thick. They are enclosed for about one-fourth of their length in a top-shaped, light reddish brown cup, whose inner surface is matted with fine hairs.

Three to five, occasionally one or two, acorns grow on the stout, downy, light brown stalks which are one to five inches long. Because of their sweet meat, live oak acorns were gathered and eaten by the Indians. Today they afford valuable food for hogs.

Bark on the trunk and large limbs is dark brown tinged with red, and is from one-half to an inch thick. It is slightly furrowed, breaking at the surface into small tight scales. The slender rigid branchlets are light gray or brown, and are downy through the first winter, but become darker and smooth the following season.

The wood is light brown or yellow with thin nearly white sapwood, and is hard, strong and tough. It is close-grained and very heavy, a cubic foot weighing nearly sixty

O. G. Babcock

Flowers appear in March or April after the new leaves which are shiny above and downy beneath with edges turned under

J. R. Dilworth

The shiny, dark brown, egg-shaped acorns are held by light reddish brown scaly cups on long stalks

pounds. It takes a fine polish, but is difficult to work. Before 1860 when all ships were made of wood, live oak was used extensively in shipbuilding. Especially important was it for ships' "knees." These were cut from the portion where the junction of large roots with the base of the trunk forms a natural "knee," so that the interwoven grain makes it far stronger than a similar piece of wood carved from a straight timber. Live oak "knees" are occasionally used in shipbuilding today. Except for fuel its present uses are few and limited. Occasional mention is made of live oak for wall panels, parquet flooring, and as axles for heavy wagons.

Because it is readily transplanted when small, and grows rapidly, and because its gnarled, spreading, picturesque branches give shade, the live oak has long been popular as a shade and ornamental tree in the South. Today there are many large, old specimens and impressive avenues of these sturdy trees. In the more southerly part of its range, the limbs are draped with thick veils of gray Spanish moss, giving it a weird picturesque appearance.

Live oak bears the distinction of being the first North American tree to be conserved for future use in a forest preserve. The value of its wood for shipbuilding was brought to the attention of Congress because of the need for ships of war to protect American commerce against pirates, and three hundred and fifty acres of live oak timberland was purchased in 1799. By 1845 the Government had obtained over a quarter of a million acres of live oak land in five southern states. With the passing of wooden ships most of this land was turned over to the General Land Office and opened for settlement.

Orlando, Florida, Chamber of Commerce

Bark on mature trunks and large limbs is dark brown and furrowed into small tight scales

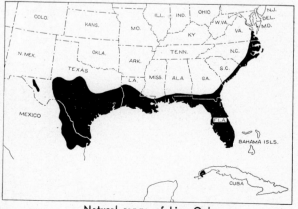

Natural range of Live Oak

WHITE OAK

Quercus alba, Linnaeus

CHIEF of all the oaks and outstanding among trees is the white oak, *Quercus alba*. *Quercus* is the Latin name for oak, while *alba* possibly refers to the light colored bark. It is easily recognized and is a favorite throughout most of the eastern half of the country from central Maine to northern Florida, and west through southern Ontario and the southern Peninsula of Michigan, through southern Wisconsin and Minnesota, most of Iowa, eastern Nebraska, Kansas, Oklahoma and along the Brazos River to southern Texas, excluding only a narrow coastal region along the Gulf. Preferring rich well drained soil, it attains its greatest size in the coves and valleys of the western slopes of the Allegheny Mountains and in the bottomlands of the lower Ohio Basin. There it attains a height of 150 feet and occasionally six or eight feet in diameter, but is more commonly sixty to eighty feet high. Individuals have been known to be 800 years old.

While trees grown in the deep woods are tall and narrow crowned, as compared with the broad round heads of open grown trees, the pale gray bark with shallow fissures and scaly ridges is usually characteristic. The bark on old trees may be two inches thick. The leaves are alternate, from five to nine inches long, narrowed toward the stem, somewhat oblong in outline but usually with the broader end forward, and with seven to nine smooth-margined finger-like lobes. They turn russet in the fall and hang on through much of the winter. The buds are round and smooth, clustered at the tips of the twigs

The wide-spreading branches of the open grown White Oak are attractive in winter as well as in summer. They form a massive low crown which becomes increasingly broad with age

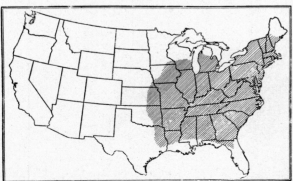

Natural range of White Oak in the United States

so as to give the effect of a clenched fist. In cross section a twig reveals a five pointed star-like pith.

In May, when the new rose colored leaves are scarcely one-third grown the fringed catkins of the staminate flowers and tiny close fitting clusters of pistillate flowers appear. The acorns mature during the early autumn of the same season. Accordingly, white oak carries no acorns during the winter. The shiny, brown nut is three-fourths of an inch to an inch long and set about one-fourth its length in a shallow cup which is attached directly to the twig or by a very short stem. Squirrels, other mammals and birds enjoy the sweet flavored nut so that comparatively few sprout into seedlings. The early colonists learned from the Indians ways of boiling and preparing them for food.

The light brown wood weighs about forty-eight pounds to the cubic foot when air dry, which is nearly twice the weight of white pine. Its uniform strength, narrow growth rings, durability and attractive color encourage a wide variety of uses, ranging from fine cabinet work and interior trim to flooring, railroad ties, piling, barrels, veneers, bridges, ships and building construction. Originally desired for its strength and durability, its beauty for furniture, floors and interior trim is now of first importance. Quarter-sawed oak reveals large numbers of "mirrors," which are the split medullary or pith rays. These form a pattern prized for many purposes. Tannic acid in the wood protects it from some fungi and insects, but results in unsightly discoloring when iron nails are used on exposed surfaces.

Lumber statistics do not distinguish the cut of white oak from that of the other commercial oaks, but fully half of the 2,163,000,000 board feet of oak reported cut during 1941 was white oak. Much of this came from Tennessee, Louisiana, Arkansas, Virginia, Mississippi and West Virginia. Reports for the past twenty years show marked decreases in annual production of oak. Recent estimates of the United States Forest Service indicate a present stand of merchantable oak sawtimber totaling 83,700,000,000 board feet, together with over 230,000,000 cords of wood on second growth areas. More than half of this is growing in the southeastern states and a quarter in the central states.

White oak has few natural enemies and the worst of them is fire. The oak timber worm or pin worm is destructive to timber values, a twig pruner causes owners of shade trees to be alarmed but is seldom fatal, and the gypsy moth may prove serious within its limited range. Several fungi cause heart rot. Fire and gypsy moth may be controlled and injuries caused by these enemies are often responsible for other difficulties.

Little attention has been given to propagating white oak either for ornamental or forest purposes. This may be due to its slow growth and the strong tap root which makes transplanting difficult, but white oak is splendidly adapted for city streets, home lawns and parks. The broadly spreading branches form a round top more than eighty feet high and fully as broad. For best development the young trees should be planted about forty feet apart, and eventually thinned to about eighty feet to give room for maximum crown development.

The acorn is the principal means by which the white oak tree reproduces itself, but under favorable conditions it will sprout from the stump. Seedlings may be grown in nurseries and transplanted, or the acorn may be planted where the tree is desired.

Pollen-bearing staminate blossoms appear in May when the first leaves unfurl. Inconspicuous pistillate blossoms from which the acorns develop are at the base of the new leaves

Light ash-gray bark with scaly plates and shallow fissures help distinguish the older white oak trees

Glossy leaves with five to nine rounded lobes and sweet-meated acorns whose shallow cup covers a fourth of the nut are characteristic

CALIFORNIA WHITE OAK

Quercus lobata, Née

THE BROAD crowned, graceful, California white oak with its massive trunk and drooping sprays of branches is peculiar to the state whose name it bears. It is the largest of fourteen oak species, only nine of which attain tree stature, native to California. It is found in low valleys and on low rolling plateaus between the Sierra Nevada and the Pacific from the Trinity River in the north to Tejon Pass in the south.

Trees forty to seventy-five feet tall are common, while a few individuals reach 100 feet or more. The trunks are short and massive with diameters ranging from two feet to occasionally ten feet. With maturity the broad crown consists of many high arching branches extending into long slender pendulous branchlets which often touch the ground.

Found most abundantly on fairly rich soil, this tree favors hot, moist valleys and avoids those which face the ocean. It grows from a little above sea level to 2,700 feet in its northern range and up to 4,500 feet above sea level in its southern range. In the foothills above the valleys it is seldom over thirty feet tall with a trunk about one foot in diameter.

The deep bayed, leathery, deciduous leaves have seven to eleven obliquely rounded lobes. They vary in size and form on the same tree, but are usually two and a half to four inches long. A covering of fine hairs on both surfaces helps the leaves resist the drying influence of days of sun and hot wind. The wedge-shaped base leads to a stout, hairy stem or petiole a quarter to half an inch long.

Heavy crops of bright chestnut-brown acorns about one and a quarter to two and a half inches long are usually produced dur-

California White Oak raises a great dome of foliage above the valley or low plateau

With the loss of leaves in winter, long pendulous branches, full of grace, are revealed

Forest Service

148

ing alternate years. They are slender and quite pointed, with a pale woolly or even warty cup which covers about one-third of the nut. Borne singly or in pairs, they have little or no stem and mature at the end of one season. Having a sweet kernel, the acorns were formerly eaten by native Indians, but are now only fed to hogs.

The staminate flowers are apparent in early spring as yellow, hairy strings two to three inches long. The less conspicuous acorn bearing pistillate flowers are borne singly, or occasionally with a few others on elongated spikes. Both sexes grow on different parts of the same tree.

The light brown to ashen gray bark of the main trunk is checked deeply to form rough irregular cubes one to two inches across. It is one to four and a half inches thick.

The wood is dull brown in color, hard, brittle and close grained. Lighter than white oak, a cubic foot weighs thirty-nine to forty pounds when air dry. It is perhaps the least valuable of the Pacific Coast hardwoods, but early settlers used logs for their cabins. In spite of the frequent cross grain, they succeeded in riving shakes and splitting out posts and rails from the trunks. Its chief value is for fuel. Large trees sometimes produce fifty to ninety cords of stove wood, but the soft texture early gave it the name "mush" oak.

Frequently referred to as valley oak, the more inclusive name California white oak is now accepted. *Quercus* —the Latin name of the oak family is derived from the ancient Celtic *quer* or fine and *cuez* for tree. This has been interpreted as "beautiful tree." The rounded lobes of the leaves are probably referred to in *lobata*. Louis Née, an eighteenth century botanist of French birth, but a Spaniard by adoption is credited with earliest description of the tree. While rounding the world with a Spaniard named Malaspina from 1789 to 1794, he made botanical collections and observations in Mexico and the Pacific Coast.

Between ages of 125 and 300 years when the tree has attained a height of fifty to 100 feet, with a form resembling American elm, long pendulous branches develop to produce a weeping stage. Its amazing vigor is shown occasionally when old trees whose branches have been lost by storm or disease develop a new crown of erect, relatively straight branches.

This white oak grows with reasonable rapidity. One tree is credited with having attained a diameter of twenty-one inches in fifty-seven years, and it may live for 400 or more years.

In spite of the heavy biennial crops of acorns, reproduction is usually poor. This may be due to the dense carpet of grass beneath some trees, or the fact that it sometimes grows in the midst of a valley long used as a wheat field. The seed also are sought by hogs, mule deer, and other wildlife. Germination can usually be assured if the acorns are well covered with fresh litter or soil.

The tree's tendency to select the best agricultural soils has resulted in the loss of many of the fine old specimen trees. It has few enemies, however, and resists long periods of excessively dry weather. Although seldom successfully cultivated outside of California it deserves to be planted to an increasing extent along the highways throughout the Sacramento and San Joaquin valleys, as well as for shade in the cities and towns. To allow for the wide spread of branches in maturity, trees should be planted at least eighty to 100 feet apart.

Woodbridge Metcalf

Leathery leaves with seven to eleven rounded lobes partly conceal the slender pointed acorns

The deeply divided bark may be ashen gray to light brown

Natural range of California White Oak

OREGON WHITE OAK

Quercus garryana, Douglas

Photographs by George C. Stephenson

velopment with a height of seventy-five to ninety feet and diameters of four or five feet. On mountain sides it is smaller, and southward in the Siskiyou Mountains, and in exposed situations along the coast, it is considerably reduced in size.

From the Santa Cruz Mountains of California, its range extends northward through western California, western Oregon, and western Washington to the shores of Puget Sound whence it follows the islands to Vancouver Island. On Vancouver it is found on the southeastern tip, and also in two small isolated stands, the farthest of which is nearly the most northern outpost of oak on this continent, being slightly outdistanced by bur oak in the southern part of Manitoba. There is also a small stand of Oregon white oak in southwestern British Columbia.

Often a gnarled, picturesque tree, it grows in a variety of soils from deep moist humus to dry, gravelly and rocky sites in the zone between grassland and forest, or on southwest slopes

OREGON white oak, or Garry oak, as it is also known, was named by the botanical explorer Robert Douglas in honor of Nicholas Garry, secretary of the Hudson Bay Company, because of the aid rendered by the latter to botanists studying the flora of the Northwest. It is a tree of dark green foliage and rugged appearance, which sometimes attains massive proportions.

In lowlands from the Willamette Valley of Oregon northward to Puget Sound this oak reaches its best de-

Upper: Reaching heights of sixty to one hundred feet, Oregon white oak develops a broadly rounded crown of dark shiny foliage

Right: Old trees are gnarled, and when growing in the open the trunk is short, and the lower branches drooping

that are excessively hot and dry in summer. It is rarely found above three thousand feet elevation. Occurring occasionally in pure stands, it is generally in mixture with Douglas fir, Kellogg oak, ponderosa pine, Oregon ash and madrona. In the bottomlands where young stands of Douglas fir crowd close about its base, it is usually tall and without lower limbs.

The light gray-brown bark is broken by shallow narrow grooves, to form square scaly plates. The young twigs are hairy, later becoming smooth and bright reddish brown, while red fuzz covers the long pointed buds. Resembling those of *Q. alba*, the leaves grow alternately, four to six inches long, and two to five inches wide, with seven to nine large rounded lobes, whose thickened margins curl under. Smooth, shiny, and dark green above, they are paler and hairy with conspicuous veins beneath. To cope with summer drought conditions, the upper surface is tough and leathery, and the under surface hairy to retain moisture.

The staminate flowers are pendent catkins that occur in clusters, and the pistillate ones are erect blooms occurring solitary or in pairs. Oregon white oak is a prolific seeder about every other year, but the rate

Bark is light grayish brown, and on old trunks is cracked and broken into fairly even plates and ridges

of germination of acorns is usually very low and therefore seedling trees are scarce. Acorns are one to one and a half inches long and about half as broad. The shallow cups are hairy, covered with thin, loose, pointed scales, and usually stemless.

This oak is the only timber oak in the coast country of the Northwest. Pale yellowish brown in color, the wood is hard, fine-grained, tough, strong and durable. It is used in furniture, ship construction, buildings, agricultural implements, vehicles, barrels, cabinet-work, fuel and interior finish. Insulator pins for electric lines, saddle trees, stirrups, and baskets are some of its more unusual uses. In 1939, the sawmill output of Oregon white oak for the two northwestern states was only 94,000 board feet.

A long-lived, slow-growing tree, it attains two hundred and fifty or three hundred and fifty years. In the northern part of its range, winters are exceedingly wet and favorable, but its growth and reproduction are limited by the excessive drought of summers.

Enemies are a leaf mold and a root rot but neither is serious. A twig girdler causes the loss of many small branches; and about once in seven years an epidemic of leaf galls produced by a small wasp reduces the vitality of many trees. The parasite mistletoe is proving an enemy of increasing destructiveness.

The approximate stand of Oregon white oak of sawtimber size is 88,300,000,000 board feet in Oregon and Washington, while the annual cut for all purposes is about 246,000 board feet.

Leaves, growing alternately along the twigs, are shiny above and hairy beneath, while the acorns, which ripen in one season, are sweet and eaten by wildlife

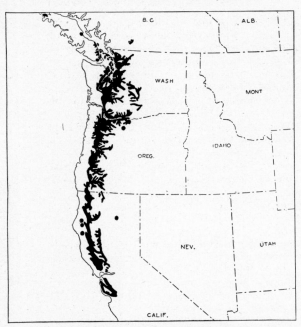

Natural range of Oregon White Oak

BUR OAK

Quercus macrocarpa, Michaux

George J. Baetzhold.

branches. In contrast to these splendid dimensions it may, on unfavorable sites live for years in thickets without attaining heights of more than six to eight feet. Under such conditions it is frequently referred to as "scrub oak."

The rounded, lobed leaves, wedge-shaped at the base, are the largest of all the oak leaves, being six to twelve inches long and three to six inches broad at the upper half. Two unusually deep wide bays or sinuses dip in near the middle of the leaf toward the stout pale midrib, which is occasionally hairy on the upper side. The five to seven rounded lobes are irregular, and the terminal one, occupying more than a third of the entire leaf has irregularly crenate margins. Crowded to the ends of the twigs are thick firm leaves, lustrous dark green above but silvery green and downy below. They turn dull yellow in the autumn, and do not hang on into the winter as do those of many other oaks.

B UR OAK is one of the largest, and next to the white oak, the most majestic of American oaks. It is characteristic of the Middle West but grows with surprising adaptability over much of the eastern half of the United States from the Turtle Mountains and Black Hills of the Dakotas, south to the Nueces River, of central Texas, east through Tennessee and West Virginia into Maryland and Delaware to the Atlantic, and north into southern Manitoba, Nova Scotia, and New Brunswick. It attains greatest size and highest commercial importance in the Wabash River Basin, of Indiana and Illinois. Typical of the "oak openings" of the Lake States, it is the most common oak of Kansas and the Prairie States.

Open grown trees develop an irregular broadly rounded crown with stiff, gnarled branches and stout, frequently crooked, corky-winged branchlets. Ordinarily seldom over eighty feet high or three feet in diameter, trees 170 to 180 feet high and six or seven feet in diameter have been reported. Under forest conditions it develops a tall, massive, clear trunk which supports a moderately broad, open crown of stout

George J. Baetzhold

With its characteristic irregular broadly rounded crown and gnarled branches, the Bur Oak is one of the largest and most majestic of the American oaks. It never grows in dense stands, but individually or in groups

In May or June the blossoms of both sexes appear as the wooly leaves unfold. The staminate or male blossoms comprise slender, yellow-green, hairy catkins from four to six inches long. On the same tree, and frequently on the same branches will be found the reddish, hairy, pistillate flowers growing without a stalk, or so close to the twig as to have only a very short one.

Being of the white oak group, the fertilized pistillate flowers develop by autumn of the first year into clumsy, short stalked, broadly egg-shaped acorns, from three-fourths of an inch to two inches long, and more than half surrounded by a deep scaly cup. This cup with its fringe of coarse elongated scales is responsible for the common names, bur oak, and mossy cup oak. Prolific crops of highly fertile seed are borne at frequent intervals. Their vitality is retained for six months to a year, with the result that seedlings are easily produced during the following spring on moist fertile soil. A strong tap root makes transplanting the seedlings difficult unless they are root pruned at an early age.

The scientific name *macrocarpa*, meaning large fruited, refers to the large nut whose sweet, white kernel is edible. The acorns of southern grown trees are usually larger than those of the north. *Quercus* is the Latin name for all the oaks, and is said to have been derived from the Celtic *quer*, meaning fine, and *cuez* meaning tree. The scientific name describing a fine tree with a large fruit is peculiarly apt in the case of bur oak.

The flaky, grayish to reddish brown bark of old trees is one or two inches thick, cut by deep fissures into firm, more or less vertical ridges. Resembling that of white oak, the bark is firmer and the ridges are usually more prominent. First year branchlets are covered with greenish gray bark, turning to a light orange color, and covered for a short time with fine hairs. Later these twigs become dark brown and develop corky ridges or wings often an inch to an inch and a half wide. As the limbs mature, sections of bark are cast off to litter the ground below.

The light brown, close grained, hard, tough heartwood with conspicuous medullary rays so resembles that of white oak that it is frequently classed with that species on the market. Under air dry conditions a cubic foot weighs about forty-five pounds, which is only two or three pounds lighter than the wood of white oak. No figures are available to show this country's existing stand of bur oak as distinguished from white oak. It is used for furniture, interior finishes, vehicles, moldings, and veneers. Because of its durability in contact with the soil it is frequently used for railroad ties and structural material.

Bur oak never grows in dense stands, but as individuals or in groups associated with other bottomland trees such as pin oak, white oak, basswood, willow, cottonwood, black walnut, the hickories, elms, and soft maples. It grows well on rich, moist bottomlands and on lower slopes, preferring areas where water is available but not excessive.

Of relatively slow growth, it reaches great ages and is not considered mature before 200 to 300 years.

Because of the damp sites on which it grows, fire damage is rare, while it is seldom injured by either insects or fungous diseases.

The sturdy unsymmetrical beauty of bur oak, its remarkable ability to withstand damage from city smoke as well as its freedom from insect and fungous injuries, its adaptability to soils and climates, and the comparative ease with which it may be raised and transplanted recommend it for use on streets and lawns.

George J. Baetzhold.

The rounded, lobed leaves of the Bur Oak, wedge-shaped at the base, are the largest of all the oak leaves, being from six to twelve inches long and three to six inches broad at the upper half. The acorns are clumsy, short-stalked, and broadly egg-shaped

The flaky, grayish to reddish brown bark of the older trees is from one to two inches thick, cut by deep fissures into firm, more or less vertical ridges. Resembling that of the White Oak, the bark of the Bur Oak is firmer and the ridges are usually more prominent

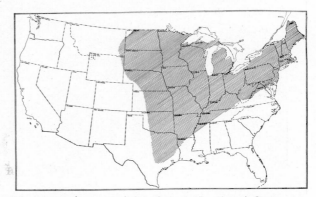

Natural range of Bur Oak in the United States

CHESTNUT OAK

Quercus montana, **Willdenow**

The trunk of Chestnut Oak may be tall and straight, or divided into large ascending limbs, with spreading branches that form a broad open head

CHESTNUT OAK is found from southern Maine westward through Ohio and southern Indiana and southward through Kentucky and Tennessee to northeastern Mississippi and Georgia. It is most abundant on the Appalachian hills from southern New York to Georgia and Alabama, and reaches its largest size on the lower slopes of the Carolinas and Tennessee. An exceptionally large specimen is the "Washington Oak" on the east bank of the Hudson River near Fishkill, New York, under which Washington used to mount his horse when he went from headquarters on the west bank of the Hudson to the army encamped at Fishkill. This tree is seven feet in diameter and its estimated age is eight hundred to a thousand years.

Although chestnut oak is generally associated with dry soil and sandy, rocky ridges, it frequently grows on rich well-drained soil close to the banks of streams. It is usually sixty to seventy feet tall with a trunk two to three feet in diameter, but sometimes reaches a hundred feet in height with a trunk six to seven feet in diameter. On rocky ridges and dry mountain slopes chestnut oak has a scrubby form about twenty or thirty feet tall with a trunk eight to twelve inches in diameter. The trunk usually divides into several large limbs not far from the ground to give the tree an open irregular spreading head.

Sometimes this tree is called rock oak or mountain oak because it grows on high, rocky slopes, but its more common name, chestnut oak, refers to its leaves which are similar to those of the chestnut except that they are scalloped or wavy on the edge instead of sharp-toothed. It belongs to the white oak group in the family *Fagaceae,* which includes all the oaks, the beech, and the chestnut.

The leaves, five to nine inches long and one and a half to four inches wide, are narrowly oval in outline with coarsely scalloped margins, wedge-shaped or rounded bases, and tapering tips. They are shiny yellow-green above, pale green and hairy below, and turn dull yellow or yellow-brown in autumn. They have short stems one half to one inch long, stout yellow midribs, and ten to sixteen pairs of conspicuous straight primary veins.

The bright rich-brown acorns of the chestnut oak are borne singly or in pairs on short stout stems. They are one to one and a half inches long and five-eighths to one inch thick. The

acorns are inclosed to about half their length by thin, rough, scaly cups. The white, sweetish kernels are eagerly eaten by squirrels. Large acorn crops occur irregularly at infrequent intervals, and prefer deep humus for germination.

The stout twigs, green with a purple or bronze cast when they first appear, are light orange or reddish brown the first winter and turn dark gray or brown the second year. The smaller branches have thin, smooth, purplish brown bark. The trunk and large limbs have thick nearly black bark, rich in tannin, and it is divided into broad scaly ridges.

The wood is hard, strong, tough, and close-grained. A cubic foot when dry weighs nearly forty-seven pounds. It is a hardy, windfirm tree, and although its wood is not as valuable as that of white oak, it is durable in contact with the soil, and is useful for ties, fencing material, mining props, and other rough products.

Chestnut oak requires much light, especially as it grows older. Its root system is adaptable; where the soils are deep the tap root is long; in rocky or shallow soils the lateral roots are strongly developed. Repeated fires reduce sprouting vitality, but the thick bark is a protection against fire.

Leaves somewhat resemble those of chestnut and the acorns which mature in the first season are useful as food for wildlife

L. W. Brownell

Bark on mature trunks is deeply fissured into long, continuous, firm ridges

Pollen-bearing flowers, shown here, appear in May or June with the acorn-producing ones which are small, and grow from the base of leaf-stems

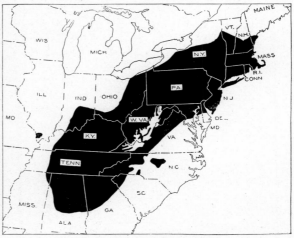

Natural range of Chestnut Oak

AMERICAN ELM

Ulmus americana, Linnaeus

THE dignified and courtly American elm is characteristic of the northeastern landscape and has been planted over most of the United States. Typically vase-shaped, it sometimes develops heavy far-reaching limbs after the manner of the oaks.

Elm belongs to the family "*Urticaceae*"—the family of the nettle. The genus *Ulmus*, which is the ancient Latin name for elm, has sixteen species distributed in the north temperate countries of the world. Six elms are native to eastern North America, with American elm the largest and most important. None are native west of the Rocky Mountains, but they grow successfully in all western states.

American elm is known as white elm, and sometimes as water or soft elm. It grows naturally in river bottoms and on low fertile hills, from southern Newfoundland to central

In summer the Elm combines grace and dignity with courtliness, while in winter it reveals the strength of its limbs and branches above a sturdy trunk

Florida, and west beyond the northern shores of Lake Superior to the Turtle Mountains of North Dakota, thence up the water courses to the base of the northern Rockies. Its western limits are confined to stream banks in western Nebraska, central Kansas and Oklahoma, through central Texas to the Gulf of Mexico.

The main trunk of open grown trees divides at ten or twenty feet to form a broad crown, while in the forest trunk lengths of thirty to sixty feet are attained. Trees two to four feet in diameter and eighty to one hundred feet high are common, but elms eight to eleven feet in diameter and 120 to 140 feet high have been known.

Field Museum

The lopsided, double-toothed, alternately placed, sharp pointed leaves are two to five inches long and one to three inches wide. Evenly spaced, parallel veins extend from the midrib to the sawtooth edges. The upper surface is slightly rough while the under surface is softly hairy. In early autumn the leaves turn golden yellow, then sere and brown and quickly leave the tree bare.

At the base of each short petiole or leaf stem is a blunt-pointed, smooth, slightly flattened bud, which appears to be at one side of a semi-circular leaf scar after the leaves drop. Before the leaves are fully open, in May or June, the seeds ripen. They are flat, entirely surrounded by a broad, slightly hairy, papery wing, which rarely exceeds three-quarters of an inch in diameter. If planted immediately, most of the seed will germinate in a few days, but some may lay dormant until spring. Each seed develops from an inconspicuous light green perfect blossom with red stamens. They hang in clusters and are produced before the leaves, when the tree appears as if covered with a purple glow.

The wood is light brown, heavy, hard, tough, so cross-grained as to be difficult to split, and weighs thirty-three to thirty-five pounds to the cubic foot when air dry. It has a broad area of lighter colored sapwood. Because of its toughness it is used for the hubs of wheels and for hoops and staves in slack cooperage, for shipbuilding, furniture, flooring, sporting goods, boxes and crates. Relatively easy to season, it works fairly well, and while it can be scoured to a clean whiteness, does not polish easily. The Iroquois Indians of western New York used the bark for canoes and twisted it into ropes.

In 1941 the total cut of all elm lumber in the United States was 129,870,000 board feet as compared with 175,833,000 board feet in 1929. Nearly one-half of the 1936 cut was produced in Wisconsin and Michigan.

American elm grows from seed, sprouts readily from the stump and from root ends. Horticultural types may be reproduced by cuttings, buds and grafts. Preferring rich, deep, well drained loam, it will grow in almost any soil. The vigorous, shallow, fibrous root system permits comparatively easy transplanting until the trees reach a large size.

Of its leaf pests, the elm leaf beetle is chief. By eating the leaves this beetle and its larvae occasionally kill

One side of each leaf is larger than the other, and parallel veins go directly from the midrib to the sawtooth edge

Bunches of light green blossoms appear from last year's buds ahead of the new leaves

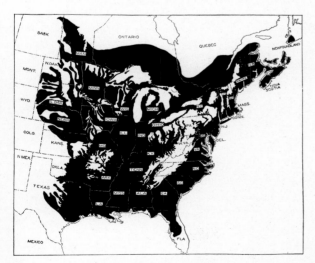

The dark, ashy gray bark of the main trunk is broken into interlacing flaky ridges

Field Museum

Natural range of American Elm

trees, but like other insect pests it can be controlled.

Much more to be feared is the Dutch elm disease, for which no cure has been discovered. In spite of enemies, however, American elm is a popular shade tree and its ability to reproduce under forest conditions encourages its use in hardwood forest management.

SLIPPERY ELM

Ulmus fulva, **Michaux**

SLIPPERY ELM has neither the graceful symmetry nor the large size of the more commonly known American elm. It is usually a tree of medium size averaging from forty to sixty feet in height with a comparatively short trunk one to two feet in diameter. Occasionally trees reach seventy or eighty feet in height and on especially favorable sites specimens 135 feet high with trunk diameters up to four feet have been found. The large, stout, spreading limbs branch haphazardly from the trunk, and form a broad, open, flat-topped crown that is often irregular in outline.

George J. Baetzhold

The flat, broadly-winged seeds
occur in clusters along the twigs

Pennsylvania Dept. of Forests and Waters

Usually slender with short trunk, Slippery Elm has stout,
spreading branches that form a broad, open crown

Of the six species of elm native to eastern North America, slippery elm is second to American elm in abundance, and has a natural range almost as extensive as the latter. It grows from Maine and the lower St. Lawrence valley in Canada, westward across southern Ontario to eastern South Dakota and southward to western Florida and eastern Texas.

Slippery elm prefers rich, moist, alluvial, well-drained soils, and is found most frequently along stream banks and on low, fertile, wooded slopes. Sometimes it grows on rocky ridges or limestone outcrops, but in such sites it makes poor growth. The region of greatest abundance and greatest size is probably in the Great Lakes states.

Bark on old trunks of slippery elm is frequently an inch thick, deeply furrowed into large, loose plates, and is ashy gray to dark, reddish brown in color. The inner bark is whitish and strongly mucilaginous. It is the latter quality which gives the tree its common name. Also aromatic, the inner bark is sometimes chewed to allay thirst; and because it has a soothing effect, it is used medicinally, for which purpose many trees are stripped of their bark and killed. In the North the tree is sometimes called moose elm because

F. W. Besley

The alternate, wrinkled, thick leaves are coated on the upper surface with rough hairs

The perfect, short-stemmed flowers appear in March or April before the leaves

moose eat both twigs and bark. Other common names are red elm, red-wooded elm, rock elm and Indian elm.

Hairy and roughened by pores and leaf scars, the twigs are at first pale gray or grayish brown, later becoming darker. They are stout, tending to turn upward, and have no buds at the tip.

The tawny hairs of winter buds offer a means of identifying slippery elm from the American elm, whose winter buds are smooth and account for the generic name *fulva*. Leaf buds are about a quarter inch long, located toward the outer ends, while the stouter, thicker flower buds are further back along the twig. Flowers appear in April or early May before the leaves and are in crowded clusters on short stalks.

Another characteristic of slippery elm is the extreme roughness of the upper surface of its leaves. Growing alternately along the twigs, these leaves are covered with stiff hairs above, and are rough to the touch when rubbed in any direction. Firm, wrinkled and dark green above, paler beneath and coated with soft hairs, especially on the midrib, the leaves of slippery elm measure four to seven inches in length and two to three inches in width, and are doubly toothed on the margins, pointed at the tip, and rounded and uneven at the base.

Wood of slippery elm is hard, strong, compact, and durable in contact with the soil. A cubic foot weighs forty-three pounds when dry. Heartwood is reddish brown and the sapwood paler. Though slippery elm is not an important timber tree, its wood is used for furniture, wheel-hubs, fence posts, railroad ties, sills, ship-building and agricultural implements.

Like other elms of this continent it is susceptible to Dutch elm disease and *phloem necrosis*.

The deeply furrowed bark has an under layer that is ruddy-brown and an inner layer that is mucilaginous and nearly white

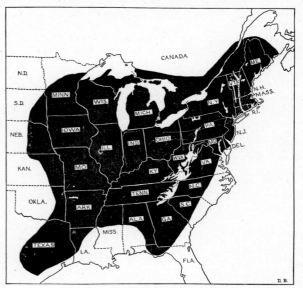

Natural range of Slippery Elm

HACKBERRY

Celtis occidentalis, (Linnaeus)

THE RAGGED and often unshapely hackberry of the open grows from Atlantic to Pacific and barely misses reaching into every state. The principal gaps are on the west coast and through the higher elevations of the Rocky Mountains. Best growth is confined to the rich bottoms of the lower Mississippi Valley, where forest trees attain heights of 130 feet and diameters approximating two to three feet. In such cases the trunk is smooth and shapely. Elsewhere the trees are frequently so isolated and so difficult

Inconspicuous pale greenish flowers of both sexes appear with the young leaves in April or May on the new growth. The staminate flowers grow in clusters at the bases of the new shoots, while the pistillate flowers grow singly or in pairs from the axils of the upper leaves. Both flowers occur on the same tree.

The dark purple, cherry-like fruits hang suspended on slender stems and ripen in September and October. They remain on the tree throughout the winter, and the sweet orange flesh provides food for various birds. Seed are thus carried miles away from the parent tree, which accounts for its wide and scattered range.

On the trunk and larger limbs the inch to inch and a half thick, light brown to silvery gray bark is broken into discontinuous ridges. Frequently the bark is roughened by irregular wart-like galls which may occur as ridges. On young trees and secondary branches

Devereux Butcher

Open grown Hackberry trees branch low and develop ragged, irregularly oval crowns of dense foliage

D. E. Ahlers

"Witches brooms" often disfigure the slender branches, the tendency of which is to be horizontal to the main trunk

of recognition as to be called the "unknown tree." Early French settlers even translated the term into *bois inconnce.*

Belonging to the *Urticaceae,* or nettle family, it is related to the elm as well as to the mulberry and fig. In fact, it is so superficially similar in appearance and size to the American elm that it is sometimes mistaken for one.

The simple, alternate, coarsely toothed, light green leaves are two and a half to four inches long, with long narrow points. Three conspicuous ribs branch from the lop-sided base. The upper surface is smooth or roughish while below it is smooth and pale. Hackberry leaves are subject to attack by numerous insects including the spiny elm caterpillar. They are seldom, however, the subject of disastrous defoliation.

it is smoother. It is rich in tannin and exudes a gum similar to that found on cherry trees. The numerous, slender branches are generally horizontal, and when grown in the open divide a few feet from the ground.

Thick clusters of twigs resembling mistletoe occur on many trees. These are caused by a fungus and are known as "witches brooms."

The clear, light yellow wood is soft and comparatively heavy — weighing about forty-five pounds to the square foot when air dry. The annual rings are marked by several rows of large open pores. It takes a good polish, but is not durable in contact with the soil, and is frequently badly riddled by wood boring insects. Hackberry is usually sold with lower grades of ash and elm, which it superficially resembles. It is hard, but not strong enough or in sufficient commercial quantities for building construction. Offering considerable resistance to shock, it is used for farm implements as well as for crates, boxes, furniture, and to some extent for carving.

Because of its wide range and remarkable tolerance of soil and moisture conditions, hackberry is often planted for shade and ornament throughout the region from the Mississippi River to the Rocky Mountains, and to some extent in other parts of the country.

Devereux Butcher

Pale greenish flowers of both sexes appear with the unfolding leaves in early spring

U. S. Forest Service

Small, warty galls often add roughness to the light brown to silvery gray bark

Devereux Butcher

Dark purple, cherry-like fruits hang from the base of simple, alternate, long pointed leaves

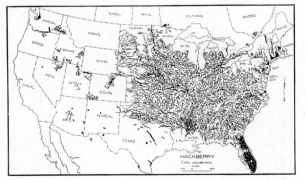

Natural range of Hackberry

OSAGE-ORANGE

Maclura pomifera, (Rafinesque) Schneider
(Synonym: *Toxylon pomiferum* Rafinesque)

ORIGINALLY confined to the rich bottom lands of the Arkansas and Red River Valleys in the region inhabited by the Osage Indians, the hardy, drought resistant qualities of Osage-orange, its adaptability for hedges and wind-breaks, and the varied uses of its wood have so widely encouraged its planting that it is now found growing throughout most of the country. It is usually a small, thorny tree with a crown of irregular, ragged contour. It reaches heights of fifty to sixty feet, with a short, stout, early divided trunk which is seldom more than two to three feet in diameter.

The glossy green leaves are simple and arranged alternately on the twigs. They have smooth margins, are three to six inches long and two to three inches wide, generally egg-shaped but terminating in a slender point. The slender leaf stem or petiole is one and a half to two inches long. When either this or the leaf is broken a thick juice exudes.

The stout, tough branchlets are centered with a thick orange-colored pith, and the pale bark is marked with pale orange lenticels. Short, stout, straight spines arm the twigs. Greenish clusters of tiny staminate and pistillate flowers develop on separate trees in June. By late summer the pistillate blooms are noticeable as yellowish

Above: Gnarled branches ramify from a short trunk to form a low, ragged crown

Left: Osage-orange trees are usually small, but may reach heights of fifty or sixty feet with a low irregular, spreading crown

162

green balls which become three to five inches in diameter before maturing in the autumn. These are compound fruits, like those of other members of the *Moraceae* or mulberry family, of which this and the fig are members. The coarse, fibrous texture and sticky, bitter, milky juice makes these fruits unpalatable for man or beast.

The orange-brown, shreddy outer bark is scarcely an inch thick. It is irregularly divided by deep furrows. The dark orange inner bark and the lemon colored sapwood were used by the Indians to dye their blankets. More recently it has been a source of yellow, tan and Khaki dyes, as well as of tannin in the treatment of leather.

Heartwood as well as sapwood is bright yellow, but the former turns brown on exposure. It weighs about forty-eight pounds to the cubic foot when air dry, is stronger than white oak, but not so stiff, and very hard. Because of its durability in contact with the soil, material of suitable size is used for fence posts, railroad ties, and cabin supports. In the horse and buggy days the hubs and rims of wheels for farm wagons were made of Osage-orange. Pulley-blocks are now made of it, but perhaps its most specialized use is by modern archers, who, like the early Indians, prize the flexible wood of straight clear-grained specimens for the construction of bows. Thus the name *Bois d'Arc*.

Although seldom used for shade or ornamental purposes, Osage-orange was, before the widespread use of wire fences, so generally planted for hedges as to be commonly known as "hedge plant."

Devereux Butcher

Clusters of greenish staminate flowers among the glossy green foliage of early summer. The leaves are three to six inches long with smooth margins and attenuated points

Devereux Butcher

This immature compound fruit will reach three to five inches in diameter. The name Osage-orange recognizes the resemblance of this fruit to an orange and the tree's relation to the Osage Indians

G. J. Baetzhold

The rough shreddy outer bark is dark orange-brown and scarcely an inch thick

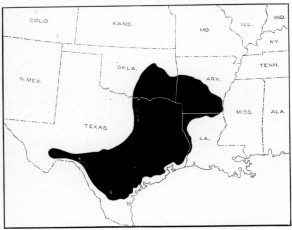

Original range of Osage-orange

CUCUMBER TREE

Magnolia acuminata, **Linnaeus**

OF seven tree-size magnolias native to the United States, the cucumber tree is most hardy. Never common, but usually scattered throughout the forest, its range extends from southern Ontario and central New York through southeastern Illinois and the Appala-

George J. Baetzhold

In the forest the cucumber tree is straight and tall, but in the open, with limbs often sweeping the ground, it develops a conical crown

chian Mountains to southern Alabama and central Mississippi. It also occurs in Arkansas and southern Missouri. Forest-grown trees are fifty, eighty, or rarely one hundred feet tall, with trunks three to four feet in diameter which may be clear of branches for fifty feet or more. The trunks of open-grown trees support long, sweeping, ground-touching limbs, while the relatively slender upper branches ascend to form a broad pyramidal outline. It is the largest of the magnolias.

A rapid grower maturing in eighty to 120 years, it does best in loose, moist, fertile soil on low mountain slopes, along the banks of streams and in narrow protected valleys. It attains maximum size and greatest abundance in narrow valleys at the base of the Smoky Mountains of North Carolina and Tennessee. Its

companions include the tuliptree, white oak, white ash, sugar maple, and the hickories.

The name *Magnolia* commemorates the work of Pierre Magnol, an early eighteenth century professor of botany at Montpelier, France; *acuminata* refers to the sharp points of the simple alternate leaves whose smooth upper surfaces are dark green, with the undersides pale and slightly hairy along the veins. They are seven to ten inches long, four to six inches wide, papery thin, with prominent midribs and smooth wavy margins. In autumn they turn pale yellow before falling and leave narrow elevated scars on the slender, shiny twigs.

Perfect, bell-shaped, green or pale yellow flowers appear from April to June. Their six petals are pointed, two to three and a half inches long, and so similar to the young leaves which precede them as to be frequently overlooked.

The fleshy fruit resembles a two or three inch long cucumber. Hence the name. First green, then pink, and at maturity a purplish red, it has several scar-

In winter the straight trunk, the drooping lower branches and ascending upper ones serve as an aid in identifying an open-grown tree

George J. Baetzhold

let, one-celled seeds which grow on the surface like scattered kernels on a corn cob. When fully ripe the seeds drop away to hang singly by slender white threads. Once on the ground, they may remain in the duff until the second spring before germinating. The many seedlings resulting from a seed crop are so intolerant of shade that few grow large enough to be noticed and even fewer reach maturity.

The firm grayish brown bark is one half to three quarters of an inch thick, broken and covered with small scales. Narrow ridges flow one into the other and are divided by long, vertical grooves.

The yellow-brown heartwood, sometimes streaked with shades of green, has narrow white sapwood similar to that of the tulip-tree. When air dry it weighs twenty-nine pounds to the cubic foot. Without special strength, it is soft, durable, close-grained, porous and works easily. Its uses include crates, boxes, cheap furniture, cabinet work, interior finish and flooring.

The bark gives little protection against light surface fires, and scale insects may attack the branches, but in general this tree has few enemies.

The symmetrical form, the almost tropical foliage and the scarlet late summer fruits encourage its ornamental use in the eastern states and in central Europe. It is readily grown from seed, but the brittle roots demand special care in transplanting. Seedlings are used as root stock on which to graft the several varieties of ornamental magnolia.

The large knobby fruit is first green, then pink, and finally red at maturity when the several scarlet seeds drop

This magnolia is easily identified from others of its kind because it is the only one with rough bark

Walter E. Rogers

The flowers of this magnolia are inconspicuous because they are of the same pale green color as the spring foliage which is present when they bloom

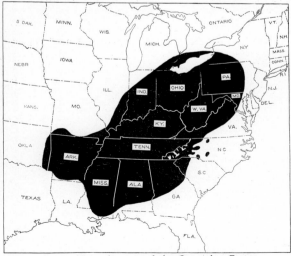

Natural range of the Cucumber Tree

TULIPTREE OR YELLOW POPLAR
Liriodendron tulipifera, Linnaeus

The Tuliptree in summer foliage, and

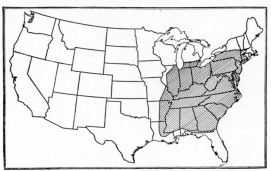

Natural range of the Tuliptree

in winter, when the upright trunk is revealed

ONE of the largest and most valuable trees of the eastern states, the tuliptree, is found in the region bounded by southern New England through New York to southern Wisconsin and south to northeastern Alabama and northern

Florida. It reaches its largest size in the deep rich soil of the lower Ohio Valley and in rich sheltered coves and valleys of the Southern Appalachian Mountains, where occasionally it attains a height of over one hundred and fifty feet and a diameter of eight or ten feet. Occasionally the trunk of forest grown trees will be eighty to one hundred feet tall before the first branch. It is always found in mixture with other trees rather than in pure stands as with some of the pines.

In some regions it is known as white-wood, while the Onondaga Indians of central New York called it the white tree, *Ko-yen-ta-ka-ah-tas*.

It is characterized by the clean-cut, glossy, fiddle-shaped leaves, which the botanist describes as truncate, or ending abruptly, as if cut off. This gives rise to the name "saddle-leaf-tree." The large greenish yellow and orange tulip-like flowers develop into dry cone-like fruits about three inches long which remain on the tree after the leaves drop, and from which the winged seeds fall and twirl to the ground. In winter when the leaves have fallen one sees the dark reddish brown buds which are alternate on the branches. The blunt terminal buds are especially noticeable.

The tuliptree belongs to the magnolia family, which is far removed from any of the poplars and cottonwoods, but because of its soft wood it is frequently called yellowpoplar. *Liriodendron* is from two Greek words describing a tree with lily-like flowers. *Tulipifera* refers to the tulip-like blossoms. It is a tree of ancient origin and with its close relatives is geologically recorded in Europe and Asia as well as in North America, where it once occupied a wider range.

The sawtimber stand of tuliptrees consists of about 9,500,000,000 board feet, of which more than half is in the southeastern states and about one-fourth in the central states. The lumber cut of 1941 was 427,187,000 board feet, of which 67,239,000 board feet came from West Virginia, 66,217,000 board feet from Virginia, 49,035,500 board feet from Georgia and 48,417,000 from Tennessee.

The wood is light yellow to brown with a creamy white margin of sapwood. It is soft, easily worked and takes paint well. When air dry it weighs only about twenty-six pounds to the cubic foot. It is used in many kinds of construction, for interior finish, in the manufacture of boxes, crates, baskets and woodenware, for excelsior, veneer wood, and also as a core upon which to glue veneers of other wood. Small amounts are cut for pulpwood to make into paper. Occasionally planks sixty inches or wider are produced.

The inner bark of the root and trunk is intensely acrid, bitter and has been used as a tonic and stimulant. It is a source of hydrochlorate of tulipiferine, which is an alkaloid possessing the power of stimulating the heart.

Tuliptree is frequently used as a shade tree and for street planting, for which it is well adapted. The size to which it may grow makes it more satisfactory for planting on wide avenues than on a narrow street. Spring transplanting is recommended.

The tree is moderately free from pests, but frequently unsightly brown spots caused by a gall insect cover the leaves. Also they may turn yellow and drop during the summer.

The deeply furrowed bark of a mature tree is sometimes two inches thick. Bark of young trees is thin and smooth

Above: The tulip-like flower growing on a slender branchlet among the early summer leaves. (About half natural size)
Below is a winter twig showing the dark red bud. The leaf scars, which are alternate, are also prominent and characteristic
Lower down to the right are the conical fruits which ripen late in September and October, and stay on the tree through the winter. The cross-section shows the flat winged seed cases attached to a central spike

SASSAFRAS

Sassafras variifolium, (Salisbury) Kuntze

FROM southern Maine to Ontario and south over the Mississippi Valley to east Texas and central Florida, sassafras is known by its flat unsymmetrical crown, or twisted branches which spread almost at right angles from the trunk to support many upward reaching branchlets.

set Indians on Long Island Sound called the wood "sasauaka-pamuch." Efforts to derive *sassafras* from Latin words meaning "rock-breaking," or "salt-breaking" are doubtful. The first refers to the power of the roots to pry rocks apart, and the latter to the manner in which the burning wood snaps and crackles, like salt. *Variifolium* refers to the three forms of yellow-green, aromatic, short stemmed, simple leaves that may grow on a single branch. Some are lance shaped and entire, others are shaped like a mitten with an oblique lobe on one side, while still others have lobes on either side. All are wedge shaped at the base three to six inches long and two to four inches wide. They are slightly hairy when young, becoming smooth, shiny and pale green on the lower surface with net-like veins. In autumn they turn yellow or orange, often tinged with red.

With the unfolding leaves come inconspicuous greenish yellow flowers in two inch clusters or racemes from the inner bud scale axils at the twig ends. The six-pointed staminate flowers grow on different trees from those which bear the pistillate flowers. By September or October these develop into dark blue, berry-like fruits about half an inch long on the enlarged end of a fleshy crimson pedicel.

Devereux Butcher

The broad, sometimes flat topped crown of Sassafras is intensified by the side branches which stand out almost at right angles from the main trunk

Little more than a shrub in the north, it reaches heights of forty to ninety feet and trunk diameters of four to seven feet from Pennsylvania on south. The largest trees are reported on the deeper soils of the Smoky Mountains of North Carolina and Tennessee. It grows moderately rapidly, but slows down after attaining a diameter of two to two and a half feet, and may live for 700 to 1,000 years.

Ancestors of this sassafras inhabited much of the northern hemisphere during early geologic periods, and a species almost identical with *sassafras variifolium* grows in China.

The name *sassafras* appears in explorers' reports as early as 1591 and evidently was in use from New England to Florida. The Narragan-

The red-brown, deeply furrowed bark with flattened ridges about an inch and a half thick appears as if washed with ashen gray. On young trees it is thin, reddish brown and evenly striated or cracked into buff colored blocks. The smooth, green, aromatic twigs are mucilaginous when chewed.

Sassafras wood is tinged with red, with seven or eight rings of light yellow sapwood. The darker shades seldom develop before the trees are fifteen or eighteen inches in diameter. Air dry wood weighs thirty-one to thirty-two pounds to the cubic foot. Without special qualities of strength, it is soft, brittle, coarse grained, and slightly aromatic. Its durability in contact with the soil accounts for its use as fence posts, split rails, sills for country homes, and light boats. The merchantable supply is limited and little is sold.

During early colonial days, the supposed medicinal virtues of the roots and bark made it one of America's chief exports. Sassafras tea has long been a spring tonic to "thin the blood and purify the system." Oil of sassafras is distilled from the bark of the roots to perfume soaps and flavor medicines. An orange dye from the bark once colored homespun woolens. The Choctaw Indians call it "gumbo file." They taught the Louisiana Creoles to make a yellow powder from the leaves for flavoring gumbo soup. It grows readily from seed, sprouts from the roots and can be reproduced from root cuttings. Insects seldom do serious harm, but grass fires injure the base of large trees and often kill young ones.

Inconspicuous, greenish yellow flowers appear with the new spring leaves. These pistillate blooms grow on trees separate from the staminate ones

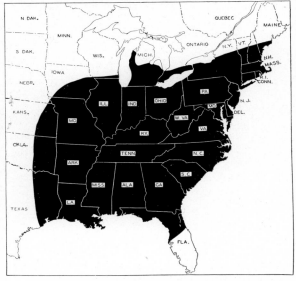

Chas. F. Steiger

The twisted ridges of the red-brown bark often appear as if washed with light gray

A three lobed leaf with partly mature fruits of Sassafras

Devereux Butcher

Natural range of Sassafras

SWEETGUM

Liquidambar styraciflua, Linnaeus

SWEETGUM — commonly called red gum — flourishes from southern Connecticut to Florida and west as far as eastern Texas, Oklahoma, Arkansas and southeastern Missouri, where it prefers rich, moist soil and, while not a swamp tree, grows vigorously on occasionally flooded land. It also grows on high land, but seldom attains as great size as along stream bottoms where it grows in mixture with red maple, elm, ash, cottonwood and several oaks. A closely related variety reappears in the mountains of central and southern Mexico and in the highlands of Guatemala. Sweetgum trees eighty to 120 feet high and eighteen inches to three feet in diameter at breast height are common. Occasionally, however, they attain heights of 150 feet and are five feet in diameter. They are most abundant and attain greatest size in the bottomlands of the lower Mississippi Valley and the southeastern coastal states. In the forest the trunk is straight and clear of side branches for approximately two-thirds of its height, but young open grown trees have a pyramidal crown with a straight central stem like that of a coniferous tree. With maturity, the side branches become heavier and develop a narrow but more irregular crown.

Sweetgum is frequently confused with black gum and the tupelos, but belongs to the witch hazel or *Hammamelidaceae* family. It has three closely related species—one in Mexico, one in central China and a third in parts of Asia Minor where the liquid storax of commerce is secured. The scientific name, *Liquidambar styraciflua*, was given by the Swedish botanist, Carl von Linne, and refers to the yellowish, fragrant, balsamic

Sweetgum becomes a tall symmetrical tree when grown on rich moist bottomland, but will do well on high, well drained soils. The clean trunk, dense glossy green summer foliage, gorgeous autumn coloring and comparative freedom from pests make it a favorite for street and ornamental planting

The slender side branches of the straight central trunk support twigs with corky wings or ridges, from which dry seed balls on long, thread-like stalks, hang through the winter

liquid which exudes from the bark. This resembles the liquid storax of commerce, for which it is frequently substituted. Trees near the northern limit of its range yield little resin, but the flow is abundant in the South.

The glossy, aromatic, star-shaped, five to seven-pointed alternate leaves give rise to the common name, "star leafed" gum. The name "red" gum refers to the color of the wood, but applies also to the brilliant autumn foliage, which compares with that of the maples.

The flowers of both sexes occur separately on the same tree. In the South they appear as early as March, and in the North during April or May, when the leaves are about half grown. The clusters of hairy, green, pollen-producing flowers are two or three inches long, and at the end of the new growth. The seed-producing flowers hang as greenish balls on long, thread-like stalks from the base of the upper leaves. These develop into brown seed balls or burs one to one and one-half inches in diameter and remain swinging on the trees through the winter. Each seed ball consists of a number of closely connected woody, horn-tipped capsules in which are enclosed the seeds. With maturity the capsules split apart permitting the half-inch long, winged seeds to escape.

The slender first year twigs are light orange to reddish brown with prominent lenticels. After the second year corky wings or ridges develop. Larger branches have a broken warty bark which gives the tree the name, "alligator wood." The soft deeply furrowed dark gray bark of the main trunk may be over an inch thick.

Sweetgum develops a long, strong tap root in deep bottomlands, which usually prevents loss from windfall and encourages vigorous growth. The lumber was long discriminated against because of its tendency to warp and twist. Technical studies of the wood structure, and development of kiln-drying during the present century have largely overcome these difficulties. Lumber production of sweetgum now ranks third among American commercial hardwoods. Gum sawtimber manufactured in 1941 was 586,-751,000 board feet but in 1927 the production exceeded a billion feet, of which over one-half came from Louisiana, Mississippi and Arkansas. Nearly one-eighth of all hardwood timber growing in this country is red gum. This was estimated in 1936 to be 28,000,000,000 board feet of sawtimber.

Sweetgum wood, because of its interlocking grain, is strong and stiff. It works moderately well with tools. Its air-dry weight is thirty-four to thirty-seven pounds to the cubic foot. The hard, straight, close-grained wood is bright brown tinged with red and it has a thin white sapwood. The heartwood has a satiny luster and pleasing, varying figure. Few American woods equal sweetgum in beauty of natural grain but, in deference to the prejudice against "gum" wood, it is frequently marketed as satin walnut, Circassian walnut and hazelwood. Furniture, interior trim, railroad ties, cigar boxes, boxing, crating material, cheap flooring, barrels, woodenware and wood pulps are among its many uses. It is also one of the most important sources of plywood.

Growing largely on lands subject to overflow, fire damage is small. Insects and fungi attack felled trees and those which have been injured by fire and wind, but loss from these sources is not serious.

Sweetgum is superb for ornamental planting, ranking with the most beautiful of our eastern broad-leaved trees. It is hardy as far north as Massachusetts, is easily planted and grows fairly rapidly. The splendid fall coloring—gorgeous scarlet, orange and yellow tints as well as purple, lilac and brown tones—together with its freedom from pests make it especially attractive on streets and lawns.

In early spring clusters of green pollen-bearing flowers, glossy green aromatic five-pointed leaves, and dry, horn-tipped seed balls of the previous year are characteristic features of Sweetgum

The soft gray bark is deeply furrowed and usually about an inch thick

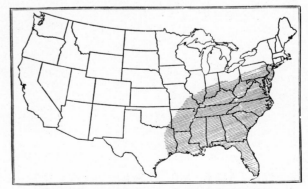

Natural range of Sweetgum in the United States

BLACKGUM

Nyssa sylvatica, Marshall

BLACKGUM grows on a variety of soils, in swamps, bottom lands, and moist uplands throughout the region

bers of the genus *Nyssa*, blackgum is the most widely distributed, and is commercially the most important. *Nyssa* refers to a Greek water nymph, because all tupelos or gums seek the swamps, and *sylvatica* designates this tree as "of the woodlands."

Fossil forms indicate that the genus was once distributed over much of North America, Europe, and Asia. A single species is now found in southeastern Asia.

From April to June inconspicuous greenish, five-toothed flowers on slender downy stems appear among the unfolding leaves. Individual trees bear perfect blossoms, while others bear only staminate or pistillate blooms. By September or October blue-black, plum-like fruits, about half an inch long are developed, whose thin oily, slightly acid pulp is attractive to many birds and animals. This may be responsible for the

east of the Mississippi River, and west through southeastern Missouri to eastern Texas. Best growth occurs in the southern Appalachian Mountains of North Carolina and Tennessee.

The densely foliaged, conical topped crown is carried on an erect trunk which frequently extends continuously into the top. The many up-reaching twigs and small branches of the upper crown give reason for the mountain name "wild pear tree." Frequently sixty to eighty feet high and two to three feet in diameter, exceptional trees reach 110 feet and may be five feet in diameter. Of the four American mem-

The densely foliaged, well rounded crown of Blackgum contains many small, up-reaching branchlets and as shown by the winter view to the left, the upright trunk frequently extends well into the top

name "blackgum," and also for the name "pepperidge"—an old English corruption of barberry, because like the barberries, the tupelo berries are acid. Tupelo is an Indian name.

The simple, alternate leaves are oval and pointed, broadest above the middle and with wavy margins. They are of leathery texture, dark green and smooth on the upper surface, slightly downy underneath, and densely clustered on the branchlets.

Similar to its relative, the dogwood, the bark of blackgum is reddish brown and broken into deep irregular ridges and lozenge-shaped plates. On old trunks the bark may be an inch or more thick. The angular plates are larger than those of dogwood.

The yellow to light brown wood has inconspicuous annual rings and a twisted grain that makes it tough and difficult to split. When air dry a cubic foot weighs about thirty-five pounds. Considerable amounts are cut into veneer to be manufactured into boxes, baskets, and berry crates, and to serve as a core on which veneers of rarer woods are glued. Without natural ability to resist decay, the wood may be successfully treated with creosote or other preservative. Because of its toughness it was formerly used for ox yokes and chopping bowls, and is now used for flooring, rollers in glass factories, hatters' blocks, gun stocks, and pistol grips.

Blackgum is included with three other gums in commercial estimates and reports. These indicate a stand of about twenty billion board feet of blackgum, with ten billion board feet of other tupelo gums. About two-thirds of the 272,093,000 board feet of gum lumber produced in 1941 were from Louisiana, South Carolina, North Carolina, Mississippi, Alabama and Virginia.

The moist location of most of the trees and the thick bark combine to protect this tree from fire, but the shallow root system frequently causes trees to give way to high winds. Mature trees are frequently subject to heart rot.

The erect trunk, shapely crown, and gorgeous scarlet autumn foliage combine to make blackgum an attractive ornamental tree, especially suited to wet or swampy soils.

Upper left: The densely clustered, dark green leaves are two to five inches long, light silvery beneath, and arranged alternately. Right: Inconspicuous greenish flowers appear with the new leaves in early spring

Irregular ridges and lozenge-shaped plates build up a reddish brown bark an inch or more thick

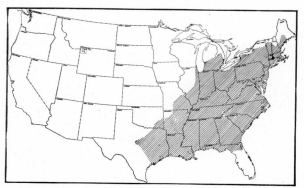

Natural range of Blackgum in the United States

occasionally one hundred feet or more across. This form gives way under forest conditions to a slightly tapering trunk whose clear length of sixty feet or more supports a relatively small crown.

The simple, alternate, palmately veined leaves are roughly three to five-lobed, with occasional coarse teeth. It is the largest single-bladed leaf native to the American forest, being four to ten inches long and equally broad. Bright green on the upper side, paler beneath but without hairs, the leaves have a leathery texture. At the base of the stout one- to two-inch leaf stem or petiole is a flaring ruffle-like stipule, while the entire stem is finely coated with hairs and the broad hollow base completely caps and encloses a long, smooth, blunt, conical bud of the coming season.

Inconspicuous flowers of both sexes are borne on the same tree but on different stalks and appear as the leaves unfold in early May. The male flowers are in dark red clusters, borne on a short base, while the small, light green, pistillate or female blooms form closely-packed, ball-like heads attached to a long, slender, thread-like stem. By October these develop into a dense ball

George J. Baetzhold

Sycamore is easily recognized in winter as well as summer by its mottled white bark, its thick buttressed trunk and its broadly oval crown

George J. Baetzhold

SYCAMORE, while not the tallest, attains the most massive proportions of any American hardwood or broad-leafed tree and is of considerable commercial importance. The wide buttressed trunk and smooth, whitish, variegated bark extending its glistening whiteness into the branches of the crown is a familiar sight along streams, on islands, and in rich, moist bottomlands. It grows throughout most of the eastern half of the country from southern Maine to northeastern Nebraska, south into Texas and along the Gulf of Mexico to northern Florida.

Averaging sixty to one hundred and twenty feet in height and two to five feet in diameter, individuals 140 feet tall and up to fourteen feet in diameter have been recorded. As the tree attains maturity the trunk becomes irregular and eccentrically buttressed. From the relatively short, rapidly tapering trunk of open grown specimens, large, wide-spreading limbs extend to form a broad irregular crown

or compound fruit dangling from a long slender stem and after hanging through the winter break up into many hairy, one-seeded nutlets. American sycamore has single seed balls, while those of the Oriental sycamore and London plane, (*P. orientalis* and *P. acernifolia*), hang in pairs or even fours. These seed balls give rise to the common name buttonwood or buttonball.

While sycamore fruits abundantly nearly every year, the vitality is low and the seeds are slow to germinate. Many seeds are carried by the water of early spring freshets and deposited on muddy flats where they germinate in considerable quantities. Even under upland woods conditions, however, the seeds require exceedingly moist surroundings in which to grow. Sycamore sprouts readily from the stump and reproduces itself by this means as well as from seeds.

The bark assumes a variety of forms and colors according to the age of the tree and the conditions under which it grows. Most easily recognized is that of young to moderately old trees in which large, thin plates peel off the trunk, exposing conspicuous areas of whitish, yellowish, or greenish inner bark. This is probably caused by the inability of the bark to stretch as the trunk expands. As trees grow older, the bark becomes two to three inches thick, broken by many shallow fissures to give a scaly appearance, and the light colored mottled look gives way to red-brown or dark gray.

Interwoven fibres make the reddish brown, clean appearing, coarse-grained wood tough and difficult to split or work. It is moderately hard and weighs thirty-five to thirty-six pounds to the cubic foot when air dry. Because it is so easily consumed by decay it is not generally used for railroad ties or fences, but its toughness results in use for butchers' blocks, saddletrees, vehicles, tobacco and cigar boxes as well as for shipping boxes, crates, and slack cooperage. It is also used for musical instruments and when quarter sawn the mottled texture makes it desirable for furniture and interior trim.

Sycamore is scattered through the forests in company with other hardwood trees characteristic of bottomlands. Because of the scattered growth, no accurate estimate of the total stand has been made, but in 1941 the Census Bureau reported the production of 49,-488,000 board feet of lumber.

American sycamore belongs to the plane tree family and is the most important of six or seven species native to the United States, Mexico and Central America, and one—*Platanus orientalis*—native to southwestern Asia.

Platanus is the classical name of the Asiatic plane tree, while *occidentalis*, meaning western, records it as belonging to the western world, and distinctly an American tree. The family was once world-wide in range and can be traced through geologic evidence to remote times.

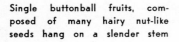

Single buttonball fruits, composed of many hairy nut-like seeds hang on a slender stem

George J. Baetzhold

George J. Baetzhold

The leaves, frequently broader than long, are palmately veined, four to ten inches across, shiny green on the upper surface and pale beneath

The mottled bark with browns, reds and greens against a background of white, is the result of inability to stretch to meet the expanding trunk

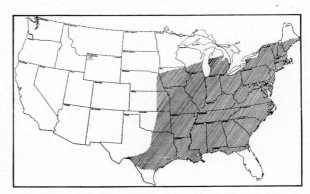

Natural range of Sycamore in the United States

BLACK CHERRY

Prunus serotina, Ehrhart

BLACK CHERRY grows in all the eastern states and Nova Scotia as far west as South Dakota, and south through the mountain ranges of western Texas, into southern New Mexico, Arizona, Mexico, Co-

George J. Baetzhold

Open-grown Cherry trees develop a spreading oval crown whose tortuous, more or less horizontal branches are clothed in summer with dark green foliage. Forest-grown trees are frequently characterized by a long symmetrical trunk, usually free of side branches

lombia, and Peru. Frequently reaching heights of sixty to eighty feet with trunk diameters at breast height of two or three feet, occasional forest trees are 100 feet high and four feet in diameter, with a clean, uniform trunk extending forty to sixty feet. In the open tortuous, more or less horizontal branches form a spreading oval crown. Best development is found in the Southern Appalachians where ex-

treme ages of 150 to 200 years are attained. It prefers deep, rich soil with uniform moisture, but thrives under many soil and moisture conditions.

The dark green, simple leaves are oval or pointedly lance-shaped, with fine incurved teeth on the margin. They occur alternately on the twigs, are two to five inches long, one inch to one and a half inches wide, smooth on both sides, pale green below, with fine hairs near the light colored midrib and veins, and one or more red glands near the base. The slender leaf stem, or petiole, is one-half to three-quarters of an inch long.

In April or May, when the new leaves are still red, four to six-inch drooping clusters of perfect, five-petaled white flowers appear. Domestic cherries produce blossoms before the leaves, so the Latin name *serotina*, meaning "appearing late," refers to the belated flowers, while *Prunus* is the classical name for all cherries and plums.

Drooping clusters of pea-sized cherries, so dark red as to be nearly black, with purple, juicy pulp develop by late summer. They have a pleasant, slightly bitter taste and are sometimes used in a beverage called

George J. Baetzhold

"cherry bounce"—hence the name "Rum Cherry." Within each fruit is a thin walled, slightly egg-shaped pit about a third of an inch long, enclosing the seed. Trees bear seed at intervals of three or four years from early youth to old age. The fruit is eagerly eaten by birds who distribute the seeds over wide areas. The seedlings demand sunlight and grow best in the open.

The dark bark of old trees is broken into irregular, easily peeled, scaly plates and is about three-quarters of an inch thick. On young trees and branches it is satin-smooth, dark red-brown, with conspicuous horizontal, pale lenticels or breathing pores. When wounded a gum similar to gum arabic exudes from the bark. The twigs are slender, smooth, red-brown, and like the leaves and inner bark contain prussic acid which gives an aromatic flavor resembling bitter almonds. This element may be responsible for its use in tonics and cough remedies. The same substance may cause severe illness or death to livestock which eat the wilted leaves.

The reddish brown, close-grained wood is hard, relatively light, and when air dry weighs about thirty-six pounds to the cubic foot. The sapwood is yellow and thin. Cherry is extensively used by the printing trade to back electrotypes and zinc etchings. Its beauty, lustre, ability to withstand knocks, and ease of working encourages its use for furniture, interior trim, veneers, and tool handles. Like mahogany, the color deepens with age, and the wood ranks close to walnut for cabinet purposes.

The commercial stand is estimated to be 453,000,000 board feet and the lumber production in 1935 was 4,899,000 board feet, coming largely from West Virginia, Tennessee and Pennsylvania. Additional amounts are cut for fuel, fence posts, and railroad ties.

Cherry trees are susceptible to many insects and diseases. Tent caterpillars feed on the leaves and sometimes fatally denude the trees, while "black knot," a fungus disease of the twigs and branches, causes severe injury. Surface fires permit the entrance of wood-rotting fungi, causing hollow butts.

Cherry is not a satisfactory street tree, but it can be planted anywhere within its natural range for its showy blossoms, its fruit which attracts birds, and its unconventional form.

Drooping racemes of white flowers, with the principal parts in fives, appear after the leaves

The dark colored bark of mature trees consists of many irregular, easily peeled, scaly plates and may be three-fourths of an inch thick

George J. Baetzhold

Drooping clusters of dark red cherries with purple, juicy pulp, ripen in late summer and early fall

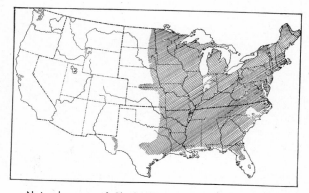

Natural range of Black Cherry in the United States

KENTUCKY COFFEETREE

Gymnocladus dioicus, (Linnaeus) Koch

THE Kentucky coffeetree is the sole North American representative of the genus *Gymnocladus.* The only other species is in southern China.

The thick, blunt-tipped twigs are a characteristic of the winter tree

Heavy, ascending branches form a high, narrow, irregularly rounded crown

From southern Ontario and western New York to Minnesota and eastern Nebraska, southward through eastern Oklahoma to northwestern Oklahoma and on rich bottomlands within the Appalachian Mountains to middle Tennessee, the coffeetree grows as a solitary specimen or, rarely, in groups.

It reaches heights of one hundred and ten feet and five feet in diameter, but more usually is forty to eighty feet high with diameters of two to three feet. Open grown trunks may be ten to twelve feet tall, with three or four heavy ascending branches turning slightly outward to form a high, narrow and irregularly round crown. Under forest conditions, trunks may be clear for seventy feet.

Gymnocladus, meaning "naked branch" is of Greek origin. The leaves break out late in the spring and drop early in the fall. During six months or more the tree shows no signs of life so that the French of southern Canada refer to it as "Chicot," or "dead tree," and the Southern mountaineers as "stump tree."

The minute leaf buds are hidden in hairy cavities of the bark or in the notches of the heart-shaped leaf scars. The large doubly compound leaf is one to three feet long and often two feet wide, with five to nine pinnately compound secondary leaves branching from the main stem. Each of some forty to sixty small, smooth-margined, abruptly pointed leaflets are two to two and one-half inches long and arranged opposite one another on a central stem. The secondary leaf stalks often occur in pairs but seldom in direct opposition. The large leaves, taken as units, grow alternately along the twigs. Their stalks are thickened at the base, while the first or second basal pair of leaflets are usually slightly lobed, and somewhat larger than the others. They are lustrous on the upper side and pale beneath. In early autumn the individual compound leaflets turn clear yellow and drop separately.

For a week or ten days in June, clusters of greenish purple flowers hang inconspicuously among the new leaves. Male and female flowers occur on separate trees, to which the specific name *dioicus* refers. This is derived from Greek words meaning "two-houses." The pollen-bearing clusters are three to four inches long, while the pistillate or seed-producers are six to twelve inches long and slightly hairy.

Belonging to the family *Leguminosae*, coffeetree is a pod-bearer after the manner of the bean and pea. The purplish brown fruit is one of the largest tree pods of this continent, being six to ten inches long, one to two inches broad, thick and full. They mature in one season and often persist, dry and rattling, into the winter. Each pod encloses six or more hard, round, flat, dark reddish brown seeds about three-quarters of an inch in diameter separated by a thick, dark colored layer of inedible, sticky pulp. The name coffeetree recalls efforts of early settlers to use the heavy bitter seeds as a source of a coffee-like beverage.

The rough, deeply fissured bark is three-quarters to one inch thick and varies from dark gray to brown. A reddish inner bark may often be seen at the bottom of the longitudinal furrows, which are separated by sharp, scaly ridges.

The light red to reddish brown wood is coarse grained, medium hard and a cubic foot weighs about forty-three pounds when air dry. It polishes well, is durable in contact with the soil, and is used locally for railroad ties, fence posts, poles, and construction material. Too sparsely distributed to be considered commercially important, the lumber is usually sold in combination with miscellaneous hardwoods.

Leaves are three to four feet long with forty to sixty leaflets, are lustrous above, and the flat pods contain six or more seeds

The dark gray or brown bark is deeply fissured, and is three quarters to one inch thick and often reveals traces of reddish inner bark

From "Some American Trees," courtesy Macmillan Co.

R. R. Paton

George J. Baetzhold

Pistillate flowers occur on long pedicels, and, like the staminate ones, are greenish purple. The two sexes are borne on separate trees

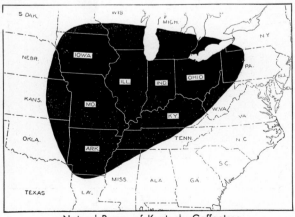

Natural Range of Kentucky Coffeetree

179

HONEYLOCUST

Gleditsia triaconthos, Linnaeus

THE honeylocust with its open plume-like crown of finely divided foliage and its thorny trunk and branches occupies a great inland region of moist, fertile soils along meadows, stream borders, and lake shores from Ontario and western New York to Nebraska, south to Texas and northern Louisiana, and northward along the western slopes of the Appalachian and Allegheny Mountains. This species is nowhere abundant and usually grows singly or scattered in small groups throughout open areas or in hardwood forests.

It is a tree of medium size with a short bole often divided near the ground. Ordinarily some seventy-five feet high with trunk diameters of two or three feet, the maximum height is about 140 feet with occasional trunks six feet in diameter. Honeylocust reaches its best growth in the valleys of small streams in southern Indiana and Illinois. Everywhere the slender, spreading, somewhat pendulous branches form an open, flat-topped crown.

While belonging to the *Leguminosae* or pea family, botanists classify it with Kentucky coffeetree and redbud, rather than with the black locust, *Robinia pseudoacacia,* with which it is often confused. Some twelve species of *Gleditsia* are scattered throughout North and South America, southwestern Asia, China, Japan, and west tropical Africa. Three species are found in eastern North America, of which honeylocust, the largest, is at best a tree of secondary commercial importance. In 1753 Linnaeus named the species *Gleditsia* in honor of Johann Gottlieb Gleditsch, then professor of botany at Berlin. The forked spines are recognized in *triacanthos,* meaning "three-thorned."

The compound and frequently doubly compound, or bipinnate leaves are seven to twelve inches long. They are arranged alternately on the branches, but the several pinnae or leaf stems, have eighteen to twenty-eight small oval or slightly pointed leaflets in opposite pairs.

Maryland State Department of Forestry

The crown of Honeylocust is like a great green plume

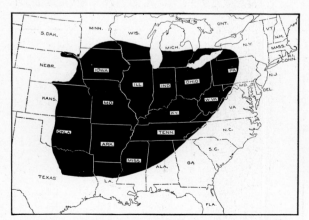

Natural range of Honeylocust

Tennessee Valley Authority

A Honeylocust tree with typical distribution of thorns on the trunk and lower branches. Proper grafting and budding methods produce entirely thornless trees

The leaves are dark green and lustrous above and dull yellow-green below—the whole becoming pale, clear yellow in the autumn.

From May to July, depending on the location, when the leaves are nearly full grown, flowers of both sexes hang from the axils of the previous season's leaves in short, inconspicuous, greenish yellow clusters. The pollen bearing blossoms are usually distinct from those which develop seeds, but all are on the same tree. They are fragrant and eagerly sought by bees for their nectar.

Flat, strap shaped, dark brown or purplish, twisted pods a foot or more long, mature in autumn and hang on the trees until early winter. The numerous, brown, oval, bean-like seeds enclosed within the pods are separated by a sweet and succulent pulp. They are eagerly sought by cattle, deer, rabbits, and squirrels who scatter the hard shelled seeds over broad areas. Bobwhite and starlings also feed on them. Names like honeylocust, honey shucks locust, or sweet bean tree are derived from the sweet pulp in the immature pod. With maturity it becomes bitter. Trees begin to bear seed early, but large crops seldom more often than three to five years. The bony coated seeds may be stored until spring, and will sprout more readily if submerged in hot water to soak and cool for several hours before being planted under about half an inch of soil.

On young trunks and branches the bark is smooth and grayish brown, while on mature trunks it is a quarter of an inch to three-quarters of an inch thick, divided into narrow ridges by deep, longitudinal fissures. It has a tendency to peel off in strips, and is grayish brown to nearly black. Relatively large, light colored, lenticils are noticeable on the smoother portions. The trunk, branches, and even the zigzag branchlets often bristle with long, slender, forked thorns. These grow from deep in the wood and are developments of true buds. Occasionally they put out leaves. A variety known as *inermis* grows without thorns.

The thick, fibrous roots are deep and wide spreading, but unlike most other legumes they are without nitrogen-fixing nodules and add no fertility to the soil. While capable of reproducing from stump and root sprouts, these seldom develop unless the tree is wounded.

The bright brown or reddish heartwood with its thin layer of pale yellow sapwood is hard, strong, coarse grained, takes a high polish, and is durable in contact with the soil. A cubic foot when air dry weighs about forty-four pounds. Its ability to resist decay encourages its use for fence posts and railroad ties, but the supply is limited. It is also used for rough construction, furniture, interior finish, and turnering.

Its ability to adjust to various soils and climates, and ease of transplanting result in wide use for ornamental, shade, and hedge purposes. It matures at about 120 years, but may live longer. In general it is sturdy, wind firm, free from diseases, and is not subject to borers as in the case of black locust.

Pale yellow-green pollen bearing blossoms grow in drooping racemes among the new foliage

George J. Baetzhold

Long forked spines grow singly or in clusters from the hard gray-brown bark

George J. Baetzhold

Twisted, strap-shaped pods a foot or more long show reddish brown among the finely divided compound and doubly compound leaves

BLACK LOCUST

Robinia pseudoacacia, Linnaeus

THE black locust, or false acacia, *Robinia pseudoacacia*, sometimes called yellow locust, belongs to the pea or legume family, and has the quality of adding nitrogen to the soil. It was originally native to the Appalachian Mountains from Pennsylvania to Georgia, and to parts of Arkansas and Eastern Oklahoma, but has been successfully planted in every state. In its natural range black locust grows along streams, in mountain coves or on the borders of forests, and usually in mixture with other hardwood trees. In many parts of the country it has escaped from cultivation and so established itself as to be generally accepted as native. It prefers deep, sweet, well drained fertile loam and soils with a limestone origin having brown or reddish brown subsoils, but will grow almost anywhere except in soils which are poorly drained or either very wet, heavy or acid.

Trees may attain heights of forty to eighty feet and trunk diameters of two or four feet, but they seldom live over 100 years.

The open branching and frond-like leaves give the crown the appearance of a plume. The alternate and pinnately compound yellow green leaves are eight to fourteen inches long and composed of seven to nineteen rounded leaflets, each on a slender stalk. They develop in April or early May. During rainy days and on the approach of evening

Black Locust forks frequently and develops a rather uneven crown which gives a plume-like appearance to the tree when in full leaf, while the seeds in their bean-like pods, flutter and rattle all winter

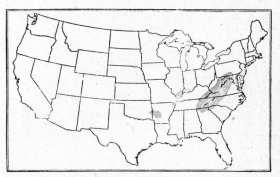

Natural range of Black Locust

the leaflets fold and the entire leaf droops slightly, after the manner of the true acacias. By the end of September or occasionally early October the leaves turn a pale, clear yellow before dropping.

The dark, reddish brown, rough, deeply fissured bark is an inch to an inch and a half thick and frequently twists diagonally across the trunk. Tonic, purgative and emetic qualities are reputed for the inner bark and roots of the trunk.

The twigs are pale green and silvery in the spring, turning reddish brown in the summer and marked with scattered pale lenticels. They bear pairs of short woody spines or thorns like those of a rose.

The new leaves are scarcely formed when clusters of fragrant white pea-like blossoms appear over the entire tree. These are perfect flowers, having a pistil as well as stamens, and are filled with nectar which attracts bees and other insects. From these come thin, smooth, bean-like pods with four to eight little dark orange seeds which ripen during Septem-

The pinnately compound leaves are alternate on the twig, but each of the seven to nineteen oval leaflets, borne opposite each other forms the full leaf

Racemes of fragrant white pea-like flowers appear in May and June. (Below) Dry bean-like seed pods with four to eight seeds

ber and October but hang on the trees through the winter.

Black locust wood weighs about forty-eight pounds to the cubic foot when air dry, and is stronger and stiffer than white oak. Freshly cut wood is greenish yellow to dark brown, coarse grained and surrounded by creamy white sapwood.

Black locust is supreme for use as insulator pins which are inserted on the cross arms of telephone and power transmission lines. Approximately 18,000 cords of high quality timber are necessary to make the 25,000,000 pins which have been manufactured in a single year for this use. Smaller amounts go into the hubs of wagon wheels, for treenails to pin ship timbers together and for fence posts, mine timbers, poles and tool handles.

The available supply of black locust was estimated in 1926 to consist of 375,000,000 board feet, of which the bulk is in Tennessee, Kentucky, West Virginia and Virginia. Few stands have as much as twenty cords to the acre, and large areas seldom average more than a cord to the acre.

It was introduced in Europe during the early part of the seventeenth century by Jean and Vespasien Robin, herbalists to the King of France and, bearing their name, is now the most generally accepted American tree in Europe. Because of its wide spreading fibrous root system, its tendency to send up new shoots from the roots, and the ability which it has with most other leguminous plants to develop nitrogen-fixing nodules on its roots, black locust is unusually adapted to the reclamation of soils and control of erosion.

Serious injury and disfigurement frequently follow attacks by the locust borer, and in some parts of the East a leaf miner gives the foliage a ragged, burned appearance.

The deeply furrowed orange-brown bark of the trunk is an inch or more thick

AMERICAN HOLLY

Ilex opaca, **Aiton**

THE glossy, yellow-green spiny leaves and red berries of holly are usually associated with the Christmas season. The tree is less well known than the foliage, but is of economic importance in several southern states, where it frequently grows forty to fifty feet high, and occasionally eighty feet. The trunk may be one or two feet in diameter, twenty feet long and tapers rapidly. Occasionally specimens four feet in diameter have been reported. The crown is frequently narrowly pyramidal with many short, spreading, nearly horizontal branches. Superficially resembling the English holly, *Ilex aquifolium* Linn, the American holly grows naturally from the coast of Massachusetts, where it is a shrub, southward into Florida, and throughout the Mississippi Valley from the Gulf to Indiana and into West Virginia. In hardwood bottomlands it grows in association with the oaks, and on the flat, sandy coastlands among the pines. Although capable of growing on poor soil, best growth is achieved on deep, fertile, moist soil, and the largest trees are found on the rich bottomlands of eastern Texas and southern Arkansas. The growth is slow but trees may reach an age of one hundred years or more.

The spiny-toothed, alternate evergreen leaves are thick, leathery, and firm, from two to four inches long and one to one and a half inches wide. They are dark, shiny green above and paler, tending toward yellow on the lower surface. The midrib and lateral veins are prominent on the lower surface, and the stout stem, or petiole, is half an inch long and grooved. Leaves remain on the tree for three years and are shed in the spring.

Ilex, the classical name of the evergreen oak of southern Europe, with leaves similar to holly, is one of five genera of the large family *Aquifoliacea*, meaning "trees with needles on their leaves." Thus the Latin name of both family and genus refers to the spiny character of the leaves. *Opaca* probably refers to the thick, opaque quality of the evergreen leaves. The name holly may be derived from its early use during the holy week. Of thirteen members of the genus *Ilex*, growing in the United States, *Ilex opaca* is the only one of economic importance.

The inconspicuous four-petaled white flowers appear in small clusters in the axils of the young leaves, or scattered along the shoots of the current year's growth. The flowers of the two sexes are borne on separate trees. The pistillate ones develop into small, red or yellow berry-like fruits and remain through the winter on the tree. The pulpy covering is relished by birds, but the four hard, ribbed nutlets within each berry are not digested. New seedlings are frequently the result of distribution by birds. Although attractive to birds, the berries should not be eaten by human beings.

American Holly frequently grows forty or fifty feet high and develops a dense, pyramidal crown with many short, nearly horizontal branches

Leaves and bark of holly, and other *Ilex* plants contain ilicin, a bitter material possessing tonic properties. Holly leaves have been used to treat fevers and rheumatism. Paraguay tea, known as *Yerbe de Maté*, is derived from one plant of this genus, and cassina tea from another.

The smooth, light gray bark is approximately a half inch thick and becomes roughened by wart-like excrescences in old trees. In color and texture, it resembles the bark of beech.

The wood is hard, tough, close-grained, not strong, but moderately heavy, weighing thirty-six to forty pounds to the cubic foot when air dry. The heartwood is creamy or ivory white when first cut, turning brownish with age or exposure, and takes a high polish. The sapwood is wide and whiter than the heartwood. It is used for cabinet work, turnery, small musical instruments, and, because of its similarity to ivory, as keys for pianos and organs. Its fine grain makes it useful for wood engraving. Present supplies of merchantable sizes are limited and scattered.

Holly is tolerant of shade, will recover from suppression after growing years under heavy shade, and young trees are capable of producing sprouts.

A deep tap root supported by numerous spreading laterals makes possible the transplanting of young trees. The best time to move them is in the fall, when the new wood is nearly ripened, or in the spring before new growth starts. When transplanting wild hollies from the woods, the tops should be severely pruned and most of the remaining leaves removed.

Holly berries may be sown in beds and covered with a heavy mulch until the spring of the second year, when the seed will germinate. Thereafter, the mulch should be removed and the seedlings given partial shade. Cuttings of the current year's ripened wood, with a little of the two-year-old wood and three or four leaves, made between August and December, may be rooted under a glass frame, or in a green-house. These should be set slanting in about six inches of mixed peat moss and soil, with the leaves lying flat on the surface. Being dioecious, those who desire trees ornamented with red berries should plant mostly pistillate ones.

The spiny-toothed, leathery, alternate evergreen leaves remain three years on the branches and are shed in the spring. These, with red berries, are widely used for Christmas decorations

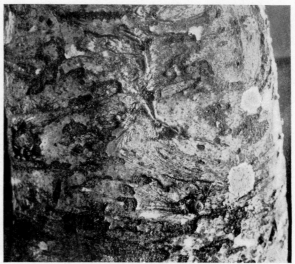

The bark is light gray, approximately a half inch thick and becomes roughened on old trees

Inconspicuous white flowers with four petals and stamens are borne from April to June in the axils of young leaves and on shoots of the current year's growth

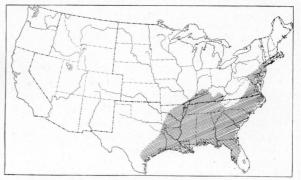

Natural range of Holly in the United States

BIGLEAF MAPLE

Acer macrophyllum, Pursh

EXTENDING some twenty degrees of latitude along the Pacific Coast from Alaska to southern California, bigleaf maple is the sole commercial species of four western maples. Demanding moisture, it occurs along the borders of foothills and on low mountains from sea level to elevations of over 3,000 feet in Washington and Oregon, and in California to 6,000 feet.

In the open this maple develops a broad, rounded crown of dense, blue-green foliage and a short trunk. Such trees may be fifty to sixty feet, or occasionally seventy-five feet high, with trunk diameters of two, three, or rarely five feet at breast height. Forest grown trees reach heights of 100 feet with a full,

may help cause its poor form. It seldom lives longer than 150 or 200 years. The simple, opposite leaves are the largest of any American maple, being six to twelve inches long and slightly broader, which accounts for the name—*macrophyllum*. They are usually deeply cut into five wavy or sub-divided lobes. The leaves vary in size on the same tree, and on trees of different ages, but are always conspicuously large as compared with those of other maples. Deep green and shiny above, and a paler green beneath, they are deciduous. In autumn the clear green of summer becomes a golden yellow, and the leaves hang on into the winter. No other native maple flowers compare with the four to six inch drooping clusters of fragrant yellow blossoms which deck the entire tree in April and May, after the leaves are fully formed. Both sexes are found on the same tree.

The winged samaras or keys are larger than those of other maples, and the seed is covered with short, stiff hairs. They are one and a half to two inches long, tawny or yellowish brown, ripen in the autumn, and hang on into the winter or early spring. Open grown trees produce abundant quantities of seed nearly every year, but production in the dense forest is sporadic. A large proportion germinate,

Open grown Bigleaf Maples have broad, dense, round-topped crowns with short trunks. Leaves and fruit frequently hang on into the winter

straight bole, clear of branches for one-half to two-thirds the total height and supporting a short, narrow crown. Best growth is in moist, gravelly, rich soils in alluvial river bottoms of Oregon and Washington. Sometimes found in pure stands, it is usually in mixture with conifers and other broadleaf trees.

In dense forests, mosses, lichens, and ferns drape the limbs well into the crown, which

George C. Stephenson

186

but only seedlings whose roots reach mineral soil before dry weather sets in survive. They will live under dense shade, but to attain any size direct overhead light is required. Supplementing reproduction by seeds are fast growing coppice sprouts from stumps. The ashy to brownish gray bark is seldom more than half an inch thick, and is broken into rough, fairly broad ridges as the tree matures.

The wood is light brown with a pale tint of red—firm, fine grained, takes a high polish, and a cubic foot weighs about thirty-four pounds when air dry. In 1936 the forests of Washington and Oregon produced 8,770,000 board feet of maple lumber. Furniture takes the bulk, but considerable quantities go into interior finish, flooring, broom handles, saddles, pulleys, boats, boxes, and baskets. Curly or wavy wood is occasionally found, and fancy grained burls command high prices for furniture veneer and novelties.

Bigleaf maple is reasonably resistant to insect attack and as part of the understory of humid forests seldom suffers from wind or fire. When fire occurs, however, the thin bark offers little resistance. Wood destroying fungi often reduce the trunk of large trees to scarcely more than a shell. Well suited for ornamental purposes within its natural range, it is a favorite street tree in many western towns. This tree does not prosper under our eastern conditions, but grows well in parts of England and western Europe.

Largest of all American maples are the deeply divided leaves. The wings of the fruit may be two inches long

The ashy gray to reddish brown bark is thin and deeply furrowed

George C. Stephenson

Large, yellow, fragrant flowers hang in clusters four to six inches long

Natural range of Bigleaf Maple

187

SUGAR MAPLE

Acer saccharum, **Marshall**

SUGAR maple grows naturally in every state east of the Great Plains but most vigorously in the northeast and in the higher elevations of the southern Appalachian Mountains. The name, sugar maple, refers to the spring crop of sugar and syrup that is boiled from its sweet sap. In autumn the leaves change from green to brilliant reds and yellows, and are an outstanding feature of the northern land-

The symmetrically rounded head of an open-grown Sugar Maple tree

In winter the relatively short stem and skeleton of many branches is revealed

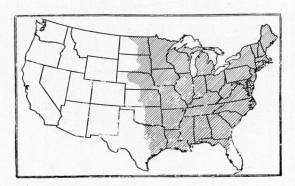

Natural range of Sugar Maple in the United States

scape. Open grown maple trees have a short trunk and a compact, globular crown. In the forest the tree lifts a relatively small rounded crown high up on a long trunk, to attain total heights from seventy to 130 feet. Forest grown maples are frequently two or three feet in diameter and have been known to attain five feet.

The smooth silvery bark of young trees becomes darker, more broken and deeply grooved as the tree matures. Frequently conspicuous shreddy flakes are developed.

Distinguishing features include the five-lobed leaf, the delicate pointed buds which grow opposite one another, the double winged seed or key, and the tendency for all branching to be opposite. Large quantities of fertile seeds mature in the early summer from inconspicuous, long-stemmed flowers that appear with the new leaves in April or May. Staminate and pistillate flowers are in separate clusters on the same tree, but occasionally a tree may have flowers of only one sex. *Acer*, the scientific name of the maple family, means hard or sharp. The Romans used European maple for pikes and lances as well as for tables and other furniture. *Saccharum* refers to the sweet sap. Most widely known as sugar maple or hard maple, it is also known as sugar tree and rock maple, while a botanical variation is known as black maple. Nearly a hundred species of maple are distributed over the northern hemisphere, of which thirteen are native within the United States. Maple trees and shrubs extend across the equator to the mountains of Java, and reach toward South America in the uplands of Central America. Most of the Old World species grow in the valleys of southeastern Asia.

The wood is known to the lumber trade as hard maple, and the bulk of maple lumber is of this species. The wide white sapwood may stain to a pale brown if improperly seasoned. The heartwood is light reddish brown, and the luster of each helps distinguish sugar maple from other maple wood. A cubic foot of air-dry maple weighs forty-four pounds. Although lighter than white oak, the wood is stronger and stiffer, and ranks as one of our more valuable hardwoods. In 1941, 614,654,000 board feet of the several maples were cut. More than half came from Michigan and Wisconsin, with considerable amounts from West Virginia, New York, Ohio and Pennsylvania. Maple is used for flooring, shoe trees, agricultural implements, musical instruments, furniture and a wide variety of materials which need a strong, firm, close-grained wood able to stay in place and capable of taking a polish. Accidental forms with contorted grain, known as curly maple and bird's eye maple, are prized for cabinet-making.

Maple syrup and sugar are important spring crops on many farms in Vermont, New York, Ohio, Pennsylvania, and Michigan. Ordinarily forty-five to fifty gallons are boiled down to make a gallon of syrup, and fifteen to twenty gallons of sap are secured from most of the trees. The census for 1939 reports the production of 2,456,400 gallons of syrup and 355,566 pounds of sugar.

Capable of growing under a variety of conditions, it grows especially well on gravelly, slightly alkaline soils. A few plantations have been established for sugar as well as lumber production, but the slow growth does not encourage such an investment. It grows readily from seed and is an important element in the management of many northern forests.

Although not so well adapted to city street conditions as some of the other maples, it is a favorite on suburban streets and country roads. Seedlings and small trees are easily transplanted. It is recommended for street and landscape use in the northern part of its natural range, in western Washington and Oregon and the northwestern counties of California.

None of the many insect and fungus pests are serious enough to discourage planting sugar maple for ornamental purposes. The sugar maple borer kills large limbs and occasionally entire trees by boring under the bark and in the outer sapwood. Similar damage is done by the larva of the leopard moth. The white grub of a twig pruner occasionally mars the trees and litters the ground by cutting off twig ends in the early autumn. Tent caterpillars, white marked tussock

Above: The five-lobed leaf with as many main ribs concentrating at the stem or petiole grow in pairs on the twigs. Below: Two winged seeds are attached to form a key or samara. Right: Winter buds, opposite one another, are tinged with purple

The ash-gray bark breaks up into hard, flinty flakes

moths and a green-striped maple worm may work on the leaves but seldom consumes all of them. Other insidious insect enemies are the scales which attach themselves to the young tender bark. Borer attacks may be met by pruning and burning the affected parts in the spring, while the leaf eaters and scales can be controlled by spraying.

Acer saccharinum, Linnaeus

Devereux Butcher

Open grown Silver Maples develop a short trunk that divides into several large ascending limbs with long pendulous branches

Bark on trunk and larger limbs of mature trees is thin, gray, and broken into broad, flaky scales

trees have trunks that rise clear of limbs for thirty to fifty feet before the branches form a medium broad crown sixty to eighty feet high. In the Ohio basin silver maple is more abundant than elsewhere in its range, where it sometimes grows to a height of one hundred and twenty feet.

During the first mild days of late winter or early spring when the leaf buds have scarcely begun to swell, the yellowish green flowers appear. Growing in short-stalked, thick clus-

SILVER maple, sometimes called soft maple, is one of sixty or seventy species of the *Acer* family distributed widely over the northern hemisphere, with one species south of the equator in the mountains of Java.

It is found as far north as New Brunswick and westward across southern Quebec, Ontario, Michigan, to southeastern South Dakota and Kansas. Although seldom found on the Atlantic coast or on the high Appalachian mountains, its range extends south to western Florida and Oklahoma. It never forms pure stands, but grows scattered through the forest in the moist soil of bottomlands, or along the borders of swamps and sluggish streams. It endures moderate shade, tolerating more shade in wet sites than in dry ones. Silver maple seldom lives over one hundred and twenty-five years, growing most rapidly during its first half century.

In the open, silver maple develops a short trunk measuring two to four feet in diameter, and dividing into several large ascending limbs that terminate in long pendulous branches to form a broad, rounded crown. Forest grown

Devereux Butcher

ters on the twigs of the preceding year, the staminate and pistillate flowers appear on the same or different trees. Later leaves appear borne on slender drooping stems. They are pale green and shiny above, smooth and silvery beneath, and measure four to six inches long and nearly as broad. They are five-lobed, deeply indented, sharply toothed with an even or heart-shaped base. The seeds occur in pairs or keys, suspended in clusters on slender, drooping stalks and have thin divergent wings one to two inches long. Some seed is produced every year, but abundant crops occur at irregular intervals. When they fall on moist soil germination follows shortly, and before the end of the summer have produced plants with several pairs of leaves. Silver maple sprouts readily from the stump, but trees begin to lose the ability to sprout or coppice after the trunk diameter exceeds a foot.

The thin gray bark on trunk and larger limbs of old trees is broken into broad scales which flake off readily, while on younger trees and on branches of mature ones it is smooth, gray, or slightly tinged with brown. Twigs are green or reddish, and when broken, give out a rank odor. Leaf-buds at the ends of the twigs are encased with three or four pairs of red scales and measure about one quarter inch in length. Buds along the sides of the twigs are borne on short stalks and are usually accompanied by the lustrous flower-buds.

The light brown wood weighs thirty-four pounds to the cubic foot when air dry, is strong, brittle, close-grained and rather hard. The sapwood is pale to almost white and with the heartwood takes a good polish and is used for cheap furniture, flooring, interior finish, woodenware, veneer and fuel. Considerable quantities are burned for charcoal, wood acetate and other products of distillation. Silver maple is sometimes mixed with the wood of other maples but is not as strong, hard or heavy. It is estimated that silver maple forms about five per cent of the total maple cut in the United States.

It is widely planted as an ornamental tree along roadsides and around homes, where its principal attribute is the comparative rapidity with which it grows. The tree, however, is not as well adapted for this purpose as are the sugar and red maples, because its limbs are brittle and are quite subject to injury by wind and ice storms. Large silver maples in cultivation are sometimes pruned as a means of helping them resist such damage.

The cottony maple scale, a sucking insect, is an enemy of the tree; while the wood is attacked by the boring leopard moth. Mature trees often have hollow trunks or show heartrot due to attack by fungus diseases. When growing in the forest, this tendency to become hollow makes the tree valuable to many forms of wildlife such as racoon, opossum, and owls. Owing to the thinness of its bark, fire is another serious enemy of the species, although the usually moist sites in which the tree grows somewhat reduces the fire danger.

There are several varieties of silver maple known as cutleaf maples. These have twigs and branches that are more drooping than those of silver maple, and leaves that are more deeply cut and decorative. These varieties are used ornamentally in parks and on estates.

Silver maple has a shallow, spreading root system with a small taproot.

Devereux Butcher

Leaves are green above, and silvery beneath, while the seeds which ripen in spring occur in pairs or keys

U. S. Forest Service

Staminate flowers occur on the same or different trees from the pistillate, and are yellowish green

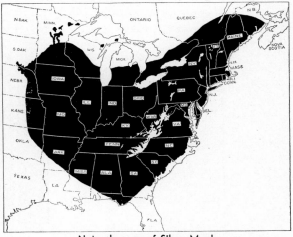

Natural range of Silver Maple

191

RED MAPLE

Acer rubrum, Linnaeus

EXTENDING over much of the eastern half of the United States and into Canada is the red maple, one of thirteen or more of the family *Aceraceae*, native to North America,

greater than 150 years. Long before reaching this age, under forest conditions a broad, round crown is developed with a moderately long clear trunk, the whole tree averaging sixty to ninety feet in height and one and a half to two and a half feet in diameter at breast height. Occasionally trees grow to a height of 125 feet and are five feet in diameter.

Red maple is best known by its three to five-lobed, doubly toothed, simple, bright green leaves which are three to four inches long, nearly as broad, and occur opposite one another on the twigs. While smooth above, the leaves are finely hairy beneath and have slender stems or petioles two to four inches long. Although basically green, the stem may be tinged with red, and in the early autumn the leaves turn to brilliant shades of scarlet, frequently mixed with orange, giving one of many reasons for the

Open-grown Red Maple develops a short trunk and a broad oval crown

George J. Baetzhold

and one of four eastern species to attain tree size. Because it occurs on low ground or in swamps, along the banks of streams where it will stand long periods of inundation, and on moist soils, it is frequently known as swamp maple. It thrives in any moist fertile soil.

Usually associated with other lowland trees such as black ash, the gums and cottonwoods, cypress and water oak, the largest sizes and best development are in the lower Ohio valley, while greatest abundance is in the lower Mississippi valley. Growth is rapid during the early stages, but trees seldom attain ages

Latin name *Acer rubrum* which translated is red maple.

The small but conspicuous clusters of ruby red flowers open in March or April considerably before the leaves. They occur as distinct male and fe-

Ruby colored staminate blossoms and the three to five-lobed leaves which appear later

George J. Baetzhold

male blossoms and may be on the same tree or segregated on different trees. By spring or early summer the fertile pistillate blossoms have developed into the characteristic key.

Red maple wood resembles that of hard maple, but the heartwood is light brown tinged with red while the sapwood is lighter colored. It is hard, close grained, easily worked and weighs when air dry about thirty-eight pounds to the cubic foot. It is used for furniture and cabinet work, flooring, interior finish, veneers, gun stocks, and woodenware, while considerable quantities are burned in kilns to produce wood acetate and charcoal. The commercial production is not distinguished from the other maples, of which red maple holds second place to the sugar maple.

Clusters of newly formed maple keys

Red Maple bark is dark gray and flaked

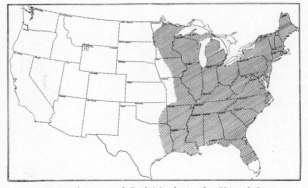

Natural range of Red Maple in the United States

BOXELDER

Acer negundo, Linnaeus

THE WINGED seeds of boxelder, whose clusters hang on the bare branches through the winter, place this tree with compound leaves within the family *Aceraceae*. Because a Malayan tree, *Vitex negundo*, has leaves similar to those of boxelder, *Acer negundo* would mean "a maple with negundo-like leaves."

It inhabits borders of streams and lakes from New England to Florida and across the eastern States and Canada to Alberta and the eastern slopes of the

or rarely a hundred years is reached. In contrast with other maples, the opposite leaves are compound, composed of three to seven, or rarely nine, short stalked leaflets. Each leaflet is irregularly toothed, two to five inches long, one to three inches wide, pointed at the tips, sometimes three-lobed, and pale on the under surface. The entire leaf turns yellow in the autumn before dropping and leaves a scar nearly surrounding the green stem.

In April or early May before or with the unfolding

Devereux Butcher

Clusters of V-shaped keyes hang for months from the branches of pistillate trees

Rocky Mountains. Usually forty to fifty feet high with two or three foot diameters, individual trees reach seventy-five feet and are four feet in diameter. The short, crooked trunk usually divides into several irregular spreading branches to form a wide bushy crown.

Boxelder is often scattered in company with bottomland hardwoods like white elm, hackberry, silver maple, and black walnut. It is most abundant in the Mississippi and Ohio valleys, but ability to thrive in dry areas has increased its occurrence in the prairie states. In good soils, diameter growth may equal an inch for each of the first fifteen or twenty years. Thereafter growth slows down until sixty

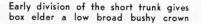

Early division of the short trunk gives box elder a low broad bushy crown

Maryland State Department of Forestry

leaves tiny yellowish green flowers appear on growth of the preceding year. Drooping clusters of pistillate **or** female flowers occur on trees separate from those which bear the hairy clusters of staminate blooms.

One to two inch V-shaped winged keys or double samara hang in six to eight-inch clusters from early summer into spring. Their broad membraneous wings converge into narrow pointed nutlets. Heavy crops of moderately fertile seeds are borne each year to be blown far from the parent tree and germinate in moist soils of open lowlands. Boxelder also sprouts from the stump collar.

The pale gray brown bark is a quarter to a half inch thick, shallowly broken into narrow, firm, flat-topped ridges which crack horizontally into thick irregular short scales. On young trunks, branches and twigs it is smooth, greenish or purplish, with conspicuous raised lenticles or pores, while the twigs are sometimes coated with a powdery white bloom.

The soft, close-grained creamy white wood, lightest of the American maples, weighs about twenty-six pounds to the cubic foot when air dry, and has scarcely half the strength and stiffness of sugar maple.

Boxelder trees frequently attain lumber size but are rarely cut for lumber. The wood is sold with that of soft maple and used for crates, boxes, slack barrels, handles, paper pulp, charcoal, cheap furniture, woodenware and fuel. Occasionally low grade maple syrup or sugar is obtained from the sap.

Until the beginning of the twentieth century boxelder was widely planted for street and windbreak purposes. These uses are now usually discouraged because of its short life, frequent injury by wind and sleet, tendency to attack by several sucking, defoliating and boring insects and its susceptibility to heartrot.

George J. Baetzhold

Yellow-green pollen-bearing flowers appear with the new leaves on staminate trees

The shallowly fissured gray-brown bark is scarcely half an inch thick

George J. Baetzhold

Each pinnately compound leaf has three to seven irregularly margined leaflets

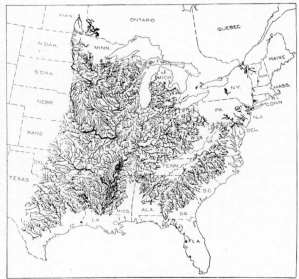

Natural Range of Boxelder

195

OHIO BUCKEYE

Aesculus glabra, Willdenow

George J. Baetzhold

to the finely toothed margin. The underside is a lighter green with fine hairs visible on the veins. In the autumn the leaves turn yellow before dropping to uncover a horse-shoe shaped scar.

In May or early June after the leaves have burst from the large shiny brown buds and have reached full size, stiff, upright clusters of greenish yellow flowers appear at the ends of many of the upturned twigs. While some are perfect with a five-lobed calyx, four petals, a pistil and seven stamens, others on the same tree may have only a pistil, or the seven stamens without a pistil. Their disagreeable, fetid odor has led some to call this the Stinking or Fetid Buckeye.

In spite of the unedible and possibly poisonous nature of the seeds of this and other members of the family, the name *Aesculus* is derived from *esca,* meaning food, and is the ancient name for a kind of oak tree. The first de-

IN THE central area east of the Alleghanies, one of the first trees to leaf out is the Ohio Buckeye. Resembling its larger and better known European relative, the horse chestnut, it differs in the five more slender finger-like leaflets, the smaller and less attractive yellow blossoms, and in other ways. Fertile bottomlands and the borders of streams from central Pennsylvania to northern Alabama, and west into northeastern Kansas, are its natural haunts.

It is of medium size, ranging from thirty to seventy feet in height with a trunk seldom more than two feet in diameter. Except in the deep woods, the stem divides low to form an irregularly broad, rounded crown, with clumsy drooping branches, and reddish brown upcurved twigs.

Twigs and leaves are arranged opposite one another. The yellow-green compound leaves consist of five or occasionally seven lance pointed, oval leaflets, diverging palmately from a common point at the end of the long stem or petiole. Each leaflet is three to six inches long, with parallel veins leading from the midrib

George J. Baetzhold

Buckeye is a medium sized tree with a broad, rounded crown. When the yellow-green foliage drops in the autumn, the opposite branching, clumsy, drooping twigs with upcurved ends are revealed.

scription was by a German botanist, Willdenow, in 1809, who selected the specific name *glabra*, meaning smooth, with reference to the buds and young leaves.

The ashy gray bark is densely furrowed and broken into large scaly flakes. On old trees it may be three-quarters of an inch thick. When bruised, or when the twigs are broken, these also give off a disagreeable odor. An extract of the bark has been used as an irritant of the cerebro-spinal system.

The white, close-grained wood weighs only twenty-five to twenty-eight pounds to the cubic foot, and like that of the larger yellow buckeye resists splitting but at the same time is easily carved or whittled. It is used largely in the making of artificial limbs, and the early settlers planed straight sections into long fine shavings with which to make summer hats. Of so little commercial importance that there are no figures to show its estimated stand or annual consumption, it is sometimes used for wooden ware, pulp, veneers, and general construction.

The younger Michaux found so many of these trees along the Ohio River during his travels in 1810 that Ohio is known as the Buckeye State. It is usually associated with beech, sugar maple, and basswood. Because the leaves and fruit are believed poisonous to livestock, the tree is frequently destroyed by landowners.

Like the horse chestnut it is subject to a fungous disease that first shows itself as brown spots or blotches on the leaves. By midsummer the entire tree may appear as if scorched by fire. Owners of ornamental trees may check this disease by promptly raking and burning all fallen leaves, leaf stalks, and fruits. Early spraying or dusting with lime sulphur or Bordeaux mixture is also helpful.

Generally considered a dirty tree, because to the dropping flowers and fruit are added the leaves which fall throughout the entire growing season, it is occasionally planted for ornamental purposes in the eastern states and in Europe. It is hardy as far north as Massachusetts.

George J. Baetzhold

In late summer and fall the five fingered foliage hides round prickly fruits which hold the glistening brown, light scarred buckeye

The densely furrowed, ashy gray bark may be three-quarters of an inch thick

Panicles of yellow, ill smelling blossoms appear among the darker foliage in May or June

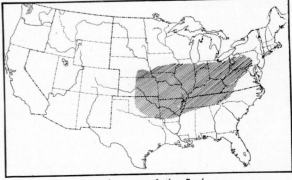

Natural range of the Buckeye

HORSECHESTNUT

Aesculus hippocastanum, Linnaeus

In winter the tree is easily recognized by its symmetrical form and stout twigs which turn upward at the ends

George J. Baetzhold

THE horsechestnut is a member of the Buckeye genus, *Aesculus*. It was introduced from Europe in the Eighteenth Century, and is a native of southern Asia, ranging from the Himalayan Mountains to northern Greece. A favorite shade tree in the Old World, it has spread in popularity in America and now appears as a planted ornamental tree in every state. Its popularity is well justified by its good form and floral display.

The leaves of the horsechestnut are from six to fifteen inches in diameter; the leaflets are four to eight inches long, extending palm-fashion from the end of a stout petiole which swells abruptly at the base. The slightly wavy margins of the leaflets are irregularly toothed and their upper surface is faintly wrinkled. Broader at the outer ends and terminating in an abrupt point, the leaflets taper toward the base, and at maturity are dark green above and paler beneath. In the fall they turn brown.

Showy, pyramidal flower clusters six to twelve inches high appear in June and July when the tree is in full foliage. The five petals are white, spotted with yellow and purple, and the long, curved stamens are yellow, extending far beyond the petals. The only other tree-sized buckeye bearing white flow-

ers is the California buckeye, and its natural range is limited to the slopes of the Sierras in California.

The fruit, ripening in September, consists of two or three reddish brown, smooth nuts, each bearing a whitish scar, and enclosed in a corky husk two or three inches in diameter covered with blunt spines. In the fall the husk turns brown, hard and leathery, and cracks into three segments to liberate the nuts. These are without economic importance in this country and so bitter as to be inedible without special treatment. Powdered dried nuts mixed with two parts of wheat flour and alum-water are said to make a vermin-repellent bookbinder's paste.

The horsechestnut may have acquired its common name from the legendary use of the fruit as a source of medicine for horses, or from the shape of the leaf scars which resemble the print of a horse's hoof. The name *Aesculus* is from the Latin for winter oak, and *hippocastanum* is a combination of two Latin words meaning "horse" and "chestnut."

The twigs are dotted with large lenticels or breathing pores, while the large reddish brown opposite buds are protected throughout the winter by a sticky shiny gum. The terminal flower buds are one-half to one inch long and below them on each side is a smaller leaf bud. The bud scales are arranged oppositely in pairs. Beneath each

Large ascending limbs and spreading branches form a rounded crown of dense foliage

Devereux Butcher

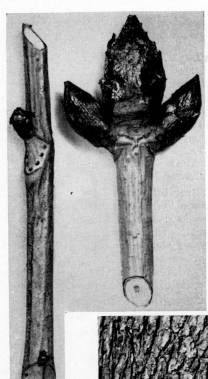

Twigs bear large terminal buds and smaller lateral ones, and have horseshoe-like leaf scars which aid identification

The showy, white flower clusters appear in June or July, and stand erect amid the large palmate leaves

The bark is dull brown or black, and on old trunks is thin, broken into large scales separated by shallow cracks or fissures. It has provided yellow dye material and tannin.

The wood weighs about thirty-five pounds to the cubic foot when air dry. It is white, soft and close-grained, but is not commercially important. In Europe and to a lesser extent in this country it is used for box-material, veneer, wooden ware, and artificial limbs and as a source of charcoal for gun powder.

Bark is thin, and on the lower trunks of old trees it is broken into flat scales by shallow fissures

Devereux Butche

side bud is a large rounded V-shaped leaf-scar marked by seven prominent dark dots.

The lower branches droop slightly with tips upturned in candelabra fashion; the crown is rounded into a broad cone by ascending limbs with spreading lateral branches. The horsechestnut grows rapidly, often reaching a height of seventy feet and a diameter of three feet. Horticulturists have produced ornamental varieties of horsechestnut with peculiar characteristics such as double flowers and deeply cut leaves.

The flowers of the dwarf, *Aesculus pavia alba,* an ornamental tree, have an apparent toxic effect on the Japanese beetle, while an extract from the seeds of red buckeye, *Aesculus pavia,* will stupefy fish. The horsechestnut flowers and leaves are preferred foods of the Japanese beetle. Its leaves are also attacked by the caterpillar of the white-marked tussock moth, while the wood-boring larva of the leopard moth causes the twigs to wilt and break off. The oyster shell scale feeds on the sap through the young bark, but rarely are any of these attacks fatal.

Courtesy Romeyn B. Hough Company

Ripening in September, the fruit consists of two or three reddish brown nuts borne within a spined husk

Tilia glabra, Ventenat

THE American basswood, American linden, or lime, forms a compact, symmetrical tree usually seventy to ninety feet high with a trunk two or three feet in diameter. Occasional trees 140 feet high with maximum trunk diameters of four and one-half feet have been reported.

It is distributed over much of the eastern half of the United States and north into New Brunswick to the eastern shores of Lake Superior. Its southern range is confused with that of the white basswood, *Tilia heterophylla*, which differs, among other features, in the leaves which are silvery white and covered with fine hairs on the lower surface. The largest and most vigorous trees are found in fertile coves and on low land near streams within the central states. It grows in mixture with other hardwoods and does not form pure stands.

This is the tree for which *Tilia americana* as given by Linnaeus was long supposed to be correct. *Tilia glabra*, as credited to the French botanist Etienne-Pierre Ventenat, probably refers to the smooth surfaces of the simple, alternate, heart-shaped leaves. The upper surface is dull dark green, and the lower surface paler with occasional tufts of rusty brown hairs in the axils of the principal veins.

The perfect five-petaled, fragrant, white or cream-colored flowers appear after the leaves are fully developed in June and early July. By early October gray, woody, spherical fruits about the size of a pea develop from the fertile blossoms and hang singly or in clusters from a stalk attached about midway to a leafy bract.

The buds are dark red or sometimes greenish. While without distinctive flavor, they become mucilaginous

American Basswood forms a handsome, compact, narrow-crowned tree from fifty feet to one hundred feet high and occasionally higher, with a full, symmetrical trunk two to three feet in diameter

Numerous slender branches, of which those at the base of the trees are strongly drooping, are revealed in symmetrical grace when the leaves have fallen

when chewed. The dark gray bark of old trees is about an inch thick, deeply furrowed into narrow, flat-topped firm ridges with characteristic horizontal cracks. That of young trees is gray, smooth and thin. The bast fibres of the inner bark have long been used in making cords, fish nets, mats and similar articles.

The white to creamy brown wood is valued for its white color, light weight and good working qualities and is used widely for woodenware, slack cooperage, boxes, veneer, excelsior, paper pulp, and many small articles. When air-dry it weighs about twenty-six pounds to the cubic foot.

Nine billion board feet of basswood are estimated to be growing in the United States, of which about five billion board feet are in the Lake States and two billion feet in the high lands of West Virginia, Kentucky and Tennessee. The basswood lumber production of 120,035,000 board feet in 1941 shows a reduction from 133,320,000 board feet cut in 1929, and about 400,000,000 board feet cut during the years 1906, 1907 and 1909.

It grows rapidly, develops from stump sprouts as well as from seeds. Trees mature at from ninety to 140 years, and when crowded by other trees form straight stems with clear lengths of fifty to seventy feet.

While the leaves are frequently disfigured by insects, the tree seldom succumbs to their attacks. Fire often causes hollow butts and permits the entrance of wood-destroying fungi.

Throughout eastern United States basswood adapts itself to difficult conditions and is frequently recommended for city streets. It is also satisfactory on the Pacific slope.

The broad, heart-shaped leaves are smooth on the under as well as the upper surface, bear coarse teeth on the margins and taper rapidly to a point. Scarcely have the leaves fully formed when clusters of white or creamy five-petaled perfect flowers appear suspended from a leafy bract (upper picture). By early autumn many of these have developed into woody fruits (lower picture) about the size of a pea. Without a true terminal bud, the smooth dark red, or sometimes greenish, lateral buds are about a quarter-inch long and are arranged alternately on the twig (right)

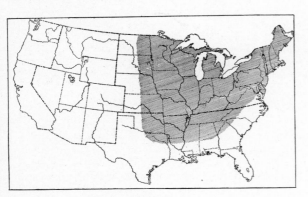

Natural range of Basswood in the United States

The furrowed bark is about an inch thick

FLOWERING DOGWOOD

Cornus florida, Linnaeus

KNOWN best for its showy blossoms, the small, irregular crown of slender spreading branches, the brilliant scarlet autumn foliage, and the highly special-

Devereux Butcher

A tracery of outreaching small twigs and branches characterizes dogwood in winter

ized commercial uses of its wood, combine to make flowering dogwood a tree to be remembered. It seldom grows more than forty feet tall, and its short, irregular trunk is usually limited to a diameter of eight inches but occasionally reaches eighteen inches. This slow growing tree usually occupies the margins or the understory beneath open forest growth, and rarely approaches the conditions of a pure stand. It prefers rich well drained soils in coves or along the banks of streams from central Florida to eastern Texas and northward throughout the Mississippi Valley and the southern Appalachians to southern Wisconsin and Michigan. lower Ontario, central New York, and southern Maine. It is also found on the uplands of northern Mexico.

An opposite branching tree, the bright green simple leaves of flowering dogwood are ovate to elliptical and

sharply pointed. They are three to six inches long, two to three inches wide, with prominent mid-ribs and five or six primary veins curving parallel with the contour of the margin. The under surface is light colored and sometimes almost white. In the autumn the upper leaf surface turns bright scarlet.

Large white, pinkish, or rarely rose red blooms appear in late April, May, or early June shortly before or with the unfolding of the first green leaves. The true flowers are inconspicuous, yellow-green, and perfect—forming a dense cluster in the center of what is usually mistaken for the blossom. What appear to be four large petals with deeply notched tips are actually bracts or forms of leaves.

Flowering dogwood gets its name from the profusion of spring flowers, and for the same reason bears the Latin name *florida*. *Cornus* is de-

Devereux Butcher

The irregularly rounded crown of bright green foliage is seldom taller than forty feet

rived from the Latin word for horn, and refers to the hard, tough wood. *Cornus florida* is the most important of some forty or fifty species of shrubs and small trees of which seventeen are native in North America.

The fruits are often in clusters, each one being

small, egg shaped and scarlet with a single hard seed. They ripen in October and are only a little less showy than the blossom.

In winter the red terminal buds are like flattened cones and are generally downy near the point. The flower buds are turnip shaped about a quarter of an inch long and broad. They are always terminal and frequently very numerous. The smooth, slender twigs are yellowish green or bright red, often covered with tiny, closely appressed gray hairs, and are bitter to the taste.

The dark red-brown to almost black bark is closely ridged and broken into four sided or rounded scales after the manner of alligator hide. It is about an eighth to a quarter inch thick and with the root bark has been used as the source of a bitter element for the treatment of fevers. The Indians also derived a form of scarlet from it for dying their blankets, feathers and belts.

The relatively small portion of reddish-brown to light chocolate colored heartwood is surrounded by a broad area of pinkish sapwood. Its fine, uniform texture with narrow annual growth rings gives a firm, stiff wood which weighs about fifty-one pounds to the cubic foot when air dry. Probably ninety per cent of all dogwood cut for commercial purposes is used in the manufacture of shuttles for textile weaving, because the hard, close-textured, smooth wood has little wearing effect upon the thread. It is also used for spool and bobbin heads, small pulleys, skewers, golf club heads, mallet heads, and jewelers' blocks.

Dogwood reproduces from seed, which are borne nearly every year. It will also sprout from the root collar to form coppice growth, and may be successfully budded or grafted. Many birds feed on the seed.

Devereux Butcher

Four large, showy, deeply notched bracts surround the cluster of inconspicuous perfect flowers

Devereux Butcher

Deeply ridged and broken, the bark resembles alligator hide

Devereux Butcher

The pointed ovate leaves are opposite one another, and the fruit cluster is bright scarlet

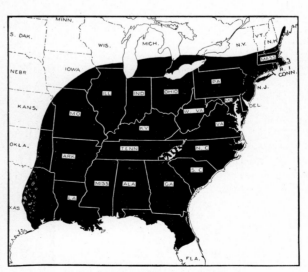

Natural range of Flowering Dogwood

PERSIMMON

Diospyros virginiana, **Linnaeus**

Ohio Forest Service

Frequently a large shrub, forming extensive thickets on abandoned land, it often attains heights of fifty feet and trunk diameters of six to twelve inches. Under favorable forest conditions it reaches 100 to 130 feet in height with trunk diameters of over two feet.

The leathery, alternate leaves are pointedly oval, three to seven inches long, and a deep, glossy green above contrasting with a pale under side. The leaf stems or petioles are one-half an inch to an inch long. Sheep, goats, and even deer will not browse the foliage, so this tree successfully maintains itself on open land and frequently prospers in spite of pasturing.

In May or June while the leaves are partly grown, yellowish green to milky white urn-shaped blossoms appear like small bells on

A TREE of moderate size, with crooked branches and a round topped cylindrical crown massed with glossy leaves, the persimmon is the most northern member of the ebony family. It is, however, more generally known for the puckery quality of its immature fruit than for its hard, firm wood. While other true ebonies are largely tropical or subtropical, this tree grows on a wide variety of soils and sites from Connecticut westward through southern Pennsylvania to southeastern Iowa, eastern Kansas, and south throughout Texas and Florida. Only one other species of persimmon, *Diospyros Texana,* occurs in the United States. This is of no commercial importance, and its range is limited to southwestern Texas.

A tree of moderate height whose irregular branches may be clothed with glossy leaves

the new shoots. The staminate blossoms are usually on one tree and the pistillate ones on another, so there are fruit bearing trees as distinguished from those which are apparently barren.

The fruit is a true berry, roughly globular and an inch to an inch and a half in diameter, with one to eight oblong, compressed seeds imbedded in the juicy flesh. Early settlers are reported to have roasted the seeds for use as coffee. Early in summer the big berries are pale orange and often red cheeked, but when dead ripe turn a blackish purple. Only then does the pulp lose its high content of astringent tannin to become sweet and delicious, with food value only second to the date.

In the same locality are trees with fruits which ripen from August or September into February or even March. Thus persimmons furnish food for birds and wildlife as well as for such domestic stock as hogs, and to some extent for humans through the fall and winter. Trees begin to bear fruit early and continue with regularity, often weighing down the branches with as much as they can support. The quality varies with different trees, some fruits being especially adapted for food, and all being capable of being reproduced through grafting or budding.

The name *Diospyros* is from two Greek words—*Dios*, which refers to the god Zeus, and *puros*, for wheat. Literally it is "food for the gods," which refers to the luscious fruits of the 200 or more varieties of persimmon. *Virginiana* refers to that great area of eastern North America named for Elizabeth, "the virgin Queen" and known as Virginia to DeSoto, who described the fruit in 1557 as a "delicious little plum."

The deep brown to black bark is closely divided into small blocks like a rough mosaic. It is an inch and a half to two inches thick.

Like other members of the ebony family, the heartwood of persimmon is dark brown or black, while the larger area of light brown sapwood is often mottled with darker spots. Comparatively little sapwood turns to heartwood until trees are close to 100 years old. The wood is close grained, hard, strong and tough, weighs about fifty-three pounds to the cubic foot when air dry, and is capable of taking a high polish. The sapwood is chosen for use as shuttle blocks, bobbins, plane stocks, and shoe lasts, is recognized as standard for the heads of golf clubs, and has other less specialized uses.

While susceptible to injury from ground fires, it is seldom seriously attacked by insects and is avoided by livestock and rabbits. A recently discovered fungus disease, known as persimmon wilt, is, however, causing severe losses throughout many portions of its range. As yet too little is known regarding the life history or possible spread of this disease to prophesy its effect on the persimmon trees of the country. Until more is known concerning this fungus and its control, the use of persimmon as a holder of the soil and as a source of food for animals or men may be left largely to nature.

The leaves are glossy green above and pale beneath, while the fruit is a large berry

The dark brown bark is deeply cut into small blocks

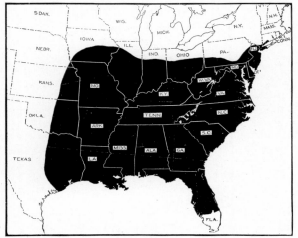

Natural range of Persimmon

WHITE ASH

Fraxinus americana, Linnaeus

George J. Baetzhold

The compact, oval crown of White Ash is clothed with rich green foliage in summer and stands stark and strong against the elements in winter

out much of its range, but the giants of one hundred and twenty feet in height and six feet in diameter were largely confined to the deep, moist soil of fertile bottomlands in the lower Ohio River Valley. In the forest the straight, symmetrical stem may be clear of branches for more than half the total height of the tree.

Like the other members of the olive family, *Oleaceae*, of which American ash is the chief commercial lumber species, the branching is opposite. The pinnately compound leaves are eight to twelve inches long, with five to nine short-stalked dark green, lance-like leaflets, each three to five inches long and one to two inches broad. They are pale green or silvery white and smooth underneath, with only the semblance of teeth on the edges.

WHITE ASH, the largest and finest of all the ashes, is one of the leading commercial hardwoods of the United States. It grows from Nova Scotia and Maine, west to Minnesota and south to the Gulf. Never forming extensive pure stands, or even a dominant part of the forest, it grows singly or in small groups in association with other hardwoods. or with hemlock, white pine, or spruce. It thrives on a variety of soils, but is most frequently found on comparatively well-drained, fertile sites along streams and on north and east slopes.

Trees seventy to eighty feet high with broadly rounded or pyramidal crowns, and a straight columnar trunk two to three feet in diameter are common through-

George J. Baetzhold

The inconspicuous, dark reddish to purple, four-lobed male blossoms are produced on different trees from the panicles of pistillate ones. Occasional trees produce perfect blossoms. They open before the leaves late in April or May, and the pistillate ones develop by midsummer into long, drooping clusters of light brown, paddle-shaped fruits, one to two inches long, in which the narrow pointed seed case extends lengthwise to form a wing about a quarter of an inch wide.

Ash may get its name from the dark brown, ashy gray bark which is one to three inches thick, and deeply divided by narrow diamond-shaped fissures into broad, flattened ridges. The thick opposite branchlets are first dark green or brown and covered with scattered hairs, but later become smooth, ashy gray and marked with pale lenticels or breathing pores.

Fraxinus is the classical name for ash, while *americana* singles this outstanding American variety from nearly fifty species distributed over the temperate and tropical regions of the northern hemisphere. Eighteen species of ash are recognized in the United States.

The hard, close grained, light brown wood is strong, tough, elastic, and free from taste or odor. When air dry it weighs about forty-two pounds to the cubic foot. It is used for tool handles, butter tubs, oars, sporting goods, furniture, vehicles, and interior trim.

The total stand of 6,150,000,000 board feet, as estimated in 1932, is largely second growth and consists of several species, of which probably forty percent is white ash. In 1909 the production reached a peak of 291.209.-000 board feet, but in 1941 only 102,091,000 board feet were cut. Commercial production is reported from each state within its range but South Carolina leads with 10,208,000 board feet.

It is relatively free from insect and fungus attack, but the thin-barked young trees are highly susceptible to fire damage. Ash reproduces sparingly from seed, but because of its high stumpage value it is generally encouraged in farm woodland management. Young trees produce vigorous sprouts, but the chief source of reproduction is by seeds.

Sturdy twigs and dark rounded buds help identify the white ash in winter

Tufts of dark red to purple staminate blossoms appear in early spring before the leaves

White ash leaves are pinnately compound with five to nine short-stalked leaflets, while light brown paddle-shaped fruits one to two inches long, hang in clusters from the previous year's growth

Deep diamond-shaped fissures cut the ashy gray bark into broad flattened ridges

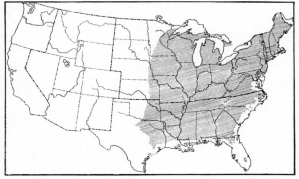

Natural range of White Ash in the United States

NORTHERN CATALPA

Catalpa speciosa, Warder, Engelmann

George J. Baetzhold

Large heart-shaped leaves and long slender seed pods make Northern Catalpa easy to recognize

In winter the long pods are often conspicuous, dangling in clusters, and rattling in the wind

Devereux Butcher

Though sometimes a hundred feet high in the forests of its natural range, Northern Catalpa is usually a medium sized tree with a broad, spreading crown

THE word *catalpa* is a Cherokee Indian name adopted by the early settlers of this continent, and *speciosa,* a Latin word meaning ornamental, has been given this irregular and picturesque tree with large decorative leaves and conspicuous flower-clusters.

In the northeastern states planted trees reach twenty-five or fifty feet in height with a trunk diameter of six to fifteen inches. The range of northern catalpa extends around the juncture of the Ohio with the Mississippi. Along the rich bottomlands of the Ohio basin in southern Illinois and southern Indiana it attains its maximum size of a hundred and twenty feet with diameters of four or rarely five feet. When growing in the open, the trunk is short and usually crooked, the crown broad and spreading with thick scraggling branches. In the forest it is taller with a narrow rounded crown and a straight, slightly tapering trunk that is sometimes clear of limbs for sixty

Devereux Butcher

feet. In deep, moist, fertile soil northern catalpa grows rapidly, maturing in one hundred years or less. It is tolerant to some shade, and seedlings require only partial sunlight.

It has been widely planted in the eastern half of the United States as far north as Massachusetts. Never forming pure stands in the forest, it is found singly or in small groups associated with other bottomland hardwoods.

Bark on the mature trunk is three quarters to one inch thick, light grayish brown, broken into longitudinal, scaly, flat ridges. Twigs are stout, smooth or downy, yellowish or reddish brown with large conspicuous lenticels, and large leaf-scars. The small lateral winter buds are embedded in the bark and covered with overlapping scales. Terminal buds are absent, and the tips of twigs in the north are often winterkilled.

The large leaves, which are almost tropical in appearance, are borne on stout cylindrical stems four to six inches long, grow opposite, whorled, or three in a group, and measure seven to twelve inches in length and five to eight inches in width. They are long-pointed at the outer end, round or heart-shaped at the base, with even edges, or one or two teeth. Mature leaves are light green and smooth above, slightly paler and hairy beneath, and at the axils of the primary veins they have clusters of dark purplish glands which are visited by honey bees. Leaves turn black and fall after the first hard frost.

Appearing in June or early July, the showy flowers, borne on slender terminal stalks, are arranged in pyramidal, few-flowered clusters five to six inches long.

The fruit ripens in autumn. It is a slender two-celled bean-like, cylindrical capsule ten to twenty inches long and one-half to three-quarters inch thick, suspended by a thick stem. Green when young, the pods later turn dark brown and remain on the tree during the winter. Toward spring they split in half liberating the many flat, winged, oblong seeds.

Catalpa wood when dry weighs twenty-six pounds to the cubic foot. It is coarse-grained, soft, not strong, but very durable in contact with soil. The heartwood is grayish brown occasionally tinged with lavender, and the thin sapwood is nearly white. It is ring-porous, and, when cut at right angles to the pith rays, resembles ash. Probably nine-tenths of all catalpa cut is made into fence posts, though occasionally it is used for handles, picture frames, interior finish and furniture.

Often severely injured by frost, its brittle limbs broken by wind, attacked by fungus, and by insects such as the catalpa sphinx, it is, nevertheless, one of the easiset hardwoods to plant. It is widely grown in parks, or along suburban streets in the eastern half of the United States.

Northern catalpa is frequently confused with the smaller common catalpa, *Catalpa catalpa,* of the South Atlantic states from Georgia to Mississippi. Common catalpa has dense clusters of flowers thickly spotted with brownish purple as compared with the more open and less conspicuously spotted flower panicles of hardy catalpa. The leaves of common catalpa are smaller, and broader in relation to their length, being only five to six inches long and four to five inches wide. The six to twenty inch long seed pod is more slender and the wells thinner than that of northern catalpa.

George J. Baetzhold

The white flowers bloom in June or July, and are arranged in showy, erect clusters at the ends of twigs

George J. Baetzhold

Bark on the lower trunk of mature trees is three-quarters to one inch thick, light grayish brown, broken into scaly, flat ridges

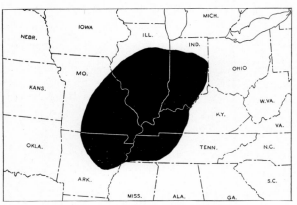

Natural range of Northern Catalpa

SELECTED BIBLIOGRAPHY

A complete list of the books and periodicals read in the preparation of these tree descriptions would cover several pages. The following, however, comprise the more important sources of technical information used in the text:

AMERICAN FOREST TREES, by Henry H. Gibson.

AMERICAN WOODS—Leaflets on individual tree species prepared by H. S. Betts, United States Forest Service.

CHECK LIST OF THE FOREST TREES OF THE UNITED STATES, by George B. Sudworth.

CULTIVATED EVERGREENS, by Liberty Hyde Bailey.

DISTRIBUTION OF IMPORTANT FOREST TREES OF THE UNITED STATES, by E. N. Munns.

FIELD BOOK OF AMERICAN TREES AND SHRUBS, by F. Schuyler Mathews.

FOREST TREES OF THE PACIFIC SLOPE, by George B. Sudworth.

HANDBOOK OF THE TREES OF THE NORTHERN STATES AND CANADA, by Romeyn B. Hough.

MANUAL OF THE TREES OF NORTH AMERICA, by Charles Sprague Sargent.

NORTHERN ROCKY MOUNTAIN TREES AND SHRUBS, by J. E. Kirkwood.

REDWOODS OF COAST AND SIERRA, by James Clifford Shirley.

SOME AMERICAN TREES, by William B. Werthner.

STANDARDIZED PLANT NAMES, by American Joint Committee on Horticultural Nomenclature.

STUDIES OF TREES IN WINTER, by Blakeslee and Jarvis.

TREE ANCESTORS, by Edward W. Berry.

TREE BOOK, by Julia E. Rogers.

TREE FLOWERS OF FOREST, PARK, AND STREET, by Walter E. Rogers.

TREES OF NORTH AMERICA, by George Rex Green.

Volume 1—The Conifers.

Volume 2—The Broadleaves.

TREES OF THE SOUTH, by Charlotte Hilton Green.

INDEX

COMMON NAME AND SCIENTIFIC NAME